The New Technology and Human Values

1971 ed

Edited by

JOHN G. BURKE

University of California, Los Angeles

Wadsworth Publishing Company, Inc., Belmont, California

L. C. Cat. Card No.: 66–12867
Printed in the United States of America

Preface

Although the results of scientific inquiry have been utilized to effect technological innovation for more than a century, in the past twenty years the pace of scientifically based technology has noticeably quickened. Aircraft regularly span the continent in four hours; we have televised communication with Europe; astronauts circle the earth in ninety minutes and stay aloft in space for days. These are engineering achievements, but their success is due ultimately to knowledge which the pursuit of pure science has made available. During the past two decades, the constant applications of scientific knowledge have brought about technological innovation and the rapid accumulation of new scientific knowledge; this new scientific knowledge then stimulates a new sequence of innovation. As a result, science is advancing like a forest fire in all directions. The outstanding example of the functioning of this process is the development of the computer, which has now become one of the most powerful research tools of modern science. This interaction between basic science—that is, pure research—and applied science, then, is what I have termed the *new technology*.

The power of modern science to effect conspicuous social change was first effectively brought home to the average individual in the awesome spectacle of the atom bomb. Since that time, there has been a dawning realization that rapid scientific progress is producing changes in every facet of life. These changes are affecting human values; choices now, as a result of scientific progress, have to be made by individuals and by governments in situations that did not exist even a quarter of a century ago. And, as the tempo of change intensifies, one finds it increasingly difficult to maintain traditional modes of life and patterns of thought. Change itself, it appears, is sought as a way of life.

The central purpose of this book of readings is to explore the effects of this advance of scientifically based technology on human values. It is an effort to bring together the writings of some men who have been concerned about the impact of scientific change upon our society. Often, these men express sharp disagreement about the proper approach to these problems, and offer different suggestions for their solution. As a result, the writings of these men highlight the basic issues involved. Other readings are expository, but they also serve a purpose in pointing to areas where the march of science may conflict with human values in the future.

The material presented in this book of readings is designed to serve two purposes. First, since it surveys one major area wherein little organized reading material is available, it may be useful in courses on the problems of contemporary society. Second, it provides a provocative basis for discussion in adult classes and groups organized through university extension divisions and other adult-education agencies.

The book was planned following suggestions of the program committee of the University Council on Education for Public Responsibility. In early 1962, this group, consisting of university extension deans and directors, agreed to work together each year in an attempt to focus public interest on a major area of public policy. For 1966, the area chosen is the subject of the present book: the issues emanating from current science and technology, including automation; and the human and social values involved in technological change.

The plan of this book and the decision on the selections to be used are my own responsibility. However, I wish to acknowledge the helpful suggestions of the members of the University Council program committee, particularly Leonard Freedman. I am also indebted to my wife, Margaret Burke, for several valuable comments, and I wish to express my thanks to Mrs. Elizabeth Singley for excellent secretarial services rendered.

JOHN G. BURKE

Contents

Part One
Science, Technology, and Society

Authors concerned with the effects on human values of scientific progress and technological change characteristically express one of three different views. The first group sees the advance of science as essentially beneficial to man, removing him from the darkness of ignorance and superstition and promising him a golden age in the future. The spokesmen of this group point with pride to the accomplishments of science and consider any ill effects as only temporary discomforts. A second group looks upon science as a curse; in Biblical terms, man has possessed himself and is eating of the forbidden apple. Man has submerged his true spiritual nature in order to gain material benefits, and he will ultimately destroy himself. The proponents of this view claim that science does not address itself to any of the more important problems of man's existence. In such areas as human relations and politics, they say, scientific findings constitute no more valid knowledge than does tradition or insight. The third group favors the advance of science but believes that the technological change which it spawns should be subject to some kind of control or planning, in order that basic human values will be preserved. Expressions of these attitudes will be made throughout this book, but they are most

1

clearly articulated in some of the readings in the first two chapters of this section.

These underlying views are particularly reflected in discussions concerning the purposes of education in our society. The advocates of continued scientific and technological advance argue that society should increase its efforts to produce scientists, engineers, and technicians in order to maintain and develop the age of science. Those who question the trend emphasize that education's traditional purpose has been individual fulfillment and the training of well-rounded, thoughtful people. This conflict is explored in Chapter 3.

1
The Impact of Scientific and Technological Change: An Historical Perspective

The changes that the findings and applications of contemporary science have effected in society and upon human values have provoked increasing controversy among scientists and non-scientists alike during the past two decades. Science is alternately attacked and defended; the changes are seen as evidencing a distinctly materialistic and hence non-humanistic trend or, conversely, as contributing to the fulfillment of man on a spiritual as well as on a material level. A study of nineteenth-century history and literature, however, shows that such debates are by no means novel. For at that time as well, there were varied reactions to the mechanization of technology and to the increasing emphasis upon science as the means to acquire a more precise knowledge of nature, which man could then exploit to his own advantage. Many saw the introduction of machines and the use of scientific knowledge as signal achievements; man could now successfully meet the challenges of his natural environment; he could live a better and a happier life. But others viewed the changes that had occurred in a different light—as threats to age-old values. The selections in this chapter are designed to mirror some of these varied reactions. "The Luddites" describes the violent resistance on the part of many English workers to the introduction of machinery that threatened their livelihood and, in turn, the reaction of society against these rioters. Granted that the actions were destructive and illegal; at the same time, does not a society have an obligation to those of its members who are engulfed by the tide of technological progress? Is it an unalterable social law, as Werner Siemens states in another selection, that all transitions must involve human suffering?

The English writer Samuel Butler, satirizing the manners of his age in his novel *Erewhon*, describes an imaginary society shut off from the rest of the world. In this utopia, the inhabitants had destroyed all machinery because they believed that machines cause men to prefer material things, that they weaken man because of his dependence upon them, and that man's devotion to machines will result ultimately in his total subservience to them. Carroll D. Wright sharply attacks these ideas. Viewing in retrospect a century of industrial progress in the United States, he judges that the introduction of machinery has had a profoundly beneficial influence upon the ethics of the individual and society as a whole.

Werner Siemens, holding the same views as Wright, stresses the idea of human progress; according to Siemens, the increase in scientific knowledge and technological change reflects a steady progression in the level of civilization. Furthermore, far from degrading man's ideals, science has elevated the human spirit by reducing superstition and fanaticism. Leo Tolstoy, on the other hand, writes of science as an essentially shallow activity, contributing little or nothing to the solution of the major problems of man's existence but, nevertheless, making absurd claims to be the fountain of knowledge.

When the impact of science and technology is thus viewed from an historical perspective, it can be seen that men have long faced several basic questions: What is meant by human progress—mere improvement in the material comfort of man and reduction of manual labor? Or must there be a concomitant elevation of man's moral standard and his spiritual life? Does the destruction of traditional values, even though they may be supersitions according to scientific standards, allow man to be better or happier? Do the values that accrue from scientific and technological progress outweigh the values that are submerged or destroyed as a result of that progress? In short, has man *really* progressed as a result of his science and his scientifically based technology?

THE LUDDITES

Mr. Baron Thomson . . . delivered the following Charge: *Gentlemen of the Grand Inquest,* we are assembled, by virtue of His Majesty's Commission, to exercise the criminal judicature in this county, at this unusual season of the year for the occurrence of such solemnities. None of us, however, can be insensible of the necessity which exists for a speedy investigation of the charges against the very numerous class of prisoners in your calendar. You will perceive I allude to those persons, who are accused of having participated (and several of them in repeated instances) in those daring acts of tumultuous outrage, violence and rapine, by which the public tranquillity has been disturbed throughout that great manufacturing district in the West Riding of this county, for a period comprising, with little intermission, almost the whole of the year which has just elapsed.

Those mischievous Associations, dangerous to the public peace, as well as destructive of the property of individual subjects, and in some instances of their lives, seem to have originated in a neighbouring country, and at first to have had for their object merely the destruction of machinery invented for the purpose of saving manual labour in manufactures: a notion, probably suggested by evil designing persons, to captivate the working manufacturer, and engage him in tumult and crimes, by persuading him that the use of machinery occasions a decrease of the demand for personal labour, and a consequent decrease of wages, or total want of work. A more fallacious and unfounded argument cannot be made use of. It is to the excellence of our Machinery that the existence probably, certainly the excellence and flourishing state, of our manufactures are owing. Whatever diminishes expense, increases consumption, and the demand for the article both in the home and foreign market; and were the use of machinery entirely to be abolished, the cessation of the manufacture itself would soon follow, inasmuch as other countries, to which the machinery would be banished, would be enabled to undersell us.

The spirit of insubordination and tumult, thus originating, has spread itself into other manufacturing districts; and when large bodies of

"Proceedings held at the Castle of York, January 1813." In *Introduction to Contemporary Civilization in the West,* 3rd ed. (New York, Columbia University Press, 1961), II, 254–261. Reprinted with permission.

men are once assembled to act against law, the transition unhappily is too easy from one irregular act to another, even to the highest of crimes against society. And thus we find that the destruction of tools has been succeeded by destroying the houses and the workshops of the manufacturers; it has led to the violent robbery of arms, to protect the tumultuous in their illegal practices, and to enable them to resist or to attack successfully; and from the robbery of arms they have proceeded to the general plunder of property of every description, and even to the murder, the deliberate assassination, of such as were supposed to be hostile to their measures. A temporary impunity (for the law, though sure, is slow) has led on these deluded persons from one atrocious act to another; from the breaking of shears to the stealing of arms, to nightly robberies, to the destruction of property, and of life itself.

The peaceful and industrious inhabitants of the country, where these enormous practices have been committed, have had the misfortune to suffer in their persons and property, from the acts of men confederated against society, and executing the purposes of their association under circumstances carrying with them the utmost terror and dismay. Armed bodies of these men, in some instances several hundred in number, apparently organized under the command of leaders, and generally with their faces blacked or otherwise disguised, have attacked the mills, shops, and houses of manufacturers and others, by day as well as by night, destroyed tools worked by machinery, and in some instances shot at the persons whose property they have thus attacked. But the worst of these misdeeds is yet behind, a most foul Assassination. While such outrages as those mentioned were carrying on in that part of the country, a person in a respectable station of life, returning from Huddersfield to his residence at Marsden, was fired at and shot from behind the wall of an inclosure near the road, receiving several wounds, of which he died shortly after. . . .

With regard to the guilt, which persons may incur by engaging in any riotous assembly, the Statute of 1 George I. commonly called the Riot Act, has enacted, That if any persons, to the number of twelve or more, who shall be unlawfully, riotously, and tumultuously assembled together, to the disturbance of the public peace, shall not disperse, but continue in that state for the space of an hour after such proclamation made as is directed in the Act, they shall be guilty of Felony without benefit of Clergy. And by the same Statute, if any persons, so unlawfully, riotously, and tumultuously assembled together, to the disturbance of the public peace, shall unlawfully and with force demolish or pull down any dwelling house or other buildings therein mentioned, they shall also be guilty of Felony without benefit of Clergy.

So also by the Statute of 9 George III. it is made a capital Felony, for persons, being riotously and tumultuously assembled, to pull down or demolish, or to begin to pull down or demolish, any wind saw-mill or other windmill, or any watermill or other mill, or to set fire to the same. In addition to which, the Act of 43 George III. cap. 58. has provided against the maliciously setting fire (among other things) to any mill, warehouse or shop, with intent to injure or defraud any of the King's subjects, by subjecting the offenders, their counsellors, aiders and abettors, to a capital punishment. . . .

The prisoners capitally convicted being . . . put to the bar, and asked what they had to say, why Sentence of Death should not be passed on them, prayed that their lives might be spared.

Mr. Baron Thomson:

John Swallow, John Batley, Joseph Fisher, John Lumb, Job Hey, John Hill, William Hartley, James Hey, Joseph Crowther, Nathan Hoyle, James Haigh, Jonathan Dean, John Ogden, Thomas Brook, John Walker, you, unhappy prisoners at the bar, stand convicted of various offences, for which your lives are justly forfeited to the injured laws of your Country. You have formed a part of that desperate association of men, who, for a great length of time, have disturbed the peace and tranquillity of the West Riding of this county. You have formed yourselves into bodies; you have proceeded to the most serious extremities against the property of many individuals. The cause of your so associating appears to have been a strange delusion, which you entertained, that the use of machinery in the woollen manufacture was a detriment to the hands that were employed in another way in it; a grosser delusion never could be entertained, proceeding probably from the misrepresentations of artful and designing men, who have turned it to the very worst purpose which riot and sedition could produce. You have proceeded to great extremities. The first object, perhaps, seems to have been that of your procuring arms, in order to carry on your nefarious designs. With that view, it seems that some of you went about inquiring for such arms at different houses, and getting them wherever you could find them.

But not stopping there, and not contenting yourselves with getting what arms you could lay your hands upon, you proceeded to plunder the habitations with a great degree of force, and took from them property of every description, which you could find in those houses. An offence of that nature is brought home, and sufficiently established against you the prisoners *John Swallow, John Batley, Joseph Fisher, John Lumb, Job Hey, John Hill, William Hartley, James Hey, Joseph Crowther,* and *Nathan Hoyle.*

You the prisoners, *Job Hey, John Hill,* and *William Hartley,* did upon the occasion, when you went to the house of your prosecutor, carrying away certainly nothing but arms, but you carried them away with great terror, and under circumstances which were sufficient unquestionably to make him deliver what he had. The other prisoners, whose names I have last recited, have been concerned in breaking a dwelling-house in the night time, some of them getting notes, money, and other things; and the last prisoners, *James Hey, Joseph Crowther,* and *Nathan Hoyle,* for robbing a person in his dwelling-house.

The evidence, that has been given against you all, was too clear to admit of any doubt; and you have all been convicted of these offences upon the most satisfactory evidence.

You, the other prisoners, *James Haigh, Jonathan Dean, John Ogden, Thomas Brook,* and *John Walker,* have been guilty of one of the greatest outrages that ever was committed in a civilized country. You had been long armed and organized, you had assembled upon this night, when the mill of Mr. Cartwright was attacked; you had assembled at the dead hour of night in great numbers; you had formed yourselves into companies under the command of different leaders; you were armed with different instruments of offence, with guns, with pistols, with axes, and with other weapons; you marched in military order and array to the mill, which was afterwards in part pulled down; you began there your attack with firearms, discharged into that mill, and kept up a most dreadful fire, and at the same time applied the instruments, which you had brought there, of a description calculated to do the worst of mischief, in beginning to demolish the mill, intending, as it is obvious, to do also mischief to and to demolish the machinery which that mill contained. The cries and exclamations that proceeded from this riotous tumultuous mob thus assembled, of which you formed a very powerful part, were such as were enough to alarm a man of less firmness than that man possessed, who was the owner of the mill so attacked. Your cry was, "Get in, get in, kill them all"; and there is but little doubt, it is to be feared, that if you had made good your entry into that mill, these threats would have been put into execution, and that the mischief done would hardly have been confined to the machinery which was there. The courage and resolution, however, which that individual displayed, had the effect of making you desist at that time from the attack, and two of your wretched companions paid the forfeit of their lives on that occasion. . . .

In the awful situation in which you, prisoners, stand, let me seriously exhort you to set about the great work of repentance, and to spend the very short time that you must be allowed to remain in this world, in endeavouring to make your peace with your God, and to reconcile him by deep repentance. A full confession of your crime is the only atonement you can make for that which you have committed. Give yourselves up to the pious admonitions of the reverend Clergyman, whose office it will be to prepare you for your awful change; and God grant, that, worthily lamenting your sins, and acknowledging your wretchedness, you may obtain of the God of all mercy perfect remission and forgiveness.

Hear the sentence which the Laws of man pronounce upon your crimes. The sentence of the Law is, and this Court doth adjudge, That you, the several Prisoners at the bar, be taken from hence to the place from whence you came, and from thence to the place of execution, where you shall be severally hanged by the neck until you are dead. The Lord have mercy upon your souls.

Samuel Butler
THE MACHINES

. . . "True, from a low materialistic point of view, it would seem that those thrive best who use machinery wherever its use is possible with profit; but this is the art of the machines—they serve that they may rule. They bear no malice towards man for destroying a whole race of them provided he creates a better instead; on the contrary, they reward him liberally for having hastened their development. It is for neglecting them that he incurs their wrath, or for using inferior machines, or for not making sufficient exertions to invent new ones, or for destroying them without replacing them; yet these are the very things we ought to do, and do quickly; for though our rebellion against their infant power will cause infinite suffering, what will not things come to, if that rebellion is delayed?

"They have preyed upon man's grovelling preference for his material over his spiritual interests, and have betrayed him into supplying that element of struggle and warfare without which no race can advance. The lower animals progress because they struggle with one another; the weaker die, the stronger breed and transmit their strength. The machines being of themselves unable to struggle, have got man to do their struggling for them: as long as he fulfils this function duly, all goes well with him—at least he thinks so; but the moment he fails to do his best for the advancement of machinery by encouraging the good and destroying the bad, he is left behind in the race of competition; and this means that he will be made uncomfortable in a variety of ways, and perhaps die.

"So that even now the machines will only serve on condition of being served, and that too upon their own terms; the moment their terms are not complied with, they jib, and either smash both themselves and all whom they can reach, or turn churlish and refuse to work at all. How

In *Erewhon: or Over the Range,* 1st edition, 1872.

many men at this hour are living in a state of bondage to the machines? How many spend their whole lives, from the cradle to the grave, in tending them by night and day? Is it not plain that the machines are gaining ground upon us, when we reflect on the increasing number of those who are bound down to them as slaves, and of those who devote their whole souls to the advancement of the mechanical kingdom? . . .

"It is said by some with whom I have conversed upon this subject, that the machines can never be developed into animate or *quasi*-animate existences, inasmuch as they have no reproductive system, nor seem ever likely to possess one. If this be taken to mean that they cannot marry, and that we are never likely to see a fertile union between two vapour-engines with young ones playing about the door of the shed, however greatly we might desire to do so, I will readily grant it. But the objection is not a very profound one. No one expects that all the features of the now existing organisations will be absolutely repeated in an entirely new class of life. The reproductive system of animals differs widely from that of plants, but both are reproductive systems. Has nature exhausted her phases of this power?

"Surely if a machine is able to reproduce another machine systematically, we may say that it has a reproductive system. What is a reproductive system, if it be not a system for reproduction? And how few of the machines are there which have not been produced systematically by other machines? But it is man that makes them do so. Yes; but is it not insects that make many of the plants reproductive, and would not whole families of plants die out if their fertilisation was not effected by a class of agents utterly foreign to themselves? Does any one say that the red clover has no reproductive system because the humble bee (and the humble bee only) must aid and abet it before it can reproduce? No one. The humble bee is a part of the reproductive system of the clover. Each one of ourselves has sprung from minute animalcules whose entity was entirely distinct from our own, and which acted after their kind with no thought or heed of what we might think about it. These little creatures are part of our own reproductive system; then why not we part of that of the machines?

"But the machines which reproduce machinery do not reproduce machines after their own kind. A thimble may be made by machinery, but it was not made by, neither will it ever make, a thimble. Here, again, if we turn to nature we shall find abundance of analogies which will teach us that a reproductive system may be in full force without the thing produced being of the same kind as that which produced it. Very few creatures reproduce after their own kind; they reproduce something which has the potentiality of becoming that which their parents were. Thus the butterfly lays an egg, which egg can become a caterpillar, which caterpillar can become a chrysalis, which chrysalis can become a butterfly; and though I freely grant that the machines cannot be said to have more than the germ of a true reproductive system at present, have we not just seen that they have only recently obtained the germs of a mouth and stomach? And may not some stride be made in the direction of true reproduction which shall be as great as that which has been recently taken in the direction of true feeding?

"It is possible that the system when developed may be in many cases a vicarious thing. Certain classes of machines may be alone fertile, while the rest discharge other functions in the mechanical system, just as the great majority of ants and bees have nothing to do with the continuation of their species, but get food and store it, without thought of breeding. One cannot expect the parallel to be complete or nearly so; certainly not now, and probably never; but is there not enough analogy existing at the present moment, to make us feel seriously uneasy about the future, and to render it our duty to check the evil while we can still do so? Machines can within certain limits beget machines of any class, no matter how different to themselves. Every class of machines will probably have its special mechanical breeders, and all the higher ones will owe their existence to a large number of parents and not to two only.

"We are misled by considering any complicated machine as a single thing; in truth it is a city or society, each member of which was bred truly after its kind. We see a machine as a whole, we call it by a name and individualise it; we look at our own limbs, and know that the combination forms an individual which springs from a single centre of reproductive action; we therefore assume that there can be no reproductive action which does not arise from a single centre; but this assumption is unscientific, and the bare fact that no vapour-engine was ever made entirely by another, or two others, of its own kind, is not sufficient to warrant us in saying that vapour-engines have no reproductive system. The truth is that each part of every vapour-engine is bred by its own special breeders, whose function it is to breed that part, and that only, while the combination of the parts into a whole forms another department of the mechanical reproductive system, which is at present exceedingly complex and difficult to see in its entirety.

"Complex now, but how much simpler and more intelligibly organised may it not become in another hundred thousand years? or in twenty thousand? For man at present believes that his interest lies in that direction; he spends an incalculable amount of labour and time and thought in making machines breed always better and better; he has already succeeded in effecting much that at one time appeared impossible, and there seem no limits to the results of accumulated improvements if they are allowed to descend with modification from generation to generation. It must always be remembered that man's body is what it is through having been moulded into its present shape by the chances and changes of many millions of years, but that his organisation never advanced with anything like the rapidity with which that of the machines is advancing. This is the most alarming feature in the case, and I must be pardoned for insisting on it so frequently." . . .

"Herein lies our danger. For many seem inclined to acquiesce in so dishonourable a future. They say that although man should become to the machines what the horse and dog are to us, yet that he will continue to exist, and will probably be better off in a state of domestication under the beneficent rule of the machines than in his present wild condition. We treat our domestic animals with much kindness. We give them whatever we believe to be the best for them; and there can be no doubt that our use of meat has increased their happiness rather than detracted from it. In like manner there is reason to hope that the machines will use us kindly, for their existence will be in a great measure dependent upon ours; they will rule us with a rod of iron, but they will not eat us; they will not only require our services in the reproduction and education of their young, but also in waiting upon them as servants; in gathering food for them, and feeding them; in restoring them to health when they are sick; and in either burying their dead or working up their deceased members into new forms of mechanical existence.

"The very nature of the motive power which works the advance-ment of the machines precludes the possibility of man's life being rendered miserable as well as enslaved. Slaves are tolerably happy if they have good masters, and the revolution will not occur in our time, nor hardly in ten thousand years, or ten times that. Is it wise to be uneasy about a contingency which is so remote? Man is not a sentimental animal where his material interests are concerned, and though here and there some ardent soul may look upon himself and curse his fate that he was not born a vapour-engine, yet the mass of mankind will acquiesce in any arrange-ment which gives them better food and clothing at a cheaper rate, and will refrain from yielding to unreasonable jealousy merely because there are other destinies more glorious than their own.

"The power of custom is enormous, and so gradual will be the change, that man's sense of what is due to himself will be at no time rudely shocked; our bondage will steal upon us noiselessly and by imperceptible approaches; nor will there ever be such a clashing of desires between man and the machines as will lead to an encounter between them. Among themselves the machines will war eternally, but they will still require man as the being through whose agency the struggle will be principally conducted. In point of fact there is no occasion for anxiety about the future happiness of man so long as he continues to be in any way profitable to the machines; he may become the inferior race, but he will be infinitely better off than he is now. Is it not then both absurd and unreasonable to be envious of our benefactors? And should we not be guilty of consummate folly if we were to reject advantages which we cannot obtain otherwise, merely because they involve a greater gain to others than to ourselves?

"With those who can argue in this way I have nothing in common. I shrink with as much horror from believing that my race can ever be superseded or surpassed, as I should do from believing that even at the remotest period my ancestors were other than human beings. Could I believe that ten hundred thousand years ago a single one of my ancestors was another kind of being to myself, I should lose all self-respect, and take no further pleasure or interest in life. I have the same feeling with regard to my descendants, and believe it to be one that will be felt so generally that the country will resolve upon putting an immediate stop to all further mechanical progress, and upon destroying all improvements that have been made for the last three hundred years. I would not urge more than this. We may trust ourselves to deal with those that remain, and though I should prefer to have seen the destruction include another two hundred years, I am aware of the necessity for compromising, and would so far sacrifice my own individual convictions as to be content with three hundred. Less than this will be insufficient."

This was the conclusion of the attack which led to the destruction of machinery throughout Erewhon. There was only one serious attempt to answer it. Its author said that machines were to be regarded as a part of man's own physical nature, being really nothing but extra-corporeal limbs. Man, he said, was a machinate mammal. The lower animals keep all their limbs at home in their own bodies, but many of man's are loose, and lie about detached, now here and now there, in various parts of the world—some being kept always handy for contingent use, and others being occasionally hundreds of miles away. A machine is merely a supplementary limb; this is the be all and end all of machinery. . . .

Carroll D. Wright

THE ETHICAL INFLUENCE OF MACHINERY ON LABOR

According to Mr. Herbert Spencer, ethics comprehends the laws of right living; and that, beyond the conduct commonly approved or

From *The Industrial Evolution of the United States* (New York, 1895). Carroll D. Wright (1840–1909) was the first Commissioner of the U.S. Bureau of Labor, Department of the Interior, and served from 1885–1905.

reprobated as right or wrong, it includes all conduct which furthers or hinders, in direct or in indirect ways, the welfare of self or others; that justice, which formulates the range of conduct and limitations to conduct hence arising, is at once the most important division of ethics; that it has to define the equitable relations among individuals who limit one another's spheres of action by coexisting, and who achieve their ends by coöperation; and that, beyond justice between man and man, justice between each man and the aggregate of men has to be dealt with by it.

This constitutes a very broad definition of ethics, and the propositions laid down by Mr. Spencer, taken by themselves, are such as no moral philosopher can for a moment reject, nor should they be rejected by economists, for a moment's reflection upon their bearing shows conclusively that material prosperity is best subserved by their incorporation as chapters in the laws of trade, commerce, and production. So the relation of the wage-receiver to his fellow-men and to society becomes ethical, purely so; but it is certainly ethico-economical, and his wages, the standard of his living; his working time, the cost of his living; his education, his interest in religious and literary matters, in art, and in all that adorns life, are features surrounding him which must be contemplated from the ethical point of view. This thought is all the more emphatic when it is considered that invention has brought with it a new school of ethics. It is the type and representative of the civilization of this period, because it embodies, so far as physics and economics are concerned, the concentrated, clearly wrought-out thought of the age. Books may represent thought; machinery or invention is the embodiment of thought. From an intellectual point of view, then, it becomes perfectly legitimate to speak of the ethical influence of inventions, and no consideration of the relation of inventions to labor or of the evolution of industry would be complete without showing in a more deeply philosophical sense their ethical influence upon the individual laborer.

We are living at the beginning of the age of mind, as illustrated by the results of inventive genius. It is the age of intellect, of brain—for brain is king, and machinery is the king's prime minister. Wealth of mind and wealth of purse may struggle for the mastery, but the former usually wins, and gives the crown to the Huxleys, Darwins, Tyndalls, Proctors, Woolseys, and Drapers, rather than to the men who accumulate great fortunes. It is natural and logical that under such a sovereignty inventions should not only typify the progress of the race, but that they should also have a clearly marked influence upon the morals of peoples, a mixed influence, to be sure, as men are what we call good or evil, but on the whole with the good vastly predominant.

Under the old hand system of labor, or, to use a better term, the domestic system, which was displaced when machinery came in and the factory system became fixed, the most demoralizing conditions prevailed. Those who believe that the old system was better than the new find something poetic in the idea of the weaver of old England, before spinning machinery was invented, working at his loom in his cottage, with his family about him, and from this reflection fall into the idyllic sentiment that the domestic system surpassed the present. This sentiment has done much to create false impressions as to the results or influence of machinery. Goldsmith's Auburn and Crabbe's Village do not reflect the truest picture of their country's home life under the domestic system of labor, for the domestic laborer's home, instead of being the poetic one, was very far from the character poetry has given it. Huddled together in his hut, not a cottage, the weaver's family lived and worked, without comfort, convenience, good air, good food, and without much intelligence. Drunkenness and theft made each home the scene of crime and want and disorder. Superstition ruled, and envy swayed the workers. If the members of a family, endowed with more virtue and intelligence than the common herd, tried to so conduct themselves as to secure at least self-respect, they were either abused or ostracized by their neighbors. The ignorance under the old system added to the squalor of the homes under it, and what all these elements failed to produce in making the hut an actual den was faithfully performed, in too many instances, by the swine of the family. The reports of the Poor Laws commissioners of England are truer exponents of conditions than poetry, and show more faithfully the demoralizing agency of pauperism and of all the other evils which were so prolific under the hand system of work.

The influence of machinery at the particular time spoken of in the history of mankind is usually over-looked, and so, too, is the fact that if there is any one thing in individuals that the present age insists upon it is work—employment of some kind, for employment means the very best ethical condition of man. The lowest and the most harmful and the most expensive ignorance which can prevail in any community is ignorance of work, the want of some technical knowledge which enables a man to earn a living outside of a penal institution, and as ethics and practical religion most assuredly have much to do with everything that affects the conduct of life, the knowledge which enables a man to do his work well indicates his ethical relations. Poverty and pure religion cannot exist among the same people, for such a religion cannot prevail unless the people are engaged in that class of employment which tends to broaden all their faculties, to awaken not only their sense of duty to their kind, but also to develop their love of beauty, of art, and of all that adorns and ennobles life; and such employment cannot be maintained without the vitalizing use of inventions which exhibit the enduring, the working, and the perfect embodiment of human ingenuity.

We are hardly aware of the silent working influence of machinery upon the morals of the world, but it is recognized in this particular thought that has been outlined, that poverty and religion are not now, as once, twin virtues. There are many other things to be learned from the influence of machinery which satisfy this thesis. Communism, which means the destruction of labor, can not coexist with machinery. Its use requires too much competition, both social and industrial, to admit of communism. The states, therefore, devoted to industries which require the use of machines to a large extent are safe from the inroads of communism and communistic socialism, for without machinery the world would necessarily retrograde to superstition and to ignorance, and the ingenuity of man would assume its old place among the unused faculties of the mind. . . .

The hours of labor have been reduced from twelve or thirteen per day in the same industry to nine and one half in England and ten generally in this country. An examination of statistical tables will convince any one that for most divisions of labor in textile factories wages have been nearly doubled during the past sixty or seventy years, and such examination will show like results for very many other industries.

This inevitable ethical result of the application of machinery has been to enable man to secure a livelihood in less time than of old, and this is grand of itself, if no other advantage had been secured; for it must be considered that as the time required to earn a living grows shorter civilization advances, and that any system which demands of a man all his time or the greater portion of it for the earning of mere subsistence must be demoralizing in all respects. The moral condition of man has been improved through the improvement of his health. In warm and comfortable clothing, in water-proof material, in heating and lighting, in a thousand ways, invention has carried with it more comfortable conditions, increased health, and an increased longevity, the average of life at present being ten percent higher than in the olden time. Low grades of labor are constantly giving place to educated labor. The man who used to do the most detestable forms of work is being displaced everywhere by men of professional and technical training, who superintend some device brought into use by invention. So the constant promotion of luxuries to the grade of necessaries of life marks the forward steps of civilization. What once were luxuries to one class are now the necessaries of life to a class that might be considered below the first. This is illustrated by the fact that there was a time when a linen sheet was worth thirty-two days of common labor, and when a gridiron cost from four to twelve days of labor.

Prior to the generation which precedes the present the fastest time that could be made was through the speed of man, or of horses, or of sailing vessels, except, perhaps, in the occasional transmission of intelligence by signals. The very first change in the way of speed in transportation or in the interchange of intelligence came to the world within the memory of men now living. Engineering enterprises are solving the problem of how to relieve congested cities and of how to give to the wage-worker, who must save time as between his lodging and his work, the benefits of healthful surroundings in the country. Rapid transit, through the application of electricity to street cars, has in many cases added from one half to three quarters of an hour of the day to the workingman's available time. This is the influence of invention, and a moral influence, for it betters his condition, helps him to a higher plane, facilitates social intercourse, and in every way gives him better opportunities for enjoying all that belongs to his environment.

Every machine that is invented marks some progress in a useful art. It accomplishes some useful end not before attained, or it does some old work better and cheaper. It makes more valuable the day's work of an operative, and it adds to everything that makes life agreeable, provided there is thrift and prudence behind the worker. If there is any ethical influence in the study of or familiarity with works of art, certainly machinery has had a very deep ethical influence, for by the aid of mechanical powers the work of artisans is rapidly making the taste of the people artistic, for trained and inventive skill, as exhibited in machinery, puts art into wood and metal, showing "the highest discipline of the mental faculties, the direction and subordination of all its manifestations for some clearly-defined purpose." But it has gone beyond and has brought to the commonest person some of the results of the highest artistic skill in the world. Copies of great pictures, the works of the great masters, are familiar to the common people. Once only one man could own a great picture; to him and to his friends all the joy that comes of beholding the artistic production was limited. To-day, while he owns the original, the people own the picture, and the artist and his influence serve all, and he is enabled not only to unlock the stores of art which the world holds, but by the cheapening of publication he can unlock the stores of knowledge.

There is one feature which belongs to the ethical influence of machinery to which attention ought to be called. The argument is often made that by its use there is brought into industrial work an ignorant class of workers, but this argument is baseless. There is no more ignorance in the world on account of inventions, but by their perfection an ignorant class can often do perfectly what an intelligent class used to bungle over, and at the same time the intelligence of the ignorant is raised. The ignorant laborer of to-day is, in all that makes up condition, more than the peer of the skilled workman of a few generations ago, and the fact that as the country increases in wealth the numbers employed in miscellaneous industries, as has been shown in the preceding chapter, and what Mr.

David A. Wells calls incorporeal functions—that is, artists, teachers, and others who minister to taste and comfort in a way that can hardly be called material—increase disproportionately to those engaged in the production of the great staples, answers the idea that inventions foster ignorance in production. Inventions have, indeed, superinduced the congregation of ignorant laborers, and thereby given the appearance of creating ignorant labor. The great fact remains that as ignorant laborers are brought together their condition attracts attention and the public proceeds at once to bring to them educational facilities. Invention was the cause of the better condition, for it was not until the factory system was thoroughly fixed as the industrial system of England that Parliament brought under educational influences the children of the factory. To machinery must be attributed the great extension of the facilities for educating the masses. The centers devoted to industrial pursuits are the centers of thought, of mental friction, of intelligence, and of progress.

Werner Siemens
THE SCIENTIFIC AGE

. . . For us older men it suffices to acquire a view of the great difference between the past and the present—to cast a brief glance back to our own youth. We can still recollect the time when steamboats and locomotives made their first feeble experimental trips; we still hear with credulous astonishment the news that light itself can be made to paint the picture which it renders visible to our eyes; that the mysterious new force, electricity, could transmit news with the velocity of lightning through whole continents and the oceans separating them; that the same force would separate metals, in fixed form, from their solutions; and that it could drive away the night with a light as clear as that of day. Who wonders to-day over these now self-evident things, without which our youth could hardly imagine a civilized life—to-day, in an age when, according to Reuleaux's calculations, several iron laborers work day and night for every civilized man; when millions of men and immense quantities of goods are carried great distances at velocities which were

From *The Popular Science Monthly*, 30 (1886), 814. Dr. Siemens (1816–1892) was a German scientist and engineer who pioneered the development of electric generators, telegraphy, electric arc lamps, and the electric railway.

once hardly conceivable; when the world-binding telegraph is not sufficient for the wants of our commerce, and has to make way for the transmission of the living word through the telephone; when photography is at the service of all classes; and when the latest fruit of the association of science and art, electro-technics, is opening to man, in its rapid unfolding, ever-new regions of inconceivable extent for further research and useful applications of the forces of Nature? To the investigator—who, more than any other class of men, is accustomed to draw conclusions from the course of observed phenomena as to the law controlling them—it is, however, not the latest state of development, but its causes, and the laws on which they depend, that are of surpassing importance. The clearly recognizable law is that of the progressive acceleration of our present advance in civilization. Periods of development, which in former times required hundreds of years for their accomplishment, which in the beginning of our age needed decades, are now completed in years, and sometimes come into being in full perfection. This is the natural result of our highly perfected system of instruction, by which the acquisitions of science, and particularly the scientific method, have been introduced into the broad stream of art and popular life in all their forms of efficacy.

Thus we see how, by virtue of our now excellent system of communications, every new scientific thought is at once flashed through the whole civilized world, and how thousands endeavor to grasp it and to apply it in the most diverse spheres of life. Sometimes it may be only modest observations, sometimes only the overcoming of small impediments that stand in the way of the recognition of the scientific relations of phenomena. They may often be the point of departure for a new course of advance, previously quite unanticipated, but important for human life. The progressive development conditioned upon these principles will therefore continue, if man does not himself in his conceit interrupt it, as long as science keeps going on to higher degrees of knowledge. The deeper insight we get into the secret processes of Nature, the more we are convinced that we are still standing in the extreme outer court of science, that an as yet immeasurable field of work lies before us, and that it still appears at least very questionable whether man will ever reach a complete knowledge of Nature. There is, therefore, no ground for doubting the continuance of the progressive ascent of scientific and technical evolution, unless man himself interferes with it by conduct inimical to civilization. But even hostile attacks can henceforth cause only temporary interruptions in the course of development, or at most only partial reversions, for, in the presence of the printing of books and the wide diffusion of the results of modern civilization, the scientific and technical accomplishments of mankind can never again be lost. Moreover, the peoples who cultivate these arts and lift them higher acquire through them such a dominant ascendency, so great a fullness of power, that their subjection in the contest with uncivilized people, and the breaking out of a new barbaric age, appear impossible.

While we thus regard the present development of civilization as incessant and impregnable, the end to which it is tending remains hidden to us; but we can discern from its beginnings the direction into which it is to turn the principles on which popular life has hitherto rested. For this purpose we need only to carry out further the changes which have been already begun. We can then easily perceive that, in the age of the reign of the sciences, severe manual labor, by which man has been very hardly and still is considerably oppressed in the struggle for existence, will be more and more reduced by the increasing utilization of natural forces in mechanical service, that the work that falls to man will become continually more of a mental character, while it will be his part to direct the work of iron laborers (or machines) but not himself to perform rough bodily labor. We see, further, that in the scientific age the necessaries of life and luxuries will be supplied with far less human toil, and that a much larger share of these products of labor will fall to each man at the expense of less working-time. We shall see, also, that, through scientific and properly directed cultivation, a very much larger quantity of food-products will be obtained from the soil than heretofore, and that the number of men devoted to this branch of industry may be correspondingly diminished. We shall find that through the improvement and greater expedition of communication and transportation an ever-more ready exchange of the products of different lands and climates will be made possible by which the life of men will be rendered more enjoyable and their existence assured against the consequences of local scarcities. It also appears very probable that chemistry in connection with electrotechnics will some time succeed in composing real food-substances out of the inexhaustible abundance of their elements everywhere present, and thereby make the number of those who may be supported independent of the ultimate productive capacity of the soil. This progressively augmenting facility in obtaining the material means of existence will, by the shortening of the working-time that will have to be applied to that purpose, afford to men the leisure they will need for their better mental cultivation; the better perfected and cheapened making of mechanical reproduction of artistic creations will also prepare the way for bringing these works into the cottages, and will make art, beautifying the life and elevating the moral standard, accessible to all mankind, instead of to privileged classes only. We are strongly of the conviction that the light of science, penetrating more deeply into the whole of human society, combats in the most effective manner degrading superstitions and destructive fanaticism, and that we shall be able therefore to go on in proud satisfaction with the building up of the age of science, in the sure prospect that it will lead mankind to a better moral and material condition than it has been or is enjoying to-day.

Our complacency on this subject has been disturbed very recently by gloomy pessimistic views which have been formed in learned circles as well as in the broad popular strata, respecting the influence which the rapid advance of science and art is exercising upon the character of popular life, and respecting the end to which that advance is tending.

The questions have been raised and discussed whether man is really better and happier for all these achievements of science and art, or whether they do not rather lead to the destruction of all ideal qualities of good, and to a coarse pleasure-seeking; whether the inequality in the division of the goods and pleasures of life will not be magnified through them; and whether the opportunities for work of individuals will not be diminished through the growth of machine-industry and the division of labor resulting from it, and the laborer himself be brought into a more restrained, dependent condition than before; or, in short, whether, instead of the lordship of birth and the sword, there will not prevail the still more oppressive rule of inherited or acquired wealth.

It can not be denied that there is now some show of justification for these gloomy anticipations. The rapid and continuous advance of scientific technics must necessarily, as it goes on, have a disturbing effect on many branches of industry. Better working methods may in many ways cause production to rise faster than consumption, and reduce the demand for labor, while manual labor, which formerly employed a much larger number of workmen to produce the same results, will no longer be able to compete with special machines. The like may be observed in the production of food-materials. Cheaper means of transportation are bringing to the old civilized lands the products in masses of thinly inhabited regions, whose virgin soils are not yet in need of artificial fertilization, but in which the scarcity of labor has led to the perfection of mechanical processes. It is true that scientific art provides means of equalizing these disadvantages by more rational methods of fertilizing and working; yet it is very hard to replace old accustomed but untenable conditions by better ones. Complaints are multiplying over the general depression in prices, and the falling off of the demand for labor, and the strangest theories are proposed for curing these evils by the isolation of certain lands against the products of others, and by forced limitations of production. The adherents of such theories go so far as to deny all utility to mankind of the scientific tendency, and to dream of a return to the methods of former presumed happier days. They do not recollect that, in this case, the number of men would also have to be brought back to the old figure. The number of happy shepherds and huntsmen is very small, and yet it must enter as an essential factor into the estimation of the greater or less prosperity of any period. It is a very hard but at the same time an unalterable social law, that all transitions to other, even if they be better, conditions, are connected with suffering. It is, therefore, certainly a humane proceeding to alleviate these sufferings to the present generation by a careful direction and partial limitation of the new, continually reverting revolutions of the social conditions of popular life; but it would be hopeless to try to stop the stream of this development, or to turn it back. It must necessarily follow its predestined course, and those countries and peoples will be least affected by its disturbing influence, and will be the first to participate in the benefits of the scientific age, which do the most to bring it on. But that the coming age will really present better conditions to mankind, and will heal again the wounds that it makes, notwithstanding the unavoidable inconveniences of the transition to new modes, is recognizable from many signs.

Is not the generally apparent lowering of the prices of all the necessaries of life and products of labor with a simultaneous, vastly increased consumption, an indubitable evidence that the human labor required to provide them has become less as well as lighter than before? And that the tendency of the development is such that men in the future will have to labor a much shorter time to provide for their needs? Does not also the fact, evident at the same time, that wages are not falling in a corresponding degree with prices, show that the lot of the working-classes will be a continuously improving one as the scientific age advances? Cheaper production of necessaries means the same thing as higher wages. Higher wages, and shorter hours of work! This louder and louder sounding demand of the so-called working-classes will be realized, therefore, as the natural result of scientific progress. For, except for crises and states of transition, no more will be made than is used, and the average time of work will of necessity diminish with the augmented speed and ease of production.

Another generally evident fact is the reduction of interest. To discern the significance of this fact, we must keep in view that capital— the savings of wages, as political economy calls it—is the standard of value of all wealth. His own or borrowed capital enables a man to obtain the usufruct of the labor of other men. If capital were really abolished, as fanatical and mistaken men are trying to have done, mankind would fall back into a condition of barbarism in which every one would be relegated to the work of his own hands for the provision of necessaries. But the demand for capital can not keep pace with its increase, because the arrangements for the production of goods are growing more facile, simpler, and cheaper. There is, therefore—always allowing for the transitional variations and violent disturbances of natural progress—a larger average accumulation of capital than can be usefully applied; or, in other words, an overproduction of capital is taking place, which must find, and is, in fact, already finding, its expression in a reduction of the rates of interest. The value of the savings of former labor, or of capital, will, therefore, continue to decline in comparison with the labor of the present, and must in the course of time be annihilated.

For the other and seemingly the most weighty objection of the opponents of our social progress—that by its operation the larger number are condemned to work in large factories, and that in the progressive division of labor no room is left for the free exertion of individuals—for this, also, the natural course of the advance of the scientific age bears the remedy in itself. The necessity of large factories for the cheap production of useful articles depends essentially on the present imperfection of machine technics. Large machines just now give cheaper effects than small ones, and the introduction of the latter into the houses of workmen is still beset with great difficulties. But ingenuity will certainly succeed in overcoming the impediments in the way of the return to competitive manual labor, by bringing cheapened mechanical powers, the basis of all industry, into the smaller shops and workmen's homes. Not a number of great factories in the hands of rich capitalists, in which the "slaves of toil" shall wear out their hard existence, is to be the ending of the development of the age of science, but the return to individual labor, or, where the circumstances call for it, the conduct of co-operative establishments by associations of workmen, for which a sound basis has first been furnished by the general spread of knowledge and training, and the possibility of a cheapened supply of capital.

The complaint is likewise unjust that the study of science, and the application of the natural forces to the arts, give a material tendency to men, making them vain in their knowledge and power, and diverting them from ideal aims.

The more deeply we look into the harmonious administration of the powers of Nature, regulated by eternally unchangeable laws, yet so profoundly veiled from our full understanding, the more, inversely, we feel ourselves moved to an humble modesty; the smaller appears the scope of our knowledge, the more earnest is our effort to draw more from this inexhaustible fountain of knowledge and power, and the higher rises our admiration of the infinite regulating wisdom which pervades the entire creation. And the admiration of this infinite wisdom gives a new stimulus to that spirit of investigation, that devout pure love of knowledge, which finds its final object in itself, which has been lifted to a position of high honor in the German scholar, where it stands a hopeful mark to future generations.

Hence we should not be disturbed in our faith that our zeal in investigation and discovery will raise mankind to higher grades of civilization, will ennoble it and make it more amenable to ideal efforts, and that the dawning scientific age will diminish its suffering and disease, heighten its enjoyment, and make it better, happier, and more satisfied with its lot. And, although we may not always see clearly the conviction that the light of truth which we are seeking for will not lead us into error, and that the fullness of power which it gives to man can not depress him, but must raise him to a higher degree of the way that leads to these better conditions, we shall yet hold fast to being.

Leo Tolstoy
THE SUPERSTITIONS OF SCIENCE

I think Edward Carpenter's article on "Contemporary Science" should be specially beneficial in our Russian society, in which, more than in any other European society, has spread and taken root the superstition according to which it is held that for the well-being of mankind the spread of true religious and moral knowledge is not at all necessary, but only the study of the experimental sciences, and that a knowledge of these sciences satisfies all the spiritual demands of mankind.

It can readily be understood what an injurious influence such a coarse superstition must have on a people's moral life,—just such an influence as religious superstition has. Therefore the spread of the thoughts of writers who take up a critical attitude towards experimental science and its methods is especially desirable for our society.

Carpenter demonstrates that neither astronomy, nor physics, nor chemistry, nor biology, nor sociology gives us a true knowledge of reality; that all the laws discovered by these sciences are only generalizations, having an approximate value as laws, and even this only when other conditions are unknown or ignored; and that even these laws seem laws to us only because we discover them in a region which is so distant from us in time or space that we cannot see the want of correspondence between these laws and reality.

Besides this, Carpenter shows that the method of science, consisting in the explanation of phenomena near to us and important for us, by

The Arena, 20 (1898), 52–60. Leo Tolstoy (1828–1910) was a Russian novelist and moral philosopher.

phenomena more distant from us and indifferent for us, is a false method, which can never lead to the desired results.

"Every science," he says, "as far as possible explains the phenomena which it investigates by ideas of an inferior order. Thus ethics is founded on questions of utility and hereditary habit. From political economy are eliminated all questions of justice between man and man, of compassion, of attachment, of efforts for solidarity, and it is based on a principle of the very lowest order that could be found in it, namely, the principle of personal interest. From biology is excluded the idea of personality, not only in plants and animals, but even in men; the question of conscious personality is set aside, and an attempt is made to reduce the questions of biology to reflex action and chemical affinity,—to protoplasm and phenomena of osmosis. Moreover chemical affinity and all the wonderful phenomena of physics are reduced to atomic motions, and atomic motions, like the motions of the heavenly bodies, are reduced to the laws of mechanics."

It is asserted that the reduction of questions of a higher order to questions of a lower order explains the questions of higher order. But this explanation is never reached, and all that happens is that, descending in its investigations ever further and further from the most real questions to less real questions, science at last reaches a region wholly foreign to man, and only coming into remote contact with him, and gives all its attention to this region, leaving all the questions which are really important for man totally unsolved.

What happens is something like the act of a man who, desiring to understand the meaning of an object standing before him, instead of going nearer to it, and examining and feeling it on all sides, should go further and further away from the object, and, finally, should reach such a distance that all the characteristics of color and inequality of surface should disappear, and only those distinctions should remain visible which separate the object from the horizon. And standing there the man should begin to describe the object in detail, holding that now he had a clear idea of it, and that this idea, formed at such a distance, would contribute to a full understanding of the subject. This is the self-delusion which is in part stripped bare by Carpenter's criticism, when he demonstrates, in the first place, that the knowledge which science gives us in the region of the natural sciences is only a convenient process of generalization, and by no means an image of reality, and in the second place that the method of science, by which phenomena of a higher order are reduced to phenomena of a lower order, can never lead us to an explanation of the phenomena of higher order.

But without prejudging the question whether experimental science will or will not ultimately lead, by its method, to a solution of the problems of life which are most important for mankind, the very action of experimental science in relation to the eternal and most legitimate demands of mankind is startling in its wrongness.

People must live. But in order to live they must know how to live. And all people have ever solved this question,—whether ill or well,—and have lived and advanced in harmony with that solution; and the knowledge of how people should live, from the time of Moses, Solomon, and Confucius, was always held to be a science, the science of sciences. And it is only in our times that the science of how to live has become no science, and that only experimental science, beginning with mathematics and ending with sociology, is held to be real science.

And from this a strange misunderstanding arises. A simple and sensible workingman holds in the old-fashioned and sensible way that if there are people who study during their whole lives, and, in return for the food and support he gives them, think for him, then these thinkers are probably occupied with what is necessary to people, and he expects from science a solution of those questions on which his well-being and the well-being of all people depends. He expects that science will teach him how to live, how to act towards members of his family, towards his neighbors, towards foreigners; how to battle with his passions, in what he should or should not believe, and much more. And what does our science tell him concerning all these questions?

It majestically informs him how many million miles the sun is from the earth, how many millions of ethereal vibrations in a second constitute light, how many vibrations in the air make sound; it tells him of the chemical constitution of the Milky Way, of the new element helium, of micro-organisms and their waste tissue, of the points in the hand in which electricity is concentrated, of X rays, and the like. But, says the simple common-sense person, none of this is necessary to me; I need to know how to live. You want to know a great deal, replies science. What you ask belongs to sociology. But before sociological questions can be answered, we must first decide zoölogical, botanical, physiological, and in general biological questions; and in order to solve these questions, we must previously solve questions of physics and chemistry, and we must come to an agreement as to the forms of infinitesimal atoms, and the manner in which the imponderable and inelastic ether conveys motion.

And people, especially those who sit on the necks of others, and for whom it is therefore quite convenient to wait, are satisfied with these answers, and sit blinking their eyes, and waiting for what is promised; but the simple and sensible workingman, on whose neck are sitting the others who are occupying themselves with science, the vast mass of people, all humanity, cannot be satisfied by such answers, and naturally asks in perplexity: When will all that happen? We cannot wait. You say yourselves that you will find out all this in several generations. But we are alive now; to-day we live; to-morrow we die; and therefore we need to know how to live the life in which we now are. Therefore teach us.

Stupid and uneducated fellow, science replies, he does not understand that science serves not utility, but science. Science studies what presents itself for study, and cannot select subjects for study. Science studies everything. This is the character of science.

And men of science are really convinced that this quality of occupying itself with trifles, and neglecting what is more real and important, is a quality not of themselves, but of science; but the simple, sensible person begins to suspect that this quality belongs not to science, but to people who are inclined to occupy themselves with trifles, and to attribute to these trifles a high importance.

Science studies everything, say the men of science. But this everything is somewhat too much. Everything is an endless quantity of subjects, and it is impossible to study everything at once. As a lighthouse cannot illumine everything at once, but only illumines the spot to which its light is directed, so science cannot study everything, but inevitably studies only that to which its attention is directed. And as a lighthouse illumines more brightly a spot which is close to it, and more faintly objects which are more remote, and does not illumine at all objects which its light does not reach, so human science, whatever its character may be, has always studied and studies in the greatest detail what appears most important to those who study, and studies in less detail what seems to them less important, and does not study at all the whole endless number of subjects which remain.

And what is very important, what is less important, and what is of no importance at all, is defined for people by their general understanding of the purpose and aim of life, that is, by religion.

But the men of science of our time, recognising no religion, and therefore having no basis for selecting subjects of study according to their importance, and separating them from subjects of less importance, and finally from that endless number of subjects which always remain unstudied, owing to the limitations of the human mind and to the endlessness of the number of these subjects, have worked out for themselves a theory of "science for science's sake," according to which science studies not what is necessary to people, but everything.

And in reality experimental science studies everything, not, however, in the sense of the union of all subjects, but in the sense of disorder and chaos in defining the subjects studied; that is, science studies especially, not what is necessary to people, and studies less, not what is less necessary, leaving unstudied what is unnecessary, but rather studies anything, according to the merest hazard. Although the Comtist and other classifications of science exist, these classifications do not guide the choice of subjects of study, but the choice of subjects is guided by human weakness, common to men of science as to all men. So that in reality men of science study, not everything, as they imagine and affirm, but what is most profitable and easy to study. And it is most profitable to study what contributes to the well-being of the upper classes to which the people who occupy themselves with science belong; and it is easiest to study what is lifeless. And this is the course followed by those who study the experimental sciences: they study books, monuments, dead bodies; and they consider this study to be the most real science. . . .

And, as always happens, the lower any human activity descends, the further it departs from what it ought to be, the stronger grows its self-confidence. And this is the very thing which has happened to the science of our time. True science was never esteemed by contemporaries, but on the contrary was for the most part rejected. And it could not be otherwise. True science shows people their errors, and points out to them new and untried paths of life. And both the one and the other are disagreeable to the ruling class of society. But the present science not only does not run counter to the tastes and demands of the ruling class of society, but rather corresponds to them completely; it satisfies idle curiosity, astonishes people, and promises them an increase of pleasures. And therefore, while everything truly great is silent, modest, inconspicuous, the science of our time knows no bounds to its self-gratulations.

All previous methods were mistaken, and therefore everything that was formerly accounted science is delusion, error, trifling; our method alone is true, and the only true science is ours. The successes of our science are such that thousands of years have failed to accomplish what we have accomplished in the last century. And in the future, following the same path, our science will solve all questions, and make the whole of humanity happy. Our science is the most important activity in the world, and we, the men of science, are the most important and necessary people in the world.

Thus the men of science of our time think and speak, and the crowd follows them, while at the same time there was never a period or a people among whom science in its complete significance stood on so low a level as our science to-day. One part of it, that which should study what makes the life of man good and happy, is occupied in justifying the existing evil conditions of life, while another part spends its time solving questions of idle curiosity.

How, of idle curiosity? I hear voices of indignation at such sacrilegious scoffing. And what about steam, and electricity, and telephones, and all the achievements of technical art? To say nothing of their scientific importance, see what practical results they have achieved. Man has conquered nature, and subjected her forces to his will; and so forth. But then all these practical victories over nature up to the present, and for a long enough time, only lead to factories which ruin the people, to weapons for destroying human life, to the increase of luxury and license, answers the simple and sensible person, and therefore man's victory over nature not only has not increased the happiness of mankind, but, on the contrary, has made its condition worse. If the structure of society is evil, as with us, where a small number of people rule over the majority, and oppress it, then every victory over nature inevitably serves only to strengthen that power and that oppression. And this is what takes place.

In the case of science, which finds its subject, not in the study of how people should live, but in the study of what is, and is therefore preëminently occupied with the investigation of dead bodies, and leaves the structure of human society as it is, no achievements and no victories over nature can improve the condition of the people.

And medicine? You forget the beneficent successes of medicine. And the inoculation of bacteria? And the present operations? exclaim, as usual, the defenders of science, as a last resource, bringing forward the successes of medicine as a demonstration of the fruitfulness of all science.

We can guard against diseases and accomplish cures by inoculation, we can perform painless operations, we can take out internal organs and cleanse them, we can straighten hunchbacks, generally say the defenders of science, holding for some reason or other that to cure one child of diphtheria from among all the children, fifty percent of whom in all Russia, and eighty percent in institutions, normally die, must convince people of the beneficence of science in general.

The structure of our life is such that not only children, but the majority of the people, owing to bad food, inordinately hard and injurious work, unhealthy dwellings, and insufficient clothing, do not live half the term of years they ought to live; the condition of life is such that children's diseases, syphilis, phthisis, and alcoholism lay hold of an ever-increasing number of people; that the greater part of their labor is perverted to preparations for war; that every ten or twenty years millions of people are destroyed by war; and all this takes place because science, instead of spreading among us true religious, moral, and social ideas, as a result of which all these evils would disappear of their own accord, occupies itself on the one hand with justifications of the existing order, and on the other with playthings, and, to demonstrate to us the fruitfulness of science, points to the fact that it cures a thousandth part of the ills which overtake us simply because science does not do its duty. If even a small fraction of the effort, attention, and labor which men of science spend on the trifles which occupy them were directed to establishing right religious, moral, social, or even hygienic ideas, there would not be a hundredth part of the diphtheria, hysteria, spinal curvature, and the like, on the cure of which science so prides itself, accomplishing these cures in its hospitals, whose accommodations cannot be extended to all.

This is just as if people who had ploughed badly a field sown badly, with bad seed, were to go about in the field, and to cure the broken ears in the crop, which grew beside diseased ears, at the same time trampling down all the rest, and were to bring forward their art in curing the diseased ears as a proof of their knowledge of agriculture.

Our science, in order to become science, and to become truly beneficent, and not injurious to mankind, must first of all renounce its empirical method, according to which it considers itself bound to study only what is, and must return to the only wise and fruitful understanding of science, according to which its object is the study of how people ought to live. In this is the aim and purpose of science; and the study of what is can only be the subject of science so far as that study contributes to a knowledge of how people ought to live.

And it is this recognition of the bankruptcy of experimental science, and the absolute necessity of adopting another method, which Carpenter's article demonstrates.

2
Science, Society, and Human Values

The progress of science affects society in two respects. First, the technological innovations that result from the application of scientific knowledge change our mode of living in many ways. As a result of technological innovation, society has become mainly urbanized; people have acquired a large degree of mobility; worldwide communication has become almost instantaneous. But probably more disturbing to man's values are the changes wrought by scientific knowledge itself. The findings of Copernicus, Kepler, and Newton destroyed man's view that the earth holds a favored position in the universe. Darwin's theory of evolution changed man's ideas about his own origin and development. Because such powerful forces for change are released by the acquisition of scientific knowledge, it is important to explore the goals and values of science itself and to determine how these may be affected by the society in which a scientist lives.

A number of questions arise when we try to analyze the relation of science to society. First, does science, considered as a disinterested search for knowledge about nature, possess any element of traditional human values? It is often characterized as an amoral activity, seeking neither to

31

confirm nor destroy societal values. What is the validity of such a description? Bronowski rejects it, stating that scientists attempt to discover truth. Second, what is the status of the results of scientific inquiry? Should society firmly build its institutions on these results—when we know that many findings of scientists in the past have later proved inexact if not completely erroneous? Many mid-nineteenth century American scientists, for example, believed that the Negro is an inferior if not a completely different species of man. This, of course, had implications in the slavery controversy. Further, scientists do not always agree on the interpretations of their findings. To what degree, then, should society trust the pronouncements of its scientists? Should it attempt to counterbalance scientific knowledge with tradition and intuition? Karl Deutsch argues that science provides society with factual knowledge that it must have in order to operate effectively. Joseph Wood Krutch, on the other hand, holds that value judgments cannot be based on scientific knowledge alone—since, from the point of view of science, there is no "good" and no "bad"; instead, he believes, we must rely on tradition and intuition. Muller, although admitting that the results of scientific inquiry may be only transitory, views science as an instrument of human purpose; science is involved rather with the means of human action, whereas value judgments are involved in the ends. Further, he warns against the assumption that scientific knowledge is the only kind of knowledge; science, he says, describes just one kind of reality and can give directions for dealing with only certain kinds of things.

In another area, how has the rise of science affected religion, certainly a traditional basic human value? W. T. Stace believes that science, in expelling the idea of purpose from the events of nature, has destroyed the foundations of all theologies and religion. Nature has come to be viewed as senseless and meaningless, so that the life of man has become meaningless as well. John K. Wood rejects this pessimistic view. He is convinced that science cannot destroy religion, for science can never successfully demonstrate that religious feelings are merely the operation of a particular set of chemical processes within the body. The important concepts embodied in all religions—faith, love, and hope—can never be invalidated by the progress of scientific knowledge.

Finally, what is the responsibility of the scientist to society? Does he have any responsibility? It is known, for example, that in a number of instances, the results of scientific research have not been beneficial to society. If it were possible, should the scientist suppress findings which he believes in the long run might be inimical to traditional human values? Deutsch argues that we must be optimistic in this regard; we must hope that the results of science will eventually promote human well-being.

Turning to another area, should the scientist interpret his findings in such a way that they will be understandable to the educated layman? As the discoverer of new knowledge, which might have a profound effect on societal values, has he discharged his responsibility by publishing his results in a scientific journal, or must he then see to it that the public at large understands the implications of his work? Herbert Muller complains that many results of science are concealed in technical jargon; and Robert M. MacIver, addressing the same problem, states that the more the findings of science are communicated and interpreted to the public, the more likely it is that social and political decisions will be enlightened. This is the duty of the scientist who, as a human being, must make value judgments. Only in this way can the scientist influence those social forces which, in a large measure, affect the development of science.

Jacob Bronowski
TRUTH AND VALUE

People who are troubled in mind by the changes which they see science working in their world usually single out the technical changes: the aeroplane, the bomb, the habit of reading newspapers, the shift from homely comforts and home music to television. But under these changes there runs in us all a deeper division between the social habits of our schooldays and new habits of thought. We are troubled by a two-sidedness in our own behavior, where one side is what we have long been taught to value, and the other is worldly success. We are faced every day with actions of which our own code of conduct makes us ashamed, but which we find compelling if we are to battle with the hard facts of society.

We do not consciously blame science for this rift until it throws out some unavoidable challenge, such as in our time has been set by the atomic bomb. But that sharp issue is merely a symbol. Beyond all our actions stands the larger shadow: how are we to choose between what we have been taught to think right and something else which manifestly succeeds? And this empirical test of success grows more pressing as we

Jacob Bronowski, *The Common Sense of Science* (Cambridge, Mass.: Harvard University Press, 1951), pp. 120–124, 131–134. Reprinted by permission of the publishers. Dr. Bronowski is a distinguished scholar and is, at present, Fellow and Deputy Director of the Salk Institute for Biological Studies.

grow used to it in science. The empirical habit never lets the traditional beliefs alone for long, even within science. And it has been busy now for quite six hundred years in changing the accepted codes of good and right conduct.

For of course, these codes have not remained fixed since the days of William of Ockham. The ideals of what is good have suffered slow but remarkable changes, even in the same Church. It is plain enough that the ideals of the Renaissance are not the same as those of the Fathers, and more recently, that the Protestant virtues differ from the Catholic, which have themselves changed. The medieval doctrine of the just price had been deeply made over before a Pope could write *Rerum Novarum* in 1891. And we see what has become of the Christian virtues in the Methodism of the early nineteenth century: how the stress has shifted from charity and loving kindness, quite unconsciously, to the socially powerful virtues of thrift, sobriety, frugality and independence. So we are in a state of change today not because we have let go of some ancient absolute of perfection, but because like every age our age is trying to re-discover its own conscience.

Nor is science the only ferment at work. I have said again and again . . . that science is a part, a characteristic part, of human activity at large. I have been at pains . . . to show scientific method as the method of all human inquiry, which differs at last only in this, that it is explicit and systematic. This is very striking when we come to problems of right judgment and good conduct. There never has been a great book or a powerful work of art which has not been thought immoral by those with an older tradition. Jews still think the New Testament immoral, and Christians the Koran. Savonarola thought Florentine art licentious, and when George Eliot wrote about him in the last century, she thought him licentious and her critics thought her so. Sidney's *Apologie for Poetrie* is a school book now, and so is Shelley's *Defense of Poetry*. Yet Sidney was defending all literature against the charge of being a corrupter of men on the very eve of the Elizabethan flowering of the arts, and a succession of men and women went to prison for selling Shelley's poems. The harsh pattern of Swift's writing was fixed because he scandalized the religious sensibilities of Queen Anne. In our own day. Thomas Hardy, James Joyce and D. H. Lawrence have been held to outrage and to undermine morality. Yet it is overwhelmingly likely that their books will survive when the thousand spruce and proper critics of the day have been forgotten.

Often the attack on a new outlook in the arts takes a slightly different ground. A book or a painting is held to be harmful to the public mind, by being not immoral but without morality at all. Raphael was criticized in this way for being amoral, and so were Whistler and the Pre-Raphaelites. In literature, Tolstoy's *Anna Karenina* was called amoral, with many other works of the Russian novelists and playwrights; and the list of English playwrights who have been charged with a lack of any moral sense goes all the way from the Restoration to Oscar Wilde and Bernard Shaw.

It is this last charge which is commonly brought against science. The claim is not that science is actively anti-moral, but that it is without morality of any kind. The implication is that it thereby breeds in the minds of those who practise it an indifference to morality which comes in time to atrophy in them the power of right judgment and the urge to good conduct.

This charge seems to me as false of the sciences as of the arts. No-one who stops to think about *Anna Karenina* today believes that it is without morality, and that it makes no judgment on the complex actions of its heroine, her husband and her lover. On the contrary, we find it a deeper and a more moving book than a hundred conventional novels about that triangle, because it shows so much more patient, more understanding and more heartbreaking an insight into the forces which buffet its men and women. It is not a conventional book, it is a true book. And we do not mean by truth some chance correspondence with the facts in a newspaper about a despairing woman who threw herself under a train. We mean that Tolstoy understood people and events, and saw within them the interplay of personality, passion, convention, and the impact on them of the to-and-fro of outside happenings. No ethic and no set of values has our respect now which does not recognise the truth in this.

There is indeed no system of morality which does not set a high value on truth and on knowledge, above all on a conscious knowledge of oneself. It is therefore at least odd that science should be called amoral, and this by people who in their own lives set a high value on being truthful. For whatever else may be held against science, this cannot be denied, that it takes for ultimate judgment one criterion alone, that it shall be truthful. If there is one system which can claim a more fanatical regard for truth than Lao-tsze and the Pilgrim Fathers, it is certainly science.

We cannot of course put their truth or any other human values quite so simply as this. We must look round and see whether, either in ethics or in science, truth does not extend beyond a simple truthfulness to fact. And we may take this inquiry into truth as a characteristic test for science, on which we can ground the larger decision, whether science does indeed possess its own values. But do not let us miss the simple point. Whatever else they have also meant by truth, men who take pride in their conduct and its underlying values do set store by truthfulness in the literal sense. They are ashamed to lie in fact and in intention. And this transcending respect for truthfulness is shared by science. T. H. Huxley was an agnostic, Clifford was an atheist, and I know at least one great mathematician who is a scoundrel. Yet all of them rest their scientific faith on an uncompromising adherence to the truth, and the irresistible urge to discover it. All of them spurn that gray appeal to expediency which is the withering thumb-print of the administrator in committee. . . .

I have singled out truth among the human values for this reason. It is common to all systems of value, and is fundamental to most of them. And it is a value. We cannot take it for granted as something self-evident in science any more than in art or morals or religion. In all of them truth rests on an act of free human judgment. In none of them of course can this judgment be exercised without experience: there is no truth, not even religious truth, which calls for no sanction from fact. There are other values: goodness, beauty, right conduct. They have their echoes even in science; and there is one value, freedom of human ideas, which is the essential condition for the health of science. But it is not my point to show laboriously that science as much as the arts creates and implies all the human values. I have wanted to show only in one example that science cannot exist without judgments of value. This example, the truth, is a critical one; and it will serve to show that science cannot exist as a blank and mechanical activity.

But there is more in science than this. It shares the values of all human action. But it also adds to these values. The human values penetrate through all our actions, and they are strikingly alike in civilisations which are thousands of years apart. The Aztecs and the Minoans, the Chaldees, the Cherokees and the Shakers held in common ideas about human dignity and value which go far deeper than the surface differences of time and place. The likenesses are as heartening in their arts and their speculations. Yet, though the values are alike, they are not identical. The human values change, slowly but not negligibly. And in this change, science plays a creative part.

For the values rest at bottom on acts of judgment. And every act of judgment is a division of the field of our experience into what matters and what does not. I spoke of this at the beginning of this book: that at the basis of human thought lies the judgment of what is like and what is unlike. In picking out what we shall call alike, we make the basic judgment, that here is something which is important to us. We do this when we say that men are like women, or that the earth is like the planets, or that the air is like wine. Aldous Huxley in his novel *Barren Leaves* speculates at length about the word "love" in different European languages; but I, coming to England as a boy, was struck more by the existence in English alone of the verb "to like."

The human values are bound up with what we judge to be like and unlike; and when science shifts that judgment, it makes as profound a shift in these values. The Greeks built a wonderful civilisation, yet it did not outrage their sense of values to hold men in slavery. They did not feel the slave and citizen to be alike men. By the end of the eighteenth century, it was felt in the western world that all white men are alike; but William Wilberforce spent a lifetime in persuading his generation that black slaves and white are alike in human dignity. Science helped to create that sensibility, by widening the view of what is like and what unlike. It helped to widen it enough to make cruelty to animals a particularly detested offence in England. In our own generation, we have seen the human values perverted in Nazi Germany into a monstrous scale of self-approval. And the perversion was bolstered by a deliberate attempt to go back on what science and humanity had struggled slowly to grasp, the likeness of man. The hateful values of the Nazi rest at bottom on this false judgment, which science for three hundred years has tried to root out: that what I do is not like what others do. . . .

Karl Deutsch
SOME PROBLEMS OF SCIENCE AND VALUES

With Tolstoi and Aldous Huxley, and to a lesser extent even Swift and Wells, the focus of interest shifts from the aesthetic to the ethical aspects of science. Science itself depends for its life on the prior acceptance of certain fundamental values, such as the value of curiosity and learning, the value of truth, the value of sharing knowledge with others, the value of respect for facts, and the value of remembering the vastness of the universe in comparison with the finite knowledge of men at any particular moment. Historically, such values have been held by outstanding scientists. One thinks of P. W. Bridgman's well-known dictum that— "in the face of the fact, the scientist has a humility almost religious"; or of Newton's description of his own work as the play of a child with pebbles on the shores of the ocean of knowledge, or his reference to the sharing of knowledge with others by describing his own achievements as being due to his having stood "on the shoulders of giants." Beyond such evidence, it

Karl Deutsch, "Scientific and Humanistic Knowledge in the Growth of Civilization," in Harcourt Brown, ed., *Science and the Creative Spirit* (Toronto: University of Toronto Press, 1958), pp. 18–21. Reprinted with permission. Dr. Karl Deutsch is a distinguished political scientist.

could perhaps be shown that the cumulative work of science could not go on if any of the values just listed were rejected.

As science rests on certain values, so do almost all values depend on knowledge, and thus to some extent in turn on science, if they are to proceed from the realm of words to that of action. This implies a circular chain of causation or a feedback process, as do many processes of social and cultural development. To act morally is in one sense the opposite of acting blindly. It is acting in the presumed knowledge of what in fact it is that we are doing. Almost every significant action of this kind implies serious assumptions in some field of science. To love one's neighbor requires at the very least that we find out where and who our neighbor is. If we are to respond to his needs we must first ascertain what his needs are and what action in fact is likely to be helpful to him. To feed the hungry requires first of all the ability to distinguish food from poison, as well as the ability to provide food or produce food when needed. The same principles apply, of course, to clothing the naked or healing the sick. Indeed, it can be said that perhaps no action can be evaluated as good or bad without some knowledge or surmise about its consequences. If we evaluate an action as good on the basis of our mere surmise of the good will of its doer, therefore, we may find ourselves forced to assume that such subjective good will—as in the Kantian Imperative—must include by implication also the will to gain and apply the best available knowledge of the probable consequences of the action chosen. The duty to have good intentions, in other words, is meaningless without the duty to try to know the facts and try to foresee correctly the consequences of one's deeds, and it is this latter duty which may distinguish in practice the responsible from the irresponsible statesman, or the well-intentioned doctor from the well-intentioned quack.

Attempts at hermetic separations of science from values are thus bound to fail. Science without at least some values would come to a dead stop; ethics without at least some exact and verifiable knowledge would be condemned to impotence or become an engine of destruction. Much of the anxious discussion of international politics between statesmen and atomic scientists, or between the so-called schools of "idealism" and "realism" among political writers, hinges upon the discrepancy between the strength of the moral convictions involved and the poverty of reliable knowledge of the probable consequences of the proposed courses of action.

The relationship of science and values thus implies a double question: the mutual interrelation of science and the general values of a civilization; and the relationship of a specific state of scientific knowledge to the pursuit of specific purposes or policies. The first of these problems, the general relationship of science and value, and thus to some extent of truth and goodness, leads us close to the heart of every civilization within which it is examined. If conceived as mutually incompatible, science and values may frustrate or destroy each other, dragging their civilization towards stagnation or decline. As a mutually productive and creative partnership, science and values may succeed in strengthening each other's powers in a self-enhancing pattern of growth, rendering their civilization increasingly open and able to learn from the hopes and dreams of the individuals within it, as well as from the universe around it.

This general vision of a mutually beneficial partnership becomes increasingly difficult to retain, however, as we proceed from the consideration of the growth of civilization on the grand scale to the effect of the timing of particular discoveries or innovations upon specific policies at specific times and places. Would it have been better for mankind if Einstein's principle of relativity, or Chadwick's discovery of the neutron, or Hahn's work on uranium fission had all come ten years later than they did, and no atom bomb had been available to drop on Hiroshima? Perhaps the most useful consideration in the face of questions such as these might be to realize the impossibility of foreseeing the ultimate consequences of even the smallest scientific or technological advance, as well as the inexhaustibility of most or all of the great contributions. Benjamin Franklin's answer to the question "What is the use of a scientific discovery?" consisted in asking the counter-question "What is the use of a baby?" Just as it seems impossible to foretell the eventual good a child may do, so it is impossible to foretell what evil he may do, and our whole attitude to children is in a sense based upon the bet that the good they do will far outweigh the evil. In civilized countries we have long ago abandoned the discussion which sometimes still echoes in mythology, whether a certain child should have been killed at birth in order to forestall the harm he did in adult life. Rather we have come to center our attention on providing a family and an environment for him in which love will outweigh hate, and in which his opportunity for free and friendly growth will be the best.

If there is merit in Benjamin Franklin's argument, we might similarly decide to bet on the potential goodness rather than on the potential evil of knowledge, and concentrate on providing a human and social environment for science in which its constructive possibilities are likely to be realized. It is possible, of course, to imagine extreme situations for some times and places in which the short-term potentialities for destruction might seem so great in the case of a particular invention or discovery, and the prevailing political régime might seem so unlikely to avoid its suicidal misuse, that a policy of temporarily restricting, delaying, or withholding such knowledge might appear as the least of several likely evils for the time being. Even granting all these assumptions, however, such a policy of fear of knowledge would have to be viewed as extremely transitory and exceptional in any modern technological civilization that is to continue to advance or indeed to survive. A civilization so prone to commit suicide that it could be saved only by concealing from it the means of its own destruction would not endure for long. Rather, for the long run and for most conditions that are likely to occur, we might do better to adopt the opposite assumption: that any modern civilization that is to endure will have to learn how to live with its new knowledge of its vast means of destruction.

Joseph Wood Krutch
THE IDOLS OF THE LABORATORY

. . . Even the most moderate proponents of a "scientific" morality seem usually unaware of the closed circle around which they lead us when they consent to consider questions concerning value. They begin by saying—and it seems reasonable enough—that value judgments should be based on knowledge rather than on tradition or intuition; and they bid us, before we make them, to consult not merely the physical sciences but also such other bodies of available knowledge as history and anthropology. Unfortunately, however, it has usually turned out that when they follow their own advice the conclusion which they arrive at is not that a true value judgment has been scientifically justified but that the impossibility of making such a judgment has been demonstrated.

As far back as the nineteenth century this pattern was set by Lecky's great *History of European Morals* which undertook to study scientifically the ethical systems which had actually prevailed. The conclusion reached was summed up in Lecky's famous statement that

From *The Measure of Man,* copyright 1953, 1954 by Joseph Wood Krutch, reprinted by permission of the publishers, The Bobbs-Merrill Company, Inc. Dr. Krutch is a noted author, critic, and lecturer. *The Measure of Man* received the National Book Award in 1954.

there is no possible line of conduct which has not, at some time and place, been condemned, and which has not, at some other time and place, been enjoined as a duty. Thus what he arrived at was not a "scientific morality" but only the conviction that such a scientific morality is impossible; that, at least from the standpoint of science, "morals" are indistinguishable from "manners" or "mores" and that "the good" is nothing more than "the prevalent."

Anthropology—which is only history with an extended scope— has more recently been more fashionable as a body of knowledge to which the moralist may appeal. But one of the most prevalent, or at least the most popular, schools of anthropology has been that which defends a cultural relativism corresponding quite closely to the moral relativism of Lecky. In the United States Ruth Benedict's *Patterns of Culture* has probably been the most widely read of all anthropological works, and *Patterns of Culture* is devoted to the thesis that the scientist must concern himself, not with any attempt to define the characteristics of a *good* society, but only with the attempt to get an adequate understanding of the fact that the "patterns of culture" which have actually existed are almost infinitely varied and that any one of them may be "good" from the standpoint of those who live in accordance with it. Thus the final conclusion seems to be, not that anthropology can tell us objectively what a good society is, but rather that the question, when considered objectively, has no meaning.

It is true that Miss Benedict falls into the inconsistency to which all who deny that they are making value judgments usually fall. She is objective enough when she compares, say, the "Apollonian" culture of the Hopis with the "Dionysian" culture of some of the Plains Indians. But when she turns, as she does, to describe the Babbitt or Middletown culture—which she takes to be predominant in the United States at the moment of writing—nearly everything she says is loaded with an adverse judgment of that culture.

To be consistent she should say that Rotary Clubs and the ceremonies of the businessman's golf game cannot be objectively pronounced either good or bad since they are, like the Hopi snake dance, simply part of a pattern of culture. What actually happens is, of course, that her objectivity deserts her just as soon as she considers the culture of her own tribe and that she makes value judgments on it just as freely—but with much less awareness of what she is doing—as they are made by those ignorant of the science of anthropology but loyal to tradition, metaphysics, or intuition.

Moreover, and in so far as those who advocate a "scientific" morality actually do consistently follow the conclusions to which they are led, the practical result is to encourage the tendency, already strongly developed in our society, to make no distinction between what men do and what they "ought" to do; to turn the quest for scientific morality into nothing except a study of prevalent behavior.

To state that "whatever is is right" and to accept that statement fully or absolutely requires a metaphysical analysis of which most men are not capable and leads to conclusions which most men would probably hesitate to accept. But many if not most men are now pragmatically accepting it already when they propose to use studies of everything from the reading habits of adolescence to the sexual behavior of homosexuals as the bases for ordering the educational system or setting up standards of sexual morality. Thus though the assumption that the concept represented in the word "ought" is radically meaningless is one not usually consciously made it is nevertheless the assumption on which many "advanced thinkers" seem willing to proceed.

Hence it appears that when the advocates of the theory that value judgments should be based on knowledge actually follow consistently their principles, they end by admitting that the only thing which science can achieve is the discovery of what the most usual conduct is like. The only guidance they can offer is the suggestion that we should not expect anything other than what we find to be happening and this in turn comes down to little more than the statement "what has been has been, what will be will be."

No sociological determinist thoughtful enough to realize the implications of his position fails to recognize that questions concerning value must be answered somehow and he usually answers them by saying that though no value judgments arrived at by metaphysical processes are valid, there is something which serves the purpose which the so-called value judgments cannot really serve and takes their place in any functioning society. This something is provided for us by the contingencies of the natural world and, in the long run, would prevent the sustained development or continued existence of such perverse horrors as Nazism achieved or imagination may fear in a Walden Three.

Since Professor Skinner is one of the clearest and most persuasive exponents of this position we may again use him for the purpose of criticizing his statement of it both as implied in *Walden Two* and as explicitly defended elsewhere. Essentially his position is defined by the statement that there are certain "values" which are "self-evident" and that no human choice is necessarily involved in the acceptance of them. We do not "make" value judgments but they are imposed upon us.

And yet, as we shall see, this thesis breaks down as it always does when confronted by the fact that these "self-evident values" are not recognized as self-evident by everyone and therefore can be called self-evident only with the proviso that those to whom they do not seem so are declared to be not "normal" or "sane"—by the arbitrary standard set up by individuals who insist that they are not setting any arbitrary standards.

Anyone who believes in the all but unlimited effect of the conditioning to which every mind has been subjected ought logically to be the first to suspect that when a man calls something "self-evident" that means merely that he has been early and firmly conditioned to believe it; not at all that it would appear self-evident to those who happen to have been otherwise conditioned. Thus those who follow Mr. Skinner's line of argument may be hoisted very neatly on their own petards. While they profess to make no value judgment they are actually making one in the most absolute and unconditional way possible, namely, by saying "it is obviously true." And whatever dangers may be involved in accepting as absolutely true conclusions arrived at by the fallible processes of human reason it does not seem as though they could be avoided by refusing to think at all—which appears to be what Mr. Skinner is proposing when faced with an ultimate problem.

In his case the value judgment which he makes while insisting that it is not really a value judgment at all comes down to this: Whatever contributes to the health of an individual or the long-continued survival of the society of which he is a part is "good," or, as he put it in the course of a debate, "The one criterion that is thrust upon us is whether the group which observes a given practice will be here tomorrow." The implication is that, granted this premise, we can easily determine how a society should be planned and to what opinions, tastes, and activities an individual should be conditioned.

But what this, in its turn, really comes down to is, of course, only a rather fancy restatement of the doctrine implied in the phrase "survival of the fittest." And the semantic emptiness of the doctrine was long ago exposed by asking the simple question, "Fittest for what?" The only possible answer is "fittest to survive" which closes the circle and thereby reduces the statement to complete nonsense by making it read: "Those survive who survive."

For the moment the question is not whether the value judgment which declares "survival" and "health" to be goods is defensible either as one of those arbitrary choices which some declare all value judgments to be or as something at which reason can arrive. The question is simply whether or not they are "self-evident" goods in the sense that all men not certifiably insane have accepted them and that they therefore demonstrate how easily we may escape the necessity of making, for ourselves, any value judgments at all. . . .

Herbert J. Muller
THE USE AND ABUSE OF SCIENCE

The practical uses and abuses of science are generally conspicuous enough. They have alike, however, confused the issue of its value.
Men consider chiefly the *results* of scientific inquiry, and build their
philosophies on current theories as if all thought labeled scientific were
necessarily valid. They neglect the logic of inquiry, the *method* that has
produced all the dazzling results and that will survive all the current
theories. The disciples of science are therefore apt to become only another
species of theologian. Still more superficial, however, is the view that
science is useful only for menial work, the chores of society, and should be
shut off from spiritual matters. This aristocratic division of labor is in
effect a return to mumbo jumbo. Its advocates are trying to achieve ends
without a realistic study of means, and ultimately they divorce ends and
means. In placing mind or spirit in an unearthly realm of its own, they do
not actually elevate it; they leave it up a creek.

To begin with, the findings of science are clearly relevant to
spiritual interests. There can be no sound judgment of any values without
a knowledge of actual conditions, the nature and possibilities of man and
his environment; about such matters the scientist has a great deal to say.
Grant that his primary interest is in processes, apart from all considerations of value, and that the critic's primary interest is in outcomes, in
which considerations of value are central; still a knowledge of processes is
always helpful in a study of outcomes.

Even more pertinent is the method of science. Theoretically it is
depressing, because it assumes determinism. Actually it gives us freedom,
freedom where we want it and can do something with it—freedom, as
Dewey says, not apart from natural events but in and among them. It is
the philosophers and theologians who have characteristically restricted
both our thought and our action; setting out from fixed truths instead of
hypotheses, they permitted less freedom than the experimental method,
which may imply determinism but which remains *experimental.* Science,

From Herbert J. Muller, *Science and Criticism* (New Haven, Conn.: Yale
University Press, 1943), pp. 69–75. Reprinted with permission. Dr. Muller is Distinguished Service Professor at Indiana University.

therefore, not only has proved an efficient instrument of human purposes but has created new purposes, liberated purposefulness from the ends arbitrarily fixed by ancient high priests of thought. Likewise its method is fundamentally more humane. The philosophers and theologians have characteristically set up absolute antitheses, of right and wrong, good and evil, and conceived their first duty to be the annihilation of most other thinkers. Scientists work more by assimilation, a reconciliation of opposites that are more apparent than real. Each new theory recaptures from a higher level the elements of truth in previous theories, and is in turn due to be included in a still higher synthesis; Newton's great contributions remain solid after Einstein devised a larger pattern. In short, despite its supposed inhumanity, science exemplifies the humanistic ideal.

Also pertinent here is the moral value of science, which is so apparent that it is often overlooked. In no other human activity is a higher premium placed upon truthfulness, or is the ideal of truthfulness more fully realized. Success in science is possible only on these terms. The eminent statesman or businessman may be unscrupulous, and indeed cannot afford too many or too fine scruples; the passionate sincerity of artists and other intellectuals may still be warped by wishful preferences, and their fervor and eloquence come by more easily because of the wishfulness; but no scientist can ever hope to succeed by misrepresenting, or by remolding according to his heart's desire. (Paul Kammerer, the well-known biologist who did fake his results, was driven to suicide by the disgrace of exposure.) His hard-won success, moreover, cannot be exploited for private gain, at least if he is to retain his professional standing. Outside his profession, needless to add, the scientist is no paragon of selfless virtue and wisdom, and within it he will cherish his brain child, hold out for his own theory as long as the facts permit. Yet the scientific community as a whole is the most impressive example history has yet known of a disinterested, coöperative enterprise, international in scope, directed toward impersonal ends and by impersonal standards. It is the most impressive demonstration of the actual possibility of "supra-personal, supra-partisan, supra-racial standards and values."

In such ways, to repeat, science can free the spirit. So can its tremendous revelations, which have also been considered alien to the human spirit. Astronomy is the striking example. Men are often depressed by the immensities it reveals: How insignificant is man, how transient his life in the perspective of the stars! Such reflections may induce a becoming humility. But neither can man lick a gorilla, or outrun an antelope, and this popular habit of measuring him by astronomical coördinates is also pointless. We may as reasonably look down on the stars, for they cannot contemplate either themselves or us. Meanwhile astronomy has other meanings for us. The stars were the first clear evidence of uniformity, regularity, harmony in the world; man might never have achieved any science at all, Poincaré remarked, had clouds always hid them. They have as well a clear imaginative or spiritual value. The spectacle lifts us out of ourselves; and if it shows how little man is, it also shows how great is his spirit, which can enjoy the immense harmony and embrace the immense mystery.

In general, science has unquestionably widened and enriched the whole context of thought, the whole background of immediate experience. The issue of whether or not to use its findings is in the end academic. Try as we will, we cannot escape its influence. We cannot walk abroad except in its shadow; it is in the air we breathe, the language we use as unconsciously. The student of esthetics, for example, may rebel against the excesses of "psychological" investigation and try once more to take his beauty straight. Nevertheless his main terms—imagination, emotion, sensation, will, intuition, expression, etc.—are charged with some kind of psychological theory. That it is usually a vague or dubious theory only emphasizes the need of his realizing what he is about. And the moment he leaves esthetics to generalize about the relation of art to other interests and purposes, he is up to his neck in matters about which scientists have had much to say. He is perforce a kind of psychologist and social scientist. He might better be an informed one.

Unhappily, however, we cannot escape the influence of pseudo-science either; and so we must go back to the beginning. The extraordinary success of scientific inquiry has also stimulated a busy shopping around to pick up some scientific dress at bargain rates. The most obvious bargains are in technical jargon, which may then clutter up not only a man's prose style but his thinking; he is apt to think that he has solved a problem when he has merely located it, as in the Unconscious, or given it a new name, such as "sublimation." But the general reason for all the awed misunderstanding is again that laymen usually pick up only the latest findings, not the logic of inquiry. With its elaborate system of fictions and symbols, which may or may not stand for something "real," science might be defined as madness with a method. To miss the method is to be left simply with madness.

Perhaps the most common and dangerous fallacy is the assumption that science tells us "all that matters." Max Eastman stated it baldly when he insisted that poets must stop "trying to tell us anything about life," because as poets they know nothing about it. This is a hard thing to tell an earnest man. It is also a very silly thing, and should embarrass scientists as much as it distresses poets; the exclusive right to say something about life is a terrible responsibility. Yet scientists, too, often talk carelessly in this way. Physicists will say that a table is "really" only a swarm of particles, or biochemists that man is "nothing but" a parcel of chemicals worth about a dollar. All that is of no value for their limited purposes—the distinctive qualities of human experience, the extraordinarily rich variety of sensation and emotion in a world of shape and color, fruit and flower, dream and song—they may then dismiss as merely "subjective," beneath the dignity of knowledge. They forget that they are always abstracting, and that their abstractions are also fictions. "It is the Nemesis of the struggle for exactitude by the man of science," writes H. S. Jennings, "that it leads him to present a mutilated, merely fractional account of the world as a true and complete picture."

The greatest victories of science have in a sense been cheap victories, for they have been won by a careful refusal to engage the more difficult, certainly no less important problems of ethics, politics, and the humanities generally. The physicist rules out all that he cannot rule, reduces what is left to the simplest possible terms. It is an excellent policy—for his purposes. But he may then forget that what cannot be measured or calculated may nevertheless be immeasurably important, have incalculable consequences, and that the terms of life as it is lived are not simple. Take even the unanswerable questions, the metaphysical questions that it is now fashionable to dismiss as meaningless. "All problems are artificial," Dewey wrote in a careless moment, "which do not grow, even if indirectly, out of the conditions under which life . . . is carried on." Roelofs answers rightly that *all* problems grow out of these conditions. Where else could they come from? Metaphysical speculation may be unproductive of strict knowledge, and is often a dangerous nuisance because it is mistaken for knowledge. Its high imaginings may also be a source of inspiration and strength. In either event the fact remains that men naturally wonder about the ultimate mysteries, give rich meaning to meaningless questions, and behave in accordance with the answers they have given the unanswerable. And so they must, for many indispensable meanings and purposes outrun all evidence.

At most, science gives us certain directions for dealing with certain things. Its abstractions are like paper money, facilitating commerce with actuality so that every transaction need not be an exchange of cows. Its abstractions are a necessary evil; and they become simply an evil if men hoard them for their own sake, forget their instrumental function and their arbitrary value. But it is especially important for the literary critic to remember that science never tells us everything about anything— that, in fact, it tells us very little about any *thing*. It leaves out of its abstractions all the unique particulars, the concrete qualities, the substantial body of direct experience that is the primary subject matter of art. The scientist's apple suggested the law of gravitation and as happily obeys the laws of biology. The apple of our experience is a unique object that may please the palate and the eye, evoke the emotions appropriate to autumn, symbolize the plight of the unemployed, enable an archer to become a national hero. Our apple is no less significant than its better behaved symbol.

Similarly the critic in particular needs to guard against the confusion commonly inspired by scientific analysis. Analysis can reduce all human behavior to its biological origins and these in turn to their physical basis; then men believe that they have completely "explained" behavior, proved that it is "simply" physical. A great deal of emotion has been generated by the elementary fallacy pointed out by Broad: because B grows out of A and C grows out of B, C is nothing but A in disguise. Scientists know that organic life is qualitatively different from inorganic matter, the conscious life of man qualitatively different from other forms of life; they may nevertheless forget that what matters most to us as men is not the common beginnings but the unique ends. Critics fall into the same fallacy when they confine science to the "economic impulse" because it is rooted there. But they also fall into it when they describe art as "merely" a compensation for some psychic maladjustment, or "essentially" an expression of class interest. They confuse the conditions of something with its cause, and both with the thing itself.

The gist of all these extravagances is that science has suffered as much from its disciples as has any faith. For it is indeed a faith, and often a very naïve one. Apart from the gross worship of time-saving and time-killing devices as ends in themselves, the disciples have displayed the artless optimism of prophets and crusaders through the centuries, based on the illusion that men always welcome light and once brought to see the truth will act upon it. They have displayed as well the frequent arrogance, intolerance, and inhumanity of the prophets and crusaders. Thomas Huxley, who declared that faith is "the one unpardonable sin," had through all his career an absolute faith in the religion of science, accepting as gospel not only its method but its current assumptions, and on the basis of these questionable assumptions erecting an often harsh philosophy. Others have been contemptuous of values other than their own devotion to verifiable knowledge, contemptuous even of the vital needs they were presumably serving. Until recently, "purpose" and "value" were the most horrid words a scientist could hear.

All in all, science is a means to a better life on earth, but cannot alone secure this end. The most that one can argue for it is that it is an indispensable means, the best investment for hope. Yet this is a sound argument; and with it I should end. Philosophy, religion, and art provide valuable experiences and suggest valuable ways of dealing with the world; science provides the most certain knowledge, the most certain means of generating more knowledge, the most certain means of manipulating this knowledge to control the natural world. Hence the necessary postscript even to preliminary discussion is that scientists now tend increasingly to think scientifically about their own activity. They are examining the implications and facing the responsibilities of the enormous power they wield. They are subjecting science to the same ruthless analysis that religion has had to endure since the eighteenth century, conducting a searching inquiry into their basic assumptions and their logic, systematically formulating the philosophy that in their naïve, exuberant youth they did not realize was a philosophy. Poincaré, Whitehead, Planck, Einstein, Jennings, Woodger, Koehler, Mannheim—such men offer a profounder criticism of science than one gets from most thinkers who are jealously defending their values from its encroachment. They are less ignorant of their ignorance.

W. T. Stace
MAN AGAINST DARKNESS

The founders of modern science—for instance, Galileo, Kepler, and Newton—were mostly pious men who did not doubt God's purposes. Nevertheless they took the revolutionary step of consciously and deliberately expelling the idea of purpose as controlling nature from their new science of nature. They did this on the ground that inquiry into purposes is useless for what science aims at: namely, the prediction and control of events. To predict an eclipse, what you have to know is not its purpose but its causes. Hence science from the seventeenth century onwards became exclusively an inquiry into causes. The conception of purpose in the world was ignored and frowned on. This, though silent and almost unnoticed, was the greatest revolution in human history, far outweighing in importance any of the political revolutions whose thunder has reverberated through the world.

For it came about in this way that for the past three hundred years there has been growing up in men's minds, dominated as they are by science, a new imaginative picture of the world. The world, according to this new picture, is purposeless, senseless, meaningless. Nature is nothing but matter in motion. The motions of matter are governed, not by any purpose, but by blind forces and laws. Nature on this view, says White-

From W. T. Stace, "Man against Darkness," *Atlantic Monthly*, 182, No 3 (1948), 54–55. Reprinted by permission. Dr. Stace is a noted Anglo-American philosopher.

head is "merely the hurrying of material, endlessly, meaninglessly." You can draw a sharp line across the history of Europe dividing it into two epochs of very unequal length. The line passes through the lifetime of Galileo. European man before Galileo—whether ancient pagan or more recent Christian—thought of the world as controlled by plan and purpose. After Galileo European man thinks of it as utterly purposeless. This is the great revolution of which I spoke.

It is this which has killed religion. Religion could survive the discoveries that the sun, not the earth, is the center; that men are descended from simian ancestors; that the earth is hundreds of millions of years old. These discoveries may render out of date some of the details of older theological dogmas, may force their restatement in new intellectual frameworks. But they do not touch the essence of the religious vision itself, which is the faith that there is plan and purpose in the world, that the world is a moral order, that in the end all things are for the best. This faith may express itself through many different intellectual dogmas, those of Christianity, of Hinduism, of Islam. All and any of these intellectual dogmas may be destroyed without destroying the essential religious spirit. But that spirit cannot survive destruction of belief in a plan and purpose of the world, for that is the very heart of it. Religion can get on with any sort of astronomy, geology, biology, physics. But it cannot get on with a purposeless and meaningless universe.

If the scheme of things is purposeless and meaningless, then the life of man is purposeless and meaningless too. Everything is futile, all effort is in the end worthless. A man may, of course, still pursue disconnected ends, money, fame, art, science, and may gain pleasure from them. But his life is hollow at the center. Hence the dissatisfied, disillusioned, restless, spirit of modern man.

The picture of a meaningless world, and a meaningless human life, is, I think, the basic theme of much modern art and literature. Certainly it is the basic theme of modern philosophy. According to the most characteristic philosophies of the modern period from Hume in the eighteenth century to the so-called positivists of today, the world is just what it is, and that is the end of all inquiry. There is no reason for its being what it is. Everything might just as well have been quite different, and there would have been no reason for that either. When you have stated what things are, what things the world contains, there is nothing more which could be said, even by an omniscient being. To ask any question about *why* things are thus, or what purpose their being so serves, is to ask a senseless question, because they serve no purpose at all. For instance, there is for modern philosophy no such thing as the ancient problem of evil. For this once famous question presupposes that pain and misery, though they seem so inexplicable and irrational to us, must ultimately subserve some rational purpose, must have their places in the cosmic plan. But this is nonsense. There is no such overruling rationality in the universe. Belief in the ultimate irrationality of everything is the quintessence of what is called the modern mind.

It is true that, parallel with these philosophies which are typical of the modern mind, preaching the meaninglessness of the world, there has run a line of idealistic philosophies whose contention is that the world is after all spiritual in nature and that moral ideals and values are inherent in its structure. But most of these idealisms were simply philosophical expressions of romanticism, which was itself no more than an unsuccessful counterattack of the religious against the scientific view of things. They perished, along with romanticism in literature and art, about the beginning of the present century, though of course they still have a few adherents.

At the bottom these idealistic systems of thought were rationalizations of man's wishful thinking. They were born of the refusal of men to admit the cosmic darkness. They were comforting illusions within the warm glow of which the more tender-minded intellectuals sought to shelter themselves from the icy winds of the universe. They lasted a little while. But they are shattered now, and we return once more to the vision of a purposeless world. . . .

John K. Wood

THE NATURE OF CONFLICTS BETWEEN SCIENCE AND RELIGION

. . . The science-religion conflict comes down to a conflict over presuppositions and the related conflict over ways of knowing. However, people do not use words like presuppositions, metaphysical foundations or epistemology in their arguments, or even the ideas which these words represent. The words are God, world, universe, evolution, miracle, and the arguments center around the origin of life and the universe, the existence and nature of God, the creator of the universe, and the relationship of man

From John K. Wood, *The Nature of Conflicts between Science and Religion* (Logan: Utah State University, 1962). Utah State University Monograph Series, Vol. IX, No. 2. Reprinted with permission. Dr. Wood is professor of physics at Utah State University.

to the universe. In short, the arguments are over cosmology and the metaphysical foundations are assumed without question. It is easy to see why these arguments can become intense and why religion is on the defensive in the conflict. It can become intense because most people defend their presuppositions emotionally rather than rationally. If a nonreligious person tries to convince a religious person that religious beliefs are based on myth and superstition, usually he will be met with violent argument or complete silence. In either case, the religious person will not listen to the argument of the non-religious person.

The advantage in the science-religion conflict is on the side of science. Knowledge, in science, comes from sense experience, reasoning or from authority. The authority, in turn, gets its knowledge from experience or reason. If anyone is in doubt about the interpretation of an experiment, the experiment can be repeated and two people can talk to each other about a definite, repeatable situation. Religious knowledge is largely based on intuition, reason and authority. The authoritative source gets its knowledge from intuition or experience. The experience can be shared with others while the intuition is private experience, and there is always some doubt as to the extent that private experience can be shared. It is possible for members of a religious group to convince each other that a private experience of one of the members does lead to knowledge which can be shared. If the members of a religious sect tried to convince someone outside the sect that a private experience of a member should be meaningful, the proof would be up to the members and it should be based on experience if it is to mean anything to the non-member. Young people of many religious sects are told by their elders that they should not attend movies on Sunday. The reasons are usually authoritative or intuitive. Authority and intuition are not convincing ways of knowing to an adolescent and as a result most of them go to movies on Sunday at one time or another, against the wishes of their elders. The "bad" effects, if any, are generally guilt feelings.

. . . one way of achieving a degree of certainty [is] to accept a certain set of presuppositions as absolute, although this results in a questionable sense of security. This leads to the authoritarian way of knowing because there is always someone who can act as the authority by expressing the presuppositions which describe as "true" those things a person wants to accept. These ideas or statements are held to be absolute or "true" by the believers or followers. This type of behavior occurs frequently in religion, and science is not free from "absolutes." The length of time which certain "absolute" concepts are maintained in science depends on the rate of growth of science. The more rapid the growth, the more likely absolutes will be challenged. It required a hundred years for the authority of Newton to be broken down in the field of optics. Several people had challenged this authority but it was not until the work of Thomas Young that Newton's concept of light was found to be untenable. Unusual ideas of modern scientists are challenged much more quickly than at the time of Newton and consequently authority is not as important in the development of ideas.

Authoritarianism in religion does not have the self-correcting system of checks and balances that is characteristic of science. It is difficult to use sense experience as a way of knowing in religion because ideas evolve so slowly. While religious concepts may well arise from experience, the history of religions indicates that the great movements arise with the insight of some strong leader into these slowly developing ideas. Insight and intuition as ways of knowing are beset with trouble because of the difficulties inherent in transmitting this knowledge from one person to another. It is legitimate to ask, why do the movements get started if the insight of one person cannot be transmitted to another except in indirect ways? The events leading up to the posting of the ninety-five theses on the Wittemburg church doors by Martin Luther were sensed by most of the people of Western Europe. Luther voiced the feelings of many people of his day, and his great insight was not sudden but based on ideas and events that developed gradually. In time, however, after the period of crisis and adjustment had passed, it became necessary to remind people about the nature of the principles for which their elders had fought. It became necessary to establish some sort of "koran for the faithful" which became the authority for the religious tradition after the experiences which led to the crisis were dimmed with time. Thus the record of the recalled insight of a leader becomes the criterion of the faithful, the dogma becomes set, the ideas of the sect become inflexible and the struggle with new ideas commences.

Those parts of religion which rely heavily on authoritarianism and mysticism or intuition are often subjected to critical analysis by the methods of science when the dogmas are questioned by an inquiring mind. This factor has played an important part in the conflicts between science and religion over the entire history of the development of modern science while its roots go even deeper into the conflict of old ideas with the new. The conflict may become acute with college students having a strong religious background who are confronted with a science class taught by a dedicated, professional scientist. The student senses two problems, one involving certainty and another involving objectivity. Both the religious background and the science are often presented to the student without mentioning the nature of the presuppositions underlying these two areas. If the student can see the contradiction then he is likely to choose one or the other or he may set up a barrier between the two. In either case the object is to reduce in his mind the areas of uncertainty. If the student is aware of the nature of the presuppositions involved, he then realizes the scope of the conflict, but now he cannot reduce the uncertainty; he has no absolute truths to fall back on. He is now faced with the "problem of existence" and must have, as Tillich puts it, "The Courage to Be." . . .

Attempts to get to the basic issues of scientific-religious conflicts are complicated by the fact that evidence acceptable to one side is not acceptable to the other. Proofs based on the authority of the Bible, on the authority of some person in the Bible, or on the authority of some person or group, do not provide acceptable evidence to those who put their trust in science and its methods. On the other hand, experiments and reason are of little value to those who believe that "God works in a mysterious way, his wonders to perform." If one is to prove a point by giving scriptural quotations, the results will be meaningless to a listener who does not accept the scriptures as a source of truth.

The present conflict between science and religion has continued at varying degrees of intensity for almost three hundred years. The arguments over cosmologies, from which the science—religion conflict stem, have gone on for a much longer time. What hope is there for a settlement of the problem? There are prophets who declare that religion is doomed and there are prophets who declare that religion will triumph over all in the end. The events of the last three hundred years show that with regard to cosmology, religion has retreated from the picture of the universe as portrayed by the ancient Hebrews. It is true there are holdouts for the cosmology of Israelite antiquity, but most Christians accept a more modern view. As mankind learns more about the universe, based on a firm foundation of scientific evidence, religions will find it less necessary to provide cosmological explanations as a substitute for primitive science.

Does this mean doom for religion? To answer this question with either yes or no would require one to reply on unproved and unprovable assumptions and this seems to lead up blind alleys. It is doubtful that science will ever be able to show that religious feelings arise from changes in body chemistry. This statement is made not to satisfy religious people but because of the inherent difficulty of finding out the things that a person really thinks. The act of probing a mind will disturb it to a point where the original thought is destroyed or seriously distorted. Because of this built-in uncertainty of finding the seat of religious feelings, there is a place in the lives of people for the rituals and symbols around such concepts as faith, hope and love. The important concepts of religion have grown out of the social contacts of one person with another. The great religious leaders have sensed these concepts in flashes of insight and passed them on to those who are not able to see the significance of their own heritage. The experiential side of religion has much to offer but this is clouded in far too many instances with authoritarianism and primitive cosmology. If people could see that to explain the origin of man and the universe in scientific terms does not necessarily destroy the concepts of respect for the individual, love, truth, justice and the historical background from which these ideas grew, the conflicts between science and religion would become less intense.

Robert M. MacIver

SCIENCE AS A SOCIAL PHENOMENON

Every society, even the most rudimentary, depends on scientific behavior in its daily pursuits. It must, in the first place, to keep alive. Certainly no sane human being undertakes any task without endeavoring to relate means to ends, without drawing conclusions from evidences, without applying his degree of rationality to a problem; in short, without being a scientist thus far. The primitive nomad depends on the art of hunting, and every practical art is the harnessing of a bit of science within its area. The hunter makes observations and deductions from evidences, from the traces of the softer earth or in the snow, from the sounds of the forest, from the direction of the wind, from the habits of the animals. Neither the method nor the attitude nor the practice of the scientist is the monopoly of the professional scientist. The hunter, the farmer, the businessman, the artist, the criminal, and the saint, all must resort to the way of science within the ambit of their interests and the limits of their intelligence.

Consequently, as arts and crafts developed and multiplied, a considerable amount of unsifted scientific lore, the product of intelligence directed to the manipulation of natural resources, was amassed before science was thought of as pursuit in its own right. The arts preceded and provided the basis for the sciences. The sciences did not develop as such, until men began to seek knowledge for itself, or at least in some detachment from the needs of everyday life.

In every society, including our own, the reach of scientific development is determined by a complex of social and environmental

Proceedings of the American Philosophical Society, 105 (October 1961), 500–505. Reprinted with permission. Dr. MacIver is Emeritus Professor of Political Philosophy and Sociology, Columbia University.

conditions. The limitations are of several kinds—limitations of the right to pursue knowledge freely, these being set by authority and social taboos; limitations to the interest in science, these being set by the level of education and the direction of education; and limitations to the opportunity to pursue science, these being set by the distribution of wealth and poverty, by class distinctions affecting the access to education, by the natural resources available to the society and the state of the industrial arts. . . .

Among these conditions we might single out the extent of industrial development as a primary determinant of opportunity and the ideology of government as the most significant factor in determining the direction and the limits of scientific activity. Industrial development means a demand for technological innovation, and therefore calls for scientific research in many directions. It also requires that class lines are flexible so as not to constitute educational or cultural barriers. It means the development of the arts of communication, thus enlarging the number of potential scientists. Furthermore, it means there is a range of leisure for non-utilitarian pursuits and thus for the free scientific inquiry from which come the major advances of science, while it also yields at length high dividends for the world of affairs.

Political power has some impact on science under all conditions, whether the government be democratic or otherwise. Its command of the national purse affects not only the amount spent on science, pure and applied, but also, in degree, the direction in which scientific effort is concentrated. Obviously, when the government is the agent of an authoritarian creed, it assumes, particularly through its control over education, the entire direction of science. Where its dogma is theological, the development of both the natural and the social sciences is likely to be severely restrained. Where the dogma is a non-religious or anti-religious philosophy, its restrictiveness in the area of the natural sciences is quite minor, but the social sciences are cut to the prescribed pattern and history is rewritten by way of corroboration. This type of enthroned political ideology is pre-eminently a product of the twentieth century, for while it is a commonplace of history that autocratic governments proscribe socio-economic doctrines that might threaten the established order, the Soviet system of government was the first to be founded squarely on the scriptures of a socio-economic doctrine, a doctrine that claimed to have irrefragable scientific proof for the future utopia it promised.

Aside from the intervention or the influence of established authority, freely operating social forces have at all times a considerable effect on the development of science, on the range of scientific inquiry, on the modes of inquiry, on the conceptual framework within which hypotheses are devised. There are fashions of thought, a readiness to welcome some new directions and to be sceptical of others. In retrospect we can see that theories to which significant evidences pointed might well have appeared much earlier than they did had it not been for the presuppositions of the times. The Newtonian theory, for example, might have arisen earlier but for the prestige and the sanctions of an older doctrine. The Darwinian theory of evolution met a great wave of indignant rejection before it became the accepted doctrine, and possibly on the other hand its final triumph may have been so complete that even yet it in turn has not evolved as much as it should to meet biological complexities it failed to answer. Perhaps even among scientists there is some truth in Bacon's saying that "the human understanding when it has once adopted an opinion . . . draws all things else to support and agree with it."

We must reckon also with the impact on the development of science of the social pressures of a highly organized society. Even in our own country in our own day we have witnessed censorial pressures on academic freedom. There have been attacks on scientists and efforts to oust them from colleges and universities—sometimes with success—because some intrusive committee or some propagandist body disliked their opinions. During the McCarthy heyday a determined assault was directed against economists who favored the point of view of Maynard Keynes or approved the expansion of social welfare legislation. Today the danger to academic freedom comes less from the idols of the tribe than from the idols of the pressure group.

We have offered so far a summary account of the manner in which social factors have affected the direction, the limitation, and the concentration of scientific inquiry. But to appreciate how science has become increasingly an aspect of the living texture of society it is necessary to take a broader perspective.

Science in the first place has become a profession, one with a quite special role and function. It is not so long ago since science was not a profession but at most a sideline, the avocation of a certain type of inquiring mind. The great names of the earlier stages of science were either amateurs or professors who professed not science nor any branch of science proper, but philosophy or mathematics or theology. Not infrequently they were churchmen, some of them monks. We might perhaps say they were all amateurs, in the better sense of that word. For some, it was a dangerous adventure. Bacon's Italian contemporaries in the approach to science, Tommaso Campanella, Galileo, and Giordano Bruno were persecuted as heretics and imprisoned—and the defiant Bruno was at length burned at the stake.

Under such conditions science played a remarkable role in society, out of all proportion to its scale or to its content. In challenging the presuppositions of the established cosmology, it was insidiously threatening the established social order as well. The hierarchical interdependence of church and state, the uneasy conflict for supremacy between the two, was at length in Western Europe partially resolved in the rise of absolute monarchy. The new science challenged, even when its practitioners claimed to be devout churchmen, the right of the church to pronounce on the laws of nature. Man's reason must patiently inquire of nature herself, instead of appealing to authority. Once the catalyst of reason was applied to authority at any point, it portended developments of a revolutionary character.

In that age, when science was still a sideline of the humanities, when science had no laboratories or special instruments, when scientists were men of letters or men of action who included the scientific interest in their ambit, there was no problem of communication between scientists and the educated public, the small aristocracy of those who combined some learning with a considerable amount of social and political influence. The age of scientific professionalism was still distant.

Scientific inquiry was then a more radical solvent than it is in our own day, when the products of science-based technology arouse far more public interest than do new scientific doctrines. Through the eighteenth and the earlier part of the nineteenth century science was still relatively unspecialized, and amateurs could still make distinctive contributions to it. Benjamin Franklin is a good example. Science continued its role as disturber of the established thought-ways, but with diminishing potency. The last intense shock to popular preconceptions was that delivered by the Darwinian theory in the middle of the century.

Today science has become a vast many-department organization, with all the advantages and the problems of highly specialized enterprise. It has been estimated that between eighty and ninety per cent of all the scientists the earth has witnessed are alive today. Scientists are an army spread over an enormous terrain, moving forward from a thousand disconnected bases. The research output is so vast that no scientist can read more than a tiny fraction of the contributions being made in his major field. Some leaders in each area are concerned with the broader strategy of the advance, but the vast majority are engaging in scouting the bit of landscape in front of their noses or in occupying for technological development the immediate territory they already possess.

The necessity for specialist concentration on meticulously limited projects has a tendency to segregate the scientist in any area from his fellows in other areas. Science speaks with no one voice on any problem of social concern. The generally educated public has no conception of what the great majority of scientists are doing. Some scientific adventures are sufficiently dramatic to receive public attention, such as the "mohole," the plumbing of the ocean depths, the Van Allen radiation belts, the mapping of the other side of the moon, and broadly, the exploration of space. There is usually one field of scientific activity that takes hold of the public imagination, although there may be little understanding of the nature or the significance of its achievements. At a crucial moment the whole world learned that the splitting of the atom had become the source of incredible power for destruction and might in time be turned to notable service for mankind. Since then, fundamental physics has held the place of honor. The atomic scientist is the wonderworker who provides governments with the horrendous secrets of new armaments and is also in demand by great corporations which are interested in the industrial applications of atomic energy.

Never has fundamental science been so much esteemed and never, perhaps, has the intrinsic significance of scientific advance been so little comprehended. Some scientists have themselves stated that the realm of the atom is so different from the macroscopic earth of tangible and visible things, so remote even from the conceptual images and abstractions that other sciences deal with, so exclusively construed in special symbols and mathematical formulas, that the new knowledge cannot be conveyed even to what we call the educated public.

No doubt it is true that the more elaborate procedures and the reasoning they embody and the background of training on which they depend are not communicable to those who lack the experience of the atomic scientist. No doubt also no one who lacks that experience can have the same quality of recognition, the same feel of the texture of things, that belongs to the specialist. To the uninitiate the mere statement of conclusions, of particular findings, remains detached, cold, unincorporate within his sketchy notions. But to some extent similar statements apply to the knowledge of every science, of every fine art, of every area that calls for *expertise*. The atomic scientist no doubt thinks in a context utterly remote from the experience of other men, in a world of infinitesimals wherein the resort to visual imagination is balked. As a total outsider from this world I would not venture to defend the position that a rough understanding of the significance of the advances in atomic science can still be communicated to a much larger public. I fall back on the words of a physicist who is himself a notable communicator, Werner Heisenberg. "Whenever we proceed from the known to the unknown," he says in his *Physics and Philosophy,*

> we may hope to understand, but we may have to learn at the same time a new meaning of the word "understanding." We know that any understanding must be based finally upon the natural language because it is only there that we can be certain to touch reality, and hence we must be sceptical of any scepticism with regard to this natural language and its essential concepts. Therefore, we may use these con-

cepts as they have been used at all times. In this way modern physics opened the door to a wider outlook on the relation between the human mind and reality.

Scientists, some scientists, may regard their particular scientific enclave as incommunicate, having nothing to say that can be translated into the language of the people, but science itself, science in some form, in some mode of social translation, is always an essential factor in the outlook of every community. Where scientific knowledge is lacking or ignored, pseudo-science is substituted. No great social controversy can be carried on without appeal either to science, which may be rightly or wrongly apprehended, or to pseudo-science. Take the conflict between the ideologies of communism and anti-communism. The lavish citation of alleged facts is always related to some doctrine that is presumptively corroborated by the alleged facts. And the doctrine is always related to presumptions about human nature, about the course of history, about the chain of consequences of different systems of production, and looming beyond such presumptions there is on the one side a philosophy of materialism that has biological implications and on the other side a variety of beliefs in the reality of non-material or spiritual values. As Francis Bacon said, it is a tendency of mankind "through the premature hurry of the understanding to leap or fly to universals or principles of things," and "great danger may be apprehended from philosophies of this kind"—at least, we may add, when, armed with power, they clash with one another. Or take the present issue over racial segregation in our own country. There are arguments on the effects of miscegenation, on the equality or superiority of racial stocks, on the lessons to be learned from history, on the psychological consequences of discrimination, on the economic benefits of equalized opportunity, and so forth—all topics where the final appeal is to science, and not to the emotions that so readily assume they have science on their side. Man is a most argumentative animal and the first premise of his endless arguments is attributed either to a science of which he knows little or to a God he does not know at all.

It seems obvious, therefore, that the more the findings of science, wherever at least they have any relevance to human affairs or human relationships or broadly to man's outlook on the world of nature or the cosmos itself, are effectively communicated and interpreted to the public, the more likely it is that social and political decisions will be more enlightened than otherwise they would be. Science is a condition and a partner of every art, including the art of living. Recently, an author who is both an effective scientist and a distinguished novelist, C. P. Snow, claimed that in our present civilization the arts and the sciences form two separate cultures, neither of which has concern for or understanding of the other. So far as this may be true, it is an unhappy divorce, unfortunate for the society they share. Science and the humanities, to use an old term that itself may be misleading, are closely interwoven into the endless process of society. Science changes more rapidly, moves only in one direction, to more advanced science. The humanities move often in a seemingly directionless manner, but they age better; their major achievements are not outmoded or replaced by superior ones. In this and in other respects the sciences and the arts are curiously complementary. Scientific advance, when translated into the products of technology, can have a disturbing or even disrputive effect on social standards, on the equilibrium of the folkways, unless there is enough recognition of the consequences and enough preparation to assure cultural adjustment to the new conditions. The salient example is the harnessing of atomic power, which renders obsolete age-old traditions concerning war and sovereignty.

In this respect scientists serve society not only by enlightening the public on the realities of the world we live in but also by helping to guide it in the intelligent use of knowledge, as at the present time many atomic scientists are notably doing. Science abjures value judgments but the scientist has no similar privilege. He is no more free than other men from the responsibilities of a citizen.

The line of communication between science and society is weakened by the habits and conditions of modern specialization, and communication is too easily dismissed as popularization, something the respectable professional abhors. The outlook of human beings is curiously compounded of scientifically valid, scientifically neutral, and scientifically invalid beliefs, and unfortunately the third ingredient, being congenial to the passions that prompt such beliefs, is often the most vehement and overbearing of the three. In times of tension and crisis it is, therefore, likely to take complete control, a phenomenon of which we have had tragic examples in recent times.

It may be too hard a task for the scientist to instill into the public mind something of his own scientific outlook, but surely the broader conceptions of the nature of the cosmos, of man's place in it, of the limitation and yet the marvelous advances of our knowledge, of the relation of mind and body, of the evolution of *homo sapiens*, could be included in the education of every educable citizen. It is this perspective, the fruit of knowledge, rather than the gobbets of information the pupil memorizes and forgets, that, properly conveyed, can subtly change the attitudes of men and blunt the gross prejudices to which the untutored imagination is so prone. Without being too optimistic about human nature, one might wonder whether, had the relevant knowledge been available and sufficiently widespread, certain pernicious doctrines would ever have gained control. One might wonder, for example, whether the early church fathers could have entertained such ignoble ideas of what was called the "flesh," which involved among other unhappy consequences the degradation of women, had there been any sufficient knowledge of the endlessly intricate marvel of reproduction. Or, to jump to modern times, had the youth of Germany been taught the relation of racial and ethnic distinctions to the common human stock, and the manner in which the diverse peoples have contributed to the greater culture of mankind, instead of the chauvinistic interpretation of history that passed muster in so many schools, would the notorious bigot, Adolf Hitler, have been so successful in his disastrous march to power? Or perhaps again, had the Southern segregationists been taught in their schoolbooks some honest anthropology, instead of the curious legends most of them still believe, would they have been so unprepared to face a decision that had to come, sooner or later? Relevant knowledge does in time change attitudes and modify our conceptions of self-interest. There is that element of truth in the old Socratic notion that knowledge is virtue. The lack of knowledge is certainly the ground of error, and every society is beset by misunderstandings of many kinds, misunderstandings of human nature, misunderstandings of our place in nature, misunderstandings of our relationships with others. Knowledge is not wisdom but it is the compass of wisdom. From all of which it surely follows that the effective communication of knowledge, of the broad findings of the sciences and of the scientific point of view, is the first obligation of science to society.

3
Education in a Technological Era

Ultimately, scientific knowledge in our society can be disseminated and applied to bring about technological change only if our educational institutions can keep abreast of the rapid sweep of change. What proposals, then, are being made with respect to education in our technological society? What are the purposes and goals of education? How can people be educated so that they can understand the complexities of modern society? Should our universities have functions other than merely educational training? What aids can the new technology offer to educators? Should traditional teaching methods be drastically revised? These questions are approached in the selections in this chapter.

A panel of UNESCO educational authorities believe that a distinction should be made between what they term "pupil-centered" and "community-structured" education. When a considerable number of students are educated above the elementary level, the panel believes that education should be community-structured—that is, in the best interests of the country and of the student. There is a necessity for a sound general education; a technical education is not sufficient. But at the same time, the educational system should prepare the student to meet the challenges of a technological way of life. He should be trained to participate actively in life, because "doing" is as characteristic of modern culture as "understanding." Children should, henceforth, be taught to comprehend the technical world.

Sharply critical of modern educational practices in this country, Admiral Rickover spells out what he considers to be the erroneous foundations of American educational philosophy; namely, that (1) little provision is made for the differences in natural ability, so that the more intelligent students receive inferior educations, and (2) in the emphasis on education as a means of providing an adjustment to life, the educators turn out people who are functionally illiterate. We must develop in our youth, Rickover argues, the intellectual attitudes and abilities that are absolutely necessary for technological progress. Students should be educated to be tough-minded and to respect the imperatives of science. We should be educating more people with the ability to transform scientific knowledge into useful products. We must also educate more skilled workers and technicians.

In his 1963 White House message on education, John F. Kennedy denies that U.S. education has been derelict, arguing that our educational system in the past has contributed materially to the strength of the nation and must be strengthened today if we are to maintain economic growth, a goal to which the nation is committed. Education, therefore, is necessary to sustain the growth of scientific knowledge; and to provide the guiding principles and leadership of the nation. Kennedy enumerates three national goals in education: the improvement of its quality; an increase in its extent; and an increase in educational opportunity, with incentives provided for individuals to complete their educations to the utmost of their abilities. To achieve these goals, Kennedy believes, we can no longer regard education as a merely local responsibility; the federal government must assume the responsibility for seeing to it that these goals are achieved.

Lewis Mumford attacks the idea, expressed by Rickover and implied by Kennedy, that education in the sciences should be emphasized and extended. It is erroneous, he argues, to slight education in the history and purpose of human culture and to make such studies subservient to the acquisition of mere scientific knowledge. Science does not consider meaningful human values, and a scientific education does not produce people capable of thought and decision in areas that are of utmost importance in contemporary society. Unless education concerns itself more with central human purposes and less with the mass production of scientists, engineers, and technicians, he warns, our society will collapse.

Julius Stratton admits that one can no longer take for granted the thesis that material progress is inevitably good. He points out some of the deleterious effects of technological change, but he believes that these can be corrected and in the future averted, if the problems are adequately understood in their total context and if programs for action are planned. The universities, he believes, are particularly qualified to meet the challenges of the present and uniquely suited to undertake the task of planning for the future.

Robert Hutchins agrees with Mumford that scientific education by itself is narrow and that American education must be reorganized. He dismisses the idea that universities at present can provide the setting for enlightened discussion of social problems. His belief is that intellectual communities must be built up outside our present educational system. The task of these communities will be to educate and inform the public.

Turning to the means by which science and technology can be used to aid the educational process, James D. Finn points to the wealth of devices now available to increase the effectiveness of teaching. He argues that the use of these new devices for instruction will prove not only beneficial but absolutely necessary if we are to educate the growing population of students effectively. Educators, he concludes, must see to it that these products of science are employed. However, many authorities, just as Mumford does, express concern with such educational innovations; the use of programmed instruction, television, and the rest, they argue, tends to depersonalize the educational process. Moreover, machine-graded examinations place too much emphasis on the remembering of isolated facts, whereas the goal of education should be to develop the powers of thought, discrimination, and judgment.

UNESCO
THE EDUCATIONAL PROBLEM IN A
TECHNOLOGICAL SOCIETY

In an age when mankind's potentialities for destruction have been enormously enhanced by such discoveries as that of atomic power, the most pressing human problem might appear to be: how can man exist?

From United Nations Educational, Scientific, and Cultural Organization, *Education in a Technological Society* (Paris, 1952) pp. 9–11, 28–31, 35–37. Reprinted by permission.

For many, however, there is another, perhaps even more important and not unrelated to the first: in a technological age such as ours, how can man more truly *live?* And the answer to this second problem is to be found largely in the field of education.

To try to provide an answer to this fundamental question without an appreciation of some of the outstanding changes which have taken place both in education and technology during the past 50 years would be unrealistic and impractical; for the nature of the changes is such as to demand a complete reorientation of our thoughts regarding the task of education today.

The quantitative and qualitative changes in education have often been described, but their gradual and cumulative nature may obscure their real impact. Quantitatively, more children are receiving education at the elementary, secondary and advanced levels than ever in the past. Qualitatively, an attempt, possibly more direct in education than in any other sphere of activity, is being made to work towards real equality of opportunity for all groups of society. The cumulative and gradual changes taking place in technology may often not be obvious; and they may be taking place at a very different speed and in a widely different direction from those in education. They have taken the form, on the one hand, of an ever more rapid introduction of modern technology into every corner of the earth; and, on the other, of the rapid transformation of technical methods, due partly to economic and political fluctuations. Whereas of old a man learning a trade could count himself equipped for a lifetime, and was encouraged by the stability of the times to arrange a comparable or identical training for his sons, today some new industrial process or politico-economic development may enforce repeated changes of occupation within the space of a few years.

Once seen in perspective, the effect of these changes in education and technology becomes clear. As long as a country educates only a small proportion of its children, and that during the earliest years only, the instruction given can hardly fail to be more or less useful. But if—to take an extreme case—a country educates almost all its young people up to the age of 16 or 18, it is most important that the education given, particularly in the later years, shall be appropriate. Otherwise, large numbers may be prepared for a type of life which they will not be able to lead. That they may wish to receive inappropriate instruction, and that the educational system meets this wish, in no way serves to set the matter right. If, for instance, in a country largely dependent upon the mining of coal or the growing of wheat the great mass of the coming generation prefers to be educated to become small clerks or shopkeepers or poets, that country will be in grave danger of wrecking itself upon the reef of its excellent intentions. It would be educating for the good life—as each separate individual understands it—but failing to secure the material basis upon which such a life depends.

In short, so long as relatively few children in a country are educated beyond the elementary standard, it is altogether suitable that education should be "pupil-centered"; i.e., that its object should be simply and solely to develop the aptitudes of a particular boy or girl. But as soon as considerable numbers are carried beyond the elementary standard, a further principle must be introduced. The educational system needs to be "community-structured"; i.e., so designed as to take due account of the means by which the country exists and prospers.

Such "community-structuring" of the educational system is, moreover, in the best interests of the pupils themselves, individually as well as collectively. This becomes evident as soon as changes in technology are taken into account. In the course of the next 50 years—the lifetime of the children now in the schools—there can be little question that the spread of technology to all peoples will have changed the whole aspect of the world. There can be little question also that the rate of transformation in technical methods will not have diminished. In these circumstances, unless education is "community-structured" with an eye to the future, it will be bad education. There can be fewer things more disastrous, for individuals no less than for a people as a whole, than that they should be educated for a way of life that does not exist.

It is at this point that the essentially international aspect of the question must be taken into consideration. In building their educational systems round the needs of the community, the peoples of the world have everything to gain in learning from one another. Those countries in the process of industrial development can profit greatly from both the successes and the mistakes of the countries with longer technological experience. Even the highly advanced countries can see their own problems, and the possible solutions, in better perspective against the background of experience other than their own.

In yet another way, international co-operation in this field has its special cogency. Failure on the part of education to meet the challenge of a technological way of life has consequences which do not stop short at frontiers. A country which makes no adequate provision for preparing its young people for the life they will actually lead, giving them instead an education based upon a conception of society long since past, is likely to expose them to great psychological, social and economic tensions. The *déclassé* intellectual, forced into work which he regards as beneath him or making a dubious living by his wits, the unskilled worker who feels himself exploited, the countryman (with no special aptitude for anything else) for whom *"la terre est trop basse,"* are typical products of educational inadequacy or misdirection. At the other end of the scale, a country whose concept of education in a technological society is to create slaves to mind its machines, is not only committing a crime against humanity; it is a source of danger to the peoples around it. The international character of the problem is thus to be seen not only in the search for solutions by means of the comparative method, but still more in the world consequences if solutions are not found and applied. . . .

Up-to-date technical education, whether in schools, in industry, or both, is not sufficient to create an effective working force. Behind the technical instruction it is essential to have a sound general education, even on purely utilitarian grounds. If there is not the underpinning of basic knowledge, no amount of training in technique can get beyond a certain stage, while the possibility of readaptation should the need arise, is greatly reduced.

At the same time, a just balance must be held between the facilities given for technical education and the attractiveness of the more traditional forms of scholarship. This is not always done. The tendency of the intellectual to create men in his own image is strong. It is also dangerous. If a country, by conferring prestige, amenities and security upon an academic type of training, sets out to produce in mass the man who never takes his coat off, it will have served its people ill.

To find a means of steering a middle way between these two extremes—emphasis entirely upon training in technique, emphasis entirely upon training for a cultured life—seemed to the Conference to be the essence of its task. . . .

The integration of all education into a continuous system extending from primary school through the various types of secondary education to the university increases equality in educational opportunities and allows the country to benefit from the special gifts of a much larger student body. The integration, however, becomes increasingly difficult as secondary education expands. If all children go to school beyond the age of 14, the secondary curriculum must be diversified and adjusted to provide for a great many occupations and careers. But then the question arises whether the universities will modify their admission requirements and accept new types of secondary curricula as adequate preparation for university work. Generally speaking, so long as the classical curriculum ranks highest with the universities, the other forms of secondary education will be regarded as inferior, although they may be closer to the practical requirements of living and to the general cultural activities in which the student will actually participate. A traditional policy of admittance to university studies has therefore a restraining influence upon secondary education and retards its adjustment to the needs of modern society. . . .

The first principle that emerges is that general education in an industrial civilization cannot content itself merely with providing knowledge but must also, in a number of different ways, prepare the student for *active* participation in life. The basic tool-subjects of general education— reading, writing, arithmetic, grammar and scientific principles—are dual purpose. They are of fundamental usefulness in helping the individual to live a good and full life in society. At the same time, learning actually to use these tools is an essential preparation for productive work. "Doing" is as characteristic of modern culture as "understanding," "know how" as important to man as the "know about" and "know why." Unless the teaching method in schools of general education is so orientated as to provide this basic appreciation of the "know how" in life it will fail to meet the needs of tomorrow's pupils and today's. General education, therefore, should not be regarded as "non-vocational" education, for it has a profound vocational significance in the broadest sense; the distinction should be made between those subjects and topics of general importance which form the background of every student's education, and those topics of special importance (such as technical training in engineering, building, or banking) which are taught to groups of students at a later stage of their educational careers when they are specifically preparing to enter the occupations concerned.

The second main principle is that the preparation for life and work provided by general education should include four main constituent elements: observation; action, co-operative as well as individual; reading and writing; and independent thought. In the past, general education concentrated primarily on the last two of these essential requirements. All four elements need to be brought together in co-ordinated action by the teacher, the student, and the school itself.

Many of our difficulties today are caused by the fact that students in school do not learn how to think, or to do and find things, for themselves—which should be the first aim of all education. Too much emphasis is laid upon the communication of second-hand information which is apt to stay in the pupil's mind only until examination time. No solution of the problem of reorientation of general education can be found, therefore, in merely adding new subjects to an already over-burdened curriculum. A new way must be found of teaching the basic subjects as they exist, a way which lays stress not merely on the student's ability to benefit by reading, but also on his capacity for using his eyes and hands and for co-operative enterprise, whether in the workshop, the theatre, the school camp or the playing field.

Furthermore, if one of the aims of a truly balanced general education is (as the Conference believed it to be) to help to build a just and ordered democratic society, opportunities must be found during the course of that education to introduce the student at first hand to political activity and the democratic procedure of self-government, with a view to widening the whole range of his interests. The examination of current national and international political and economic issues should enable him to understand, among other things, that the study of history is not mere chronology, but an all-embracing view of the technical, economic, political, social and cultural organization by which peoples live.

While general education is universally recognized as of supreme importance in introducing youth to literature, history, the arts and science, and as doubly effective if this introduction can be so ordered that it includes the acquirement of creative skill, can general education also introduce the youth of the world to technology and all that it involves in the present age?

With the help of modern technology, man is acquiring more and more goods, but understands less and less of their production, construction and operation. It has been well said that people find it terrible if told that a child has never seen a cow, but take it as a matter of course if a child has never seen a factory. Occupational specialization and the removal of production from the household have made it infinitely more difficult for man to comprehend the technical world in which he lives. And what we do not understand we are liable to distrust and fear, or at best ignore.

If general education is to provide a broad and realistic introduction to life, it must help the student to close this gap in his experience and understanding. The success of general education in this scheme will depend greatly on workship facilities and the quality of workshop instruction. The practical side of school life needs to be increasingly recognized for the contribution it is able to make to general education—it is an opportunity for children to develop their inherent manual and artistic skills, without in any way leading to specific vocations. Workshop activities give a training to eye, hand and mind which may prove invaluable in later life. And for those who eventually follow a non-manual occupation, workshop instruction is no less vitally essential, since its emphasis on direct creative activity helps to build a general self-reliance in the individual and to develop a well-rounded personality.

Thus, in brief, the Conference concluded that:

A. There need be no antagonism between learning through observation and action and the acquisition of knowledge through books. Each form of activity supplements and supports the other. The schools should therefore carefully cultivate them together.

B. While the individual child is at the center of the educational system and must remain so, he will not find himself as a maturing personality, able to meet the shocks and tensions of a disturbed and often unhappy society, unless he also engages in creative and co-operative activity with his fellows.

C. The hands as well as the head need to learn; not only because this may have some possible occupational usefulness but, still more, because it contributes to the all-round development of the growing human being.

D. What is required is not so much a new kind of curriculum (although this also may be necessary) as a new kind of teaching; and with it a new kind of aim in education—the fitting of the young person to master technology, not merely to become one of its cogs. . . .

H. G. Rickover
EDUCATION FOR ALL CHILDREN

. . . How can I, who am engaged in a specialty—nuclear propulsion—qualify as a critic of education? It so happens that this specialty has in it all the elements that go into modern technology. When you find out what it takes to accomplish an engineering project for developing atomic energy you know what it takes to do almost any other new development job. The educational qualifications of the people who do the technical work and of those who direct it as administrators are roughly the same. In fact, our nuclear project is a pretty good touchstone of the effectiveness of our schools. It calls for flexibility and toughness of mind, for understanding the basic principles in physics, chemistry, and all types of engineering. Also for what I'd like to call an impersonal "scientific" attitude toward the work that must be done. This means, first of all, a readiness to go back to fundamental principles, for it is these that must be applied in a novel way to develop a new item such as a nuclear reactor. It requires readiness to shed accustomed routines—nothing new can be created by routine methods. It means on the part of nontechnical administrators, who are set above the technical people doing the actual development work, that they must forget their organizational "status" when it comes to dealing with technical problems. Because here they are inferior in knowledge to the experts who are organizationally their subordinates. It isn't easy for people whose jobs give them power, not to use this power but to respect the imperatives of science and engineering

Portion of a statement of Admiral Rickover before House Committee on Appropriations, 87th Congress, 2nd Session.

and to bow to the judgment of technical subordinates in *all* technical matters.

Bureaucracy, Conformity, and American Educational Philosophy

Unlike basic scientific research, engineering projects are not self-contained group efforts. By choosing and training the technical people in my organization with utmost care, I have been able to assemble and train an engineering group with high competence in reactor technology. But the country does not obtain full benefit of their broad and long experience, of their spirit of cooperative endeavor and their ability to produce nuclear ships that are ready to go to war immediately after their sea trials. Much of their time is frittered away "educating" a constantly changing stream of administrators and doing the needless paperwork these people order. Once, when a particularly useless report was requested, one that would have tied up a considerable number of engineers for weeks, I demanded to know how thick the report should be, 9 inches, 13 inches, or 17 inches. The 9-inch thick report would require 4 weeks full-time work, the others correspondingly more. As you know, many people judge the value of a report by its thickness. It so happened that right at the time we were having many technical difficulties and not one engineer was available to take care of these—they were all busily writing useless reports.

It is too bad that the "personality cult" and the desire to "manipulate" people rather than to produce useful practical products so permeates our powerful administrators that, instead of helping new projects, they often hinder them. I have never had any technical help from nontechnical administrators. Their human deficiencies are, I believe, a result of the educational philosophy that has permeated the American public school system since Dewey and his followers diverted our schools from traditional objectives and methods into the dead end of life adjustment, permissiveness, and the use of the schools as social levelers instead of developers of our children's intellectual powers.

The schoolmen could not have thought up a more inappropriate concept of education for this day and age. They could not have dreamed up a worse way to educate young Americans for the tough days ahead. Particularly bad is the excessive emphasis laid in our schools on making oneself popular by conforming to the ways of the "peer" group, on assiduously cultivating an "image" of oneself that will enhance one's status, on personalizing human contacts even when these involve accomplishing tasks which must depend on knowledge and intellectual competence. A generation has grown up that puts "getting along" above competence on the job and above the intellectual courage of sticking by one's considered judgment; especially when it means objecting to orders by superiors whose own judgment may be ill considered since they lack the necessary technical knowledge. There is no surer way to become unpopular than to set oneself against a technically incompetent superior bent on using the power of his position to enforce his will. And though one may do this from the most sincere motives, he will be castigated by everyone as a "controversial nonconformer," and today in this country there is no worse term of opprobrium.

Here is the sort of thing I mean: One day one of my superiors asked that I reduce the amount of radiation shielding in our nuclear ships. He said I was using civilian radiation safety standards but that in military units, personnel casualties of 20 to 30 percent were sometimes accepted. I told him I was sorry I could not do what he asked. I couldn't ignore the fact that where radiation is involved we are dealing not just with the health of the men aboard one ship, but with the genetic future of mankind. The official replied that no one knew much about evolution anyway, and if we raised radiation exposures we might find that the resultant mutations were helpful rather than harmful and that mankind might "learn to live with radiation." You can see what utter nonsense this was. Yet this man had authority. Had I not been obstreperous, had I been a good "organization man," I would have gone along and reduced the shielding and gained favor with him at the expense of some unlucky Navy men and their descendants.

I mention this merely to illustrate how important it is today that we educate our youth to respect the imperatives of science, and to insist on their superiors likewise respecting these imperatives—even at the risk of losing one's job.

I have a legitimate concern with American education simply because I am a citizen of this country and would be derelict in my duties if I did not express my worries over what will happen to our badly educated young people in a world where the United States finds itself increasingly in competition with other nations—politically, militarily, scientifically, economically, culturally; in fact, in every area of human activity. Besides this, I have a personal concern with American education because my own engineering projects are representative of many that simply must be carried through if our Nation is to remain in top position. These projects are often being harassed and delayed by human deficiencies which a good school system could have done much to prevent.

Current Evidence of the Nation's Educational Inadequacies

Naturally, I am aware that many types of human competencies are needed in a complex society. But among these ability to translate new scientific discoveries into useful products is surely one that is of crucial importance at the present time. I have often spoken of the danger in our lengthening leadtimes, especially since leadtime in the Soviet Union has been contracting and in some important items now seems to be shorter than ours. Short leadtimes are a result of skill in planning and carrying through complex new development projects; that is, in recognizing what is needed in personnel, funds, and equipment and providing them in adequate quality and quantity. Essentially, it is a skill that can be deliberately cultivated through proper education, just as the needed personnel can be produced by proper education. Our lengthening lead-times are therefore an indicator that something is radically wrong in our school system. Whatever other tasks it may have to accomplish, surely a public school system in a country such as ours must develop in youth the kind of intellectual attitudes and abilities that are an absolute necessity if we are to progress technologically, and at a pace at least as rapid as that of competing nations.

That our schools fail in this task has worried me for a long time. As you know, knowledge now doubles every 10 to 15 years; we lack the educated manpower to make full use of the great opportunities this growth of knowledge offers. Also, since we no longer live in geographic isolation from world affairs we suffer in our contacts abroad from a lack of educated manpower to make our national goals effective. We are plagued with serious deficiencies in virtually every class of occupation that makes demands upon a person's general and specialized education, whether it is at the level of the "learned" professional, the semiprofessional, the skilled craftsman, or the technician. Despite our enormous and costly educational establishment, this country has more functional illiterates than most other industrially advanced nations. We have more people who do not possess minimum knowledge of the elements of language, mathematics, history, and geography that are considered part of *elementary education in advanced European countries and which every normal person there appears to absorb at school.* Recently, the Army published the fact that 25 percent of draftees were *unqualified* to be modern soldiers—25 percent of a cross section of young America! In most cases the deficiencies were mental. In Switzerland, where every male does military service, the rejection rate is about 7 percent. Swiss standards for draftees are certainly no more lenient than U.S. Army standards. I refuse to accept this appalling difference between rejection rates of 7 percent and 25 percent as reflecting on the intelligence and educability of American youth. I blame American schools for this.

The Need To Improve and Extend Education of Skilled Workers and Technicians

For a modern industrial nation, it seems to me evident we have too few skilled workers. This shows up glaringly in advanced technologies as nuclear power, missiles, satellites, for here we need precision hardware that cannot be produced by our usual mass production techniques, but requires craftsmanship. We put less effort into systematic education of adequate numbers of skilled workers and technicians than either Europe or Russia. Our high school vocational courses are of little practical use and are positively dangerous when they replace courses in basic education. The modern craftsman—like the professional person—needs a good general education as well as specialized training in his particular craft. We make a mistake in trying to provide both in a "general" school such as our high school. A high school makes the best contribution to the educational needs of future skilled craftsmen when it gives them a first-rate basic education. To teach the innumerable craft skills needed in a modern industrial nation is beyond its capacity. High school vocational courses are bound to lag behind industry's rapidly changing needs. I suggest we examine the diverse postschool apprenticeship and technical school courses—full and part time—by means of which Europe produces proportionally far more skilled workers than do we.

Russia has a tremendous training program for technicians. England's work force is 50 percent skilled, 12 percent semiskilled. Switzerland produces virtually no unskilled labor and must import it from abroad—currently 25 percent of her workers are foreigners. In most European countries there is a shortage of *unskilled* workers; here the shortage is among the *skilled*. A little over a decade ago American educational officialdom, under the sponsorship of the U.S. Office of Education, declared in the so-called Prosser resolution, that our schools could not educate more than 20 percent of their pupils for skilled labor, and another 20 percent for what we call "college preparatory goals." The remaining 60 percent were to be fobbed off with unintellectual life-adjustment training.

Automation was certainly in the air even then. It is incomprehensible that the schoolmen did not foresee what is now so tragically evident to all of us: that workers lacking a good basic education are badly handicapped in learning a new skill when their jobs become obsolete because of automation. The schools, I feel, must share part of the blame that, even while there is a shortage of *skilled* workers and technicians, we have a surplus of poorly educated *unskilled* labor for whom it is becoming increasingly difficult to find jobs. Children who get substandard education will cost State and Federal Governments large sums of money in later years, both through lost taxes and through increased welfare payments.

Shortages in Professional Fields

Our shortage is even greater in the category of "professionals." I need not elaborate on our lack of genuinely qualified scientists and engineers; you are only too well aware of this. Despite efforts to encourage more young people to enter engineering, the Nation's deficit in this field grows steadily. Secretary of Health, Education, and Welfare Ribicoff, reported a few months ago that we graduate each year about 45,000 engineers but need 72,000; he warned that the balance of brainpower may tip dangerously against us if the Nation does not soon awake to the importance of education to the freedom of the Western World. Russia is graduating 120,000 engineers annually.

We have similar shortages in medicine. Currently we graduate about 7,400 physicians. This is just three quarters of our minimum requirement. To fill our doctor gap we import physicians, most of them from Far and Middle Eastern countries. About 8,000 of these are now serving in our hospitals. If these foreign doctors remain here, they will constitute a loss to the countries that paid for their training, a loss these countries can ill afford. This is a shameful situation. It doesn't make sense for us to give billions of dollars to underdeveloped countries and then to take their few trained professionals away from them. This is reverse foreign-aid with a vengeance. It defeats the basic intent behind the program. We are, I believe, the only Western nation that cannot manage to produce enough doctors for its needs. We have a similar shortage in nurses. I read in the papers that we now lure them from Canada. The "professionals" shortage extends into many other spheres. One of the worst deficits, and to my mind the most important, is in teachers.

Our Philosophy of "Identical Education" and Our Trained Manpower Shortages

Now all these shortages are in large part a result of our having a public school system with a built-in bias against bright youngsters. We have committed ourselves to an educational philosophy of identical education for all. To provide for the needs of the talented, our education-ists constantly tell us, would be "elite" education. This is a loaded word that seeks to engage our emotions and prevent straight thinking. "Elite" education, as I see it, would be education where good schooling can be had only at high cost, thus barring from it the majority of children whose parents could not pay school fees. In the past, education like other amenities of life was a private expense. Children of the rich not only got better education, but also nicer homes, more expensive clothes, better medical care, and all sorts of other things. We have removed education, up to the end of high school, from this list. Most countries abroad have gone beyond us by doing this also for bright students preparing for the professions.

When schooling is tuition free, it automatically ceases to be "elite" education. What you have when you make realistic provision for differing scholastic aptitudes and needs of children is *acceleration* for those who can learn fast. These are the children who are intelligent enough to become professionals. They have to absorb a lot *more education* than the majority of our children. So what on earth is undemocratic about letting them go ahead at their own fast pace so they will not be handicapped by having to postpone overlong the time when they can earn a living?

American "professional" educators can rarely be moved by this argument. To them only *identical* education in a comprehensive school is "democratic." They are not content with eliminating "ability to pay" in our public school system. They also want to eliminate "ability to learn" as a criterion for the kind of education a child pursues. They are not content with equality of *opportunity* in our schools. They want to manipulate schooling so as to cancel out any advantages a child may possess by innate endowment or favorable home background, which would enable him to learn at a more rapid pace than the average. In this way they hope the schools may serve to level out social and economic inequalities which always get muddled in their thinking with *intellectual* inequalities. It seems to them just as "undemocratic" to provide a more challenging academic secondary school for children with academic talent as it is to permit such schools to be so expensive that in effect they are available only to children of the rich.

Their eyes are set firmly on the average pupil. American education therefore moves at the snail's pace of the child of average ability, average motivation, average home background. This is one of the chief causes of our shortage of professionals. Until quite recently the public school system even refused to concern itself seriously with the educational needs of the minority that would go on to higher education.

Professional Education: the European System and Ours

Europe, which now shares our ideal of eliminating "ability to pay" as a bar to educational advance, could not possibly afford the educational stretchout we practice as the consequence of our insistence that not only "ability to pay," but also "ability to learn," must be eliminated. I doubt very much that even we will be able to afford the stretchout much longer. Abroad it is considered sensible to allow bright youngsters to proceed through their general education at their own proper pace and to reach the bachelor's or maturity degree in 12 or 13 years. Our bright youth are dragged through the primary school and the high school at a pace adjusted to the average learner. To make up for lost time they must then take an expensive college course, ending up no better educated than their

European counterparts but 3 to 4 years older and many thousands of dollars poorer.

For example, our schoolmen's obsession with undifferentiated schooling adds 3 to 4 years to the time it takes to become a physician in this country. *Someone* must pay the student's living costs as well as the cost of schooling during these needlessly imposed additional years. As a result, the number of applicants to our medical schools is currently *decreasing*, yet with a soaring population we need *more* doctors. Since in this country 80 percent of the cost of a medical education must be borne by the student, the school stretchout will inexorably bring us to a point where only children of the rich can afford to become physicians! Even today families with incomes under $5,000 supply only 14 percent of our medical students, yet these families make up 50 percent of the population. Abroad there are not only scholarships for bright students preparing to become physicians; general education is either free or extremely cheap for *all* students. Fees in medical schools are low as well, and the *whole* process takes *3 to 4* years less time than here.

In all professions where the importance of good general education has been recognized and a bachelor's degree is now required for admission to a professional school, our public school stretchout creates severe shortages. In all the professions, where a compromise has been made with the student's desire to get on with specialized training, the stretchout has another unfortunate consequence. I refer to professions where a student may take his specialized training at the college level, entering directly from high school. In such cases, the prescribed college program must attempt to squeeze some general education into an already heavy course of professional studies, to the detriment of the student's professional training. Moreover, little will be done for his general education except to make up for a few of the most glaring gaps. The student will not emerge a genuinely educated person. His counterpart abroad, on the contrary, will be quite as well trained professionally and will *in addition* have obtained a good all-around liberal education, at least equivalent to an American bachelor's degree. The student here and abroad will be about the same age, but the difference in his educational background will be great.

Most professions are studied at the undergraduate level in this country—agriculture, business, elementary school teaching, etc. This was once true of medicine and law as well, but medicine upgraded itself half a century ago, and now the better law schools also require a bachelor's degree for admission. Engineering and a few other professions are in process of upgrading themselves. Meanwhile American professionals who receive only undergraduate training are at a disadvantage compared to Europeans, who have had a much better general education.

Summary: Achievements of American Education Mediocre

To sum up: Our schoolmen's bias against giving bright children an education appropriate to their talents and educational objectives has two unfortunate consequences. In professions where we require the members to be educated persons, the needless stretchout produces severe shortages. In professions where we compromise this requirement, Americans will be inferior in educational background to similar Europeans. Doubtless the reply will be "but we like it this way." There was a time when we could afford to say this; when we could set lower educational requirements without suffering any great damage. But that was when we lived in isolation and didn't have to meet competition from abroad. Today we simply must see to it that our people are educationally equipped to hold their own in every sphere of human activity.

As it is, many of our brightest people who have attained positions at the top of public and private enterprise, in administrative as well as in technical or professional work, lack the foundation of a broad and thorough education in the humanities and the sciences. Without this foundation they become what the Spanish philosopher Ortega y Gasset "calls learned ignoramuses"—persons who know much about a narrow specialty and little about all else; persons who, in dealing with each other, lack a common medium that would permit cross-fertilization of ideas. Even in their own specialty, such people will be less effective because they do not possess the educational background that would enable them to evaluate their own work against that of other professionals or, for that matter, against basic national interests and needs.

Here then is my indictment of American education: Its scholastic achievements are mediocre. Its pace is so slow that our children fall behind young Europeans almost from their first day at school. It does not produce the educated people we must have.

The Present National Crisis

In the past this could be tolerated for, protected by two friendly oceans, we could live as we pleased in splendid isolation. Our wealth in land and resources made up in part for our educational deficiencies. But the favorable ratio of land to population which until recently gave us *unique* advantages is now contracting. Wasteful habits, notably the whole idea of "planned obsolescence," are rapidly exhausting our nonrenewable resources while population grows apace—at almost three times the European growth rate. I estimate the day is but a generation ahead when we will no longer have *any* advantage over Russia or a united Europe as far as the material foundations of our society are concerned. Against this inexorable shrinking of special advantages in geographic isolation and natural wealth, the crisis in American education stands forth in all its gravity. The trouble we have holding our own *intellectually* against rival world powers presents a "clear and present danger" to the United States. Newspaper columnist J. A. Livingston, during last year's Berlin crisis, asked the pertinent question: "Were our horizons in diplomacy, space and propaganda limited by our way of life?" I would like to add, "or by our education?"

This state of affairs has concerned me for a long time. I have devoted much effort familiarizing myself with the problem and I have frequently spoken out for educational reform. Many "professional" educators accuse me of meddling in matters that are none of my business. But to my way of thinking every *national* problem is also the *private* problem of *every* American citizen. I think there can be no greater gift than to live in the United States—to live in our politically free society. But this is a gift not to be enjoyed passively. It comes at the cost of personal involvement with the fate of the Nation. To withdraw into one's private world and leave national problems to be solved by "others" is to me about as despicable as for an able-bodied person to evade his military obligations or to refuse to earn his living and sponge on relatives or on society. It is pure parasitism. The Greeks called citizens who took no interest in public affairs but were concerned only with themselves—with their ids—*idiotes*, from which the modern world idiot derives . . .

John F. Kennedy
THE WHITE HOUSE MESSAGE ON EDUCATION

Education is the keystone in the arch of freedom and progress. Nothing has contributed more to the enlargement of this Nation's strength and opportunities than our traditional system of free, universal elementary and secondary education, coupled with widespread availability of college education.

Portion of "The White House Message on Education," January 29, 1963, Senate Committee on Labor and Public Welfare, Sub-Committee on Education, 88th Congress, 1st Session.

For the individual, the doors to the schoolhouse, to the library, and to the college lead to the richest treasures of our open society: to the power of knowledge—to the training and skills necessary for productive employment—to the wisdom, the ideals, and the culture which enrich life—and to the creative, self-disciplined understanding of society needed for good citizenship in today's changing and challenging world.

For the Nation, increasing the quality and availability of education is vital to both our national security and our domestic well-being. A free nation can rise no higher than the standard of excellence set in its schools and colleges. Ignorance and illiteracy, unskilled workers and school dropouts—these and other failures of our educational system breed failure in our social and economic system: delinquency, unemployment, chronic dependence, a waste of human resources, a loss of productive power and purchasing power and an increase in tax-supported benefits. The loss of only 1 year's income due to unemployment is more than the total cost of 12 years of education through high school. Failure to improve educational performance is thus not only poor social policy, it is poor economics.

At the turn of the century, only 10 percent of our adults had a high school or college education. Today such an education has become a requirement for an increasing number of jobs. Yet nearly 40 percent of our youths are dropping out before graduating from high school; only 43 percent of our adults have completed high school; only 8 percent of our adults have completed college; and only 16 percent of our young people are presently completing college. As my Science Advisory Committee has reported, one of our most serious manpower shortages is the lack of Ph.D.'s in engineering, science, and mathematics; only about one half of 1 percent of our school age generation is achieving Ph.D. degrees in all fields.

This Nation is committed to greater investment in economic growth; and recent research has shown that one of the most beneficial of all such investments is education, accounting for some 40 percent of the Nation's growth and productivity in recent years. It is an investment which yields a substantial return in the higher wages and purchasing power of trained workers, in the new products and techniques which come from skilled minds and in the constant expansion of this Nation's storehouse of useful knowledge.

In the new age of science and space, improved education is essential to give new meaning to our national purpose and power. In the last 20 years, mankind has acquired more scientific information than in all of previous history. Ninety percent of all the scientists that ever lived are alive and working today. Vast stretches of the unknown are being explored every day for military, medical, commercial, and other reasons.

And finally, the twisting course of the cold war requires a citizenry that understands our principles and problems. It requires skilled manpower and brainpower to match the power of totalitarian discipline. It requires a scientific effort which demonstrates the superiority of freedom. And it requires an electorate in every State with sufficiently broad horizons and sufficient maturity of judgment to guide this Nation safely through whatever lies ahead.

In short, from every point of view, education is of paramount concern to the national interest as well as to each individual. Today we need a new standard of excellence in education, matched by the fullest possible access to educational opportunities, enabling each citizen to develop his talents to the maximum possible extent. . . .

A century of experience with land-grant colleges has demonstrated that Federal financial participation can assist educational progress and growth without Federal control. In the last decade, experience with the National Science Foundation, with the National Defense Education Act, and with programs for assisting federally affected school districts has demonstrated that Federal support can benefit education without leading to Federal Control. The proper Federal role is to identify national education goals and to help local, State, and private authorities build the necessary roads to reach those goals. Federal aid will enable our schools, colleges, and universities to be more stable financially and therefore more independent.

These goals include the following:

First, we must improve the quality of instruction provided in all of our schools and colleges. We must stimulate interest in learning in order to reduce the alarming number of students who now drop out of school or who do not continue into higher levels of education. This requires more and better teachers—teachers who can be attracted to and retained in schools and colleges only if pay levels reflect more adequately the value of the services they render. It also requires that our teachers and instructors be equipped with the best possible teaching materials and curriculums. They must have at their command methods of instruction proven by thorough scientific research into the learning process and by careful experimentation.

Second, our educational system faces a major problem of quantity—of coping with the needs of our expanding population and of the rising educational expectations for our children which all of us share as parents. Nearly 50 million people were enrolled in our schools and colleges in 1962—an increase of more than 50 percent since 1950. By 1970, college enrollment will nearly double, and secondary schools will increase enrollment by 50 percent—categories in which the cost of education, including facilities, is several times higher than in elementary schools.

Third, we must give special attention to increasing the opportunities and incentives for all Americans to develop their talents to the utmost—to complete their education and to continue their self-development throughout life. This means preventing school dropouts, improving and expanding special educational services, and providing better education in slum, distressed, and rural areas where the educational attainment of students is far below par. It means increased opportunities for those students both willing and intellectually able to advance their education at the college and graduate levels. It means increased attention to vocational and technical education, which have long been underdeveloped in both effectiveness and scope, to the detriment of our workers and our technological progress.

In support of these three basic goals, I am proposing today a comprehensive, balanced program to enlarge the Federal Government's investment in the education of its citizens—a program aimed at increasing the educational opportunities of potentially every American citizen, regardless of age, race, religion, income, and educational achievement.

This program has been shaped to meet our goals on the basis of three fundamental guidelines:

(a) An appraisal of the entire range of educational problems, viewing educational opportunity as a continuous lifelong process, starting with preschool training and extending through elementary and secondary schools, college, graduate education, vocational education, job training and retraining adult education, and such general community educational resources as the public library;

(b) A selective application of Federal aid—aimed at strengthening, not weakening, the independence of existing school systems and aimed at meeting our most urgent education problems and objectives, including quality improvement; teacher training; special problems of slum, depressed, and rural areas; needy students; manpower shortage areas such as science and engineering; and shortages of educational facilities; and

(c) More effective implementation of existing laws, as reflected in my recent budget recommendations.

To enable the full range of educational needs to be considered as a whole, I am transmitting to the Congress with this message a single, comprehensive education bill—the National Education Improvement Act of 1963. For education cannot easily or wisely be divided into separate parts. Each part is linked to the other. The colleges depend on the work of the schools; the schools depend on the colleges for teachers; vocational and technical education is not separate from general education. This bill recalls the posture of Jefferson: "Nobody can doubt my zeal for the general instruction of the people. I never have proposed a sacrifice of the primary to the ultimate grade of instruction. Let us keep our eye steadily on the whole system."

In order that its full relation to economic growth, to the new age of science, to the national security, and to human and institutional freedom may be analyzed in proper perspective, this bill should be considered as a whole, as a combination of elements designed to solve problems that have no single solution.

This is not a partisan measure—and it neither includes nor rejects all of the features which have long been sought by the various educational groups and organizations. It is instead an attempt to launch a prudent and balanced program drawing upon the efforts of many past Congresses and the proposals of many Members of both Houses and both political parties. It is solely an educational program, without trying to solve all other difficult domestic problems. It is clearly realistic in terms of its cost—and it is clearly essential to the growth and security of this country. . . .

In all the years of our national life, the American people—in partnership with their governments—have continued to insist that "the means of education shall forever be encouraged," as the Continental Congress affirmed in the Northwest Ordinance. Fundamentally, education is and must always be a local responsibility, for it thrives best when nurtured at the grassroots of our democracy. But in our present era of economic expansion, population growth, and technological advance, State, local, and private efforts are insufficient. These efforts must be reinforced by national support, if American education is to yield a maximum of individual development and national well-being.

The necessity of this program does not rest on the course of the cold war. Improvement in education is essential to our Nation's development without respect to what others are doing. Nevertheless, it is worthwhile noting that the Soviet Union recognizes that educational effort in the 1960's will have a major effect on a nation's power, progress, and status in the 1970's and 1980's. According to a recent report prepared for the National Science Foundation, Soviet institutions of higher education are graduating three times as many engineers and four times as many physicians as the United States. While trailing behind this country in aggregate annual numbers of higher education graduates, the Soviets are maintaining an annual flow of scientific and technical professional manpower more than twice as large as our own. At the same time, they have virtually eliminated illiteracy, with a 23-fold increase since the turn of the century in the proportion of persons with an education beyond the seventh grade. This Nation's devotion to education is surely sufficient to excel the achievements of any other nation or system.

The program here proposed is reasonable and yet far reaching. It offers Federal assistance without Federal control. It provides for economic growth, manpower development, and progress toward our educational and humanitarian objectives. It encourages the increase of the knowledge, skills, attitudes, and critical intelligence necessary for the preservation of our society. It will help keep America strong and safe and free. I strongly recommend it to the Congress for high-priority action.

Lewis Mumford
THE AUTOMATION OF KNOWLEDGE

The problems I propose to bring to your attention . . . first shaped themselves in the course of preparing a book on which I have long been at work, as a historian of technology, on the human origins of mechanization. In tracing the machine back to its earliest manifestations in the great human machines that built the pyramids and canals and irrigation works of the Bronze Age, I found that these wonderful feats were coupled to, and repeatedly nullified by the equally destructive and irrational activities of the military machines that came into existence at the same time.

Even at the earliest stage, beneath the imposing facade of mechanical order that made it possible to build the Great Pyramid of Gezeh with almost a watchmaker's accuracy, I discovered all sorts of demonic compulsions and infantile ambitions, which I recognized as very similar to those that have erupted again in our own age under a similar magnification of human power and technical adroitness.

Without my exploration of this historic background, I would not have found it possible, perhaps, to come to grips with these present day forces, which have turned so many of our achievements in science and technics into monumental absurdities. But in our time I detected a peculiar factor that had no parallel in the Pyramid Age: the automation of knowledge. The institutions that have promoted this special kind of automation are now the main power plants and the control centers of the grand system of mechanized production and depersonalized consumption and machine-fed leisure that characterizes our western way of life. Nowhere has this become more evident than in our recent educational programs.

From *Vital Speeches of the Day*, 30 (May 1, 1964), 441–446. Reprinted by permission. Lewis Mumford is a noted author and is Senior Fellow, Center for Advanced Studies, Wesleyan University.

Those who have been instrumental in the automation of knowledge, from Francis Bacon onward, have from the beginning coupled this method with the economy of abundance that mankind for so many ages had vainly dreamed of achieving: an economy under which, as Aristotle said, the shuttle would weave by itself, the lyre would play by itself, and loaves of bread would spring out of the oven untouched by human hand. The dreams of such an economy, with its promise of wealth and freedom for all, date back to the earliest urban civilizations; and it was then that other dreams that have now been realized, the dream of human flight, of instantaneous communication, of total control over the physical environment, were first expressed as heavenly marvels in art and fable. Our age has seen those dreams come true. Powers that only the gods of the Bronze Age possessed are now our daily commonplaces. So perhaps it is no wonder that the leading exponents of automation, inflamed by their success and still prompted by ancient dreams of godlike omnipotence and omniscience, now seek to extend automation to every other human activity.

But as often happens when fairy stories come true, we are at last beginning to discover that there was a concealed catch in the original promise. The scientific ideology that made possible these colossal benefits cannot, we now find, be easily attached to historically valid and purposeful human ends. In order to enjoy all these abundant goods one must strictly conform to the dominant system, faithfully consuming all that it produces, meekly accepting its quantitative scale of values, never once demanding more essential human goods, above all a more meaningful life, for that is what automation, by its very nature and on its own strict premises, is utterly impotent to produce. This is not so strange an outcome as might at first seem, for when we examine the basic ideology of modern science, as formulated in the seventeenth century, we find that the very words, *human, history, value, purpose,* and *end* were excluded as extraneous and undesirable for any method of quantitative measurement and statistical prediction.

This situation, if I read it aright, constitutes the basic problem of education today. Shall we extend the processes of automation into every department of our lives and, in order to achieve this dubious result, proceed more rapidly than ever with the automation of knowledge; or shall we bring back, as essential to the further development of life, the complex organic components, above all the full human personality, that we have too peremptorily repressed and rejected? Shall we, in other words, restore man to his central position as the actor and director in a historic drama; or shall we banish him into the wings, first as a mere agent of an automatic control system, but eventually as a desperately bored supernumerary with no more active responsibility than a union stagehand in a modern drama that doesn't use scenery? Unless we tackle this question swiftly, we shall soon find that the last word in automation is automatic Man. . . .

My purpose is to challenge, as scientifically outdated as well as humanly inadequate, the whold constellation of mechanical ideas that now dominate our civilization, beginning with the automation of knowledge. The notion of concentrating on power, profit, and productivity alone and of seeking to establish total control over both man and his environment dates definitely back to the Pyramid Age when the center of this original pyramid of power, the Pharoah, was sustained by religion in the paranoid delusion that he was a god. This gross delusion lay behind the effective political and technical regimentation that made possible the construction of the great pyramids, those monuments of technological perfection and human futility; and the irrational nature of that drive, irrational in the sense that it ignored the complex ecological cooperations favorable to human development, has not been altered today, now that Nobel Prize winners have reconstructed the ancient Pyramids in the form of space rockets, designed to reach the same heaven by a new route. But so completely has automation taken over today that even the personality of the divine King, who was necessary to the older system, has been eliminated. Only the paranoid compulsions and the docile conformities now remain.

In challenging these moribund conceptions I shall suggest that our present system of higher education, focussed almost exclusively on the unlimited mass production of scientific truths, is utterly incapable of dealing with the most pressing problem of our age: namely that of coping with the larger system of automation of which it is a part. Our task, I shall urge, is rather to restore to man, as the central agent and creator, the wide span of capabilities and potentialities he voluntarily surrendered or suppressed when he took it upon himself to develop the machine and consigned to automations the absolute powers once exercised by divine kings. In my reading, the mischief we now confront began when the scientific leaders of western thought dismissed as unworthy of their attention that immense fund of accumulated human experience which was embodied in language, religion, art, literature, morals, folklore, and in the annals of human history as a whole. Without that foundation, it is impossible to create fully dimensioned human beings.

This deliberate rejection of that large realm of human life which cannot be explored except peripherally, by the scientific method was made with open eyes, in so many declared words, when the Royal Society was founded in London in 1660; but the ground for this rejection had already been stated by Rene Descartes in his "Discourse on Method." By turning the subjective contributions of man over to theology and poetry, the scientist said, in effect, that for him the inner world of man, and the rich fabrications of human culture, no longer mattered. At the time scientists had excellent practical reasons for making that temporary simplification and clarification: this was a first step toward fabricating the exact knowledge needed to interpret physical phenomena and control mechanical operations. But how can we still cling to this naive limitation today, in a period during which man's inward realm, with all its creative and destructive possibilities, has been opened up and audaciously explored by Freud, Jung, and their followers? To do this is to forget how far science itself has traveled since the seventeenth century.

When the procedures of science were originally laid down, both Bacon and Descartes correctly anticipated that the new method would in time transform every aspect of human life. That prophecy and hope have been more than fulfilled. But what no one foresaw was that the ultimate effect of using an underdimensioned mechanical model, capable of effecting the mass production of both goods and knowledge, would be ultimately to introduce the process of automation into every province of existence. Still less did they suppose that the Advancement of Learning might lead to the Regression of Man. Certainly no one guessed that our vast gains in physical power would be accompanied by human inpotence and frustration or that these conditions in turn would be unconsciously compensated for by massive increases in demoniac disorder, rabid violence, and psychic disintegration.

Yet all these things have been happening, before our eyes and it is fatuous to keep on thinking that there is no connection between our mechanical triumphs and our equally unparalleled human failures. Perhaps the most sinister aspect of thoroughgoing automation is one that I unfortunately have no time to explore tonight: the fact that this underdimensioned system of thought requires for its smooth operation equally underdimensioned men. The new operators of this system, the elite, now constitute a recognizable ideal type, that of Bureaucratic or Organization Man whose future dominance was predicted by the German sociologist Max Weber more than a generation ago. Such ideal types are now coming out of our great megalopolises of learning in large quantities as on an assembly line, cut to a uniform pattern, and directly feeding into the great mechanical collectives, military or industrial, that will eagerly employ them.

As the facilities of our educational institutions expand—with their nuclear reactors, their cybernetic IBM machines, their computers, their television sets and tape recorders and learning machines, their machine-marked *yes* or *no* examination papers—the human contents necessarily shrink, for the very presence of the human personality disturbs this complex mechanism which operates increasingly as a single unit and can be managed only by remote control under centralized direction.

The only values recognized by automation are those necessary for the operation and continued expansion of the system itself. The minds that are now completely conditioned to these processing mechanisms are incapable of imagining any alternatives. Having opted for automation, they are committed to wiping out human autonomy. Not merely are the operators of our new mechanical cosmos ill at ease in the real world of cooperating organisms and self-directing personalities but they often show active hostility toward the world of the living, if only as a neurotic tactic of self-defense.

Here, at the core of automation, lies its principal weakness, once the system becomes universal. Its exponents see no way of overcoming its deficiencies except by a further extension of automation. Thus, a large-scale automation of compulsory leisure is now in process in order to find profit-making substitutes for the vanished pleasure of work that once brought an immediate human reward. The fact is that this system as a whole, if I may use the academic slang of the day, has no *feedback* and therefore no method of evaluating its deleterious results of correcting its mistaken postulates. The give-and-take that has always existed between man and the rest of his environment and the constant dialogue that is so necessary both for self-knowledge and social cooperation have no place in an automatic regimen.

When Job's life miscarried, he was able, at least in imagination, to confront God and criticise his ways. But the suppression of personality is so complete in an automated economy that the reputed heads of our great organizations are as incapable of intervening in their operations as the lowliest filing clerk. As for anyone's confronting them in person, our automatic agencies are as obscure and inaccessible as the authorities that Franz Kafka pictures in that accurate anticipatory nightmare, *The Trial*. Humanly speaking, the proper name for automation is organized impotence; and the archetypal hero of our time is no other than Eichmann, the correct functionary, the perfect bureaucrat, proud to the end that he never allowed a moral scruple or a human sentiment to keep him from carrying out the orders that came from above.

The radical defects that are now patent could not possibly have been anticipated by those who first put together the abstract elements of automation; and though they are largely the result of the original ideological shortcomings of seventeenth century science, they have been doubled by now, being mated to much more ancient bureaucratic and military absolutisms. By attempting to eliminate the human factor, by reducing all experience to supposedly ultimate atomic components describable in terms of mass and motion, science discarded mankind's cumulative knowledge of history and biography and paid attention only to discrete passing events. The typical vice of this ideology, accordingly, is to overvalue the contemporary, the dynamic, and the novel and to neglect stability, continuity, and the time-seasoned values of both collective history and individual human experience. The scientific intelligence, however magnified, by its capacity to handle abstractions, is only a partial expression of the fully dimensioned personality, not a substitute for it.

As a result of this one-sided objectivity so-called, decisions of critical importance to the human race are being taken today on the basis of ten-year-old knowledge, confidently applied by highly disciplined specialists who too often display the shortcomings of ten-year-old minds, for they regard as a special merit their deliberate practice of cutting their minds off from ten thousand years of human experience and culture. Overproud of their one-generation acquisitions, they point to the fact that there are now more scientists alive than in the whole history of the world before our generation. Strangely, they have not even a suspicion that the vast quantity of exact knowledge now at our disposal is no guarantee whatever of our having sufficient emotional sensitiveness and moral insight to make good use of it; if anything, the exact contrary has already proved true. The current belief in mechanical quantification without constant human qualification makes a mockery of the whole educational process.

Fortunately, the original ideological framework of seventeenth century science has long been under fire. A whole generation ago Alfred North Whitehead, in his 'Science and the Modern World,' published his fundamental critique of its logical naivete and its metaphysical absurdity. Especially in advanced physics today, still more in biology, the sacred mechanical model that for so long set the fashion for all human activities has turned out to be too crude, except for limited practical applications. Physicists have finally acknowledged that even matter and energy have a history; if one stays with the chemical elements three billion years one finds that some of them may become alive.

So if I feel free to speak disparagingly of the still current ideological background for the automation of knowledge, it is with the assurance that the more alert scientific minds of our generation have themselves led the way. Today our fundamental irreducible unit is not the atom but the human personality, in all its biological complexity and cultural multiformity. And it is now plain that only by restoring the human personality to the center of our scheme of thought can mechanization and automation be brought back into the services of life. Until this happened in education, there is not a single advance in science, from the release of nuclear energy to the isolation of DNA in genetic inheritance that may not, because of our literally absent-minded automatism in applying it, bring on disastrous consequences to the human race. These consequences would have no parallel in previous history, since in both cases they would be irreversible and irretrievable. For that possible miscarriage, our educational institutions would have to take no small share of the blame.

In calling attention to the need for deliberately controlling and correcting the automation of knowledge by addressing education to larger and more central human purposes, I must, I realize, cause a certain discomfort, perhaps acute pain; in many minds here tonight. Certainly I share much of this discomfort, for there are no easy answers to the problem I am raising. Who supposes that a method of thought which has been in operation for three centuries, and which has in every area produced so many humanly valuable results, can be corrected overnight? We cannot re-introduce the historic components that have long been missing without slowing down the pace of automation. Merely to overcome the inertia of the present system may well require something like a catastrophic breakdown before we can resume full control and go forward in a quite different direction, subordinating the improvement of mechanisms to the development and perfection of men. But it is high time that we recognized our situation and made a fresh start on sounder premises; and it is in the realm of higher education that, if anywhere, this change is due to begin. . . .

Even as late as a generation ago, there was still a large margin for free activity and independent thinking within higher education. Many of those here tonight had the benefit of those more humane and spacious practices. But today, most of our institutions of higher learning are as thoroughly automated as a modern steel plant or a telephone system: the mass production of scholarly papers, discoveries, inventions, patents, students, Ph.D.'s, professors, and publicity goes on at a comparable rate; and only those who identify themselves with the humanly irrelevant goals of automation are in line for promotion, for big research grants, for the political power and the financial rewards allotted to those who "go with" the system. . . .

In so far as our colleges and universities are not expanding their physical plants in order to engage more effectively in the mass-production of scientists, technicians, and engineers on the present obsolete model—I repeat, on *the present obsolete model*—they are but hastening the moment when the whole system will collapse of its own aimless and insensate productivity, even if more ominous irrational factors, such as the catastrophic misuse of nuclear energy, do not halt the automation of knowledge at a much earlier point. Are you sure then that your duty as responsible educators is to push on as fast as possible toward this culminating absurdity, this ironic "final solution?"

Perhaps I should leave the problems I have put before you with this final question. But it would be unwise if I did not, before closing, anticipate the all-but-automatic response some here may be tempted to make: for the easiest way of dismissing this whole argument, even if you are troubled by it a little, would be to ask me: *"Do you suppose we can set the hands of the clock back?"* The figure of the mechanical clock, that first great triumph of automatism, is indeed wonderfully appropriate here. But it is strange that those who use it do not see that it demolishes their defense and supports the position I have taken. I have nothing against clocks. But who would harbor a clock whose hands could not be turned back?—that is, a clock that could not be regulated in accordance with an independent standard of time? In the case of the clock, that independent standard is the daily revolution of the earth; in the case of all human institutions, including automation, our standard derives from the nature and history of man and his fathomless creative potentialities for further development.

Our task today is to make the genuine goods derived from the automation of knowledge subservient to the superior, history-laden functions and purposes of human culture. And we may well require as many centuries to develop an adequate ideology capable of uniting physical processes and organic functions with human purposes, the cosmos without and the microcosm within, the outer with the inner world, as our predecessors did to produce the present sterile, underdimensioned world of the machine. There is no easy way out. No multiplication of existing facilities, no shifting of budgets from the sciences to the humanities, no interdisciplinary regrouping can possibly suffice. We must settle down to the long process of rethinking our basic premises and re-fabricating our whole ideological and cultural structure. But there is one thing that those of us who wield authority in education can do here and now: *We can stop saying 'yes'—so automatically!—to the automation of our knowledge.*

Julius A. Stratton

THE M.I.T. 1964 COMMENCEMENT ADDRESS

. . . Within the infinitely complex network of intellectual, emotional, and spiritual forces that make up this strange body we call mankind, one may discern two primitive impulses that trace back to the beginning of time.

From *Technology Review*, 69 (July 1964), 20–21. Reprinted with permission. Dr. Stratton is President of the Massachusetts Institute of Technology.

The first is the desire to understand—the passionate quest for knowledge for its own sake—about the stars, about matter, about living things.

The second is the urge to do, the drive towards action and mastery of our physical environment.

The systematic interpretation of nature into a framework of law we call science; the effort to convert pragmatic experience and understanding to useful account is engineering.

For countless centuries the quest for knowledge through science has been moving forward, slowly gathering momentum, while the engineer has provided shelter, assured our supplies of food and water, built our roads and bridges, and created our massive industrial technology. And now, suddenly—almost within your own generation—the whole sweeping line of advance seems to have taken fire. In some strange unforeseen way, we have come to a critical threshold, beyond which the forces of technical progress appear to be self-sustaining. The processes of discovery, invention, and production feed upon each other. In every domain of the physical and biological sciences, there is a bursting out into new fields and new theories. The translation of ideas into action is taking place at an ever-accelerating pace, so that the functional line of demarcation between scientist and engineer has almost vanished. From the factories and commercial laboratories of our country pours a mounting stream of new products, new versions of old devices—from jet airplanes to transistor radios, from nuclear reactors to household appliances, from a multitude of new drugs to synthetic building materials. We are at the point of being overwhelmed by the very bulk of our accumulated information, bewildered by the diversity of our manufactures. And we are failing today to assess clearly the implications of these developments for tomorrow.

Yet through this maelstrom of scientific and technological enterprise runs the almost mystical conviction that somehow every technical advance will contribute ultimately to the good society. Every responsible physicist believes intuitively or subconsciously that each new insight into the structure of matter will stir someone else—some engineer—to the development of a useful piece of hardware; and every engineer, in turn, expects that each new product or service will in some way add to our health, comfort, and material well-being.

There is nothing new in this idea of technology as the driving force of progress. It is an idea that took form during the Enlightenment of the Eighteenth Century and emerged from the industrial revolution of the Nineteenth as a well-defined philosophy. M.I.T. has its historical roots in that concept of the usefulness of science. Nor is there any need for me to demonstrate to this audience by examples how the advance of technology has improved the material condition of mankind.

Yet for all my own faith in and dedication to the work and methods of science, I do not believe that we can any longer afford to take such a thesis for granted; and I fear that a blind confidence in the inevitable good of material progress can lead only to disillusionment. The stupendous revolution of the Twentieth Century is doing more than adding theories, data, and apparatus to the accumulated store of the past. It has provided an entire new dimension to human affairs on a total change of scale.

To use words that you are particularly well qualified to understand, science, technology, and society now form a tightly coupled system. Each new technical advance adds a component to that system. In years gone by we have isolated these components and assessed their usefulness in terms of a specified purpose. We measured the value of a military weapon solely by a military requirement; a new drug by its immediate effectiveness in dealing with a particular pain; a new highway simply by the number of cars it carried; or a chemical waste-disposal plant by the interests of local inhabitants. But now, because such components are coupled into an immensely complex system on a huge and massive scale, it is only by an examination of the impact upon society as a whole that we can pass judgment on the degree of progress.

To draw upon a biological analogy, I am saying that we must advance from the anatomy of components to the physiology of the organic whole—which indeed is now the society itself. One may prescribe an aspirin for a headache or build a turnpike to ease a traffic jam. But the headache may be merely an isolated symptom of a deeper disorder—a disease that may be identified only by a diagnosis which itself is the product of many specialists working together.

And so, too, our society—the body politic—is subject to old, chronic disorders and to new ailments. These diseases of the system are emerging in increasing number; and we must be courageous in recognizing that they are themselves the by-products of our highly technological environment.

Consider the transformation of our cities—the physical and social degradation of large areas—the loss of serenity and beauty. We have never before produced so many cars or such fast airplanes; yet transportation in the United States is rapidly approaching a point of crisis. The shift to automation in industry is accelerating and will have profound effects upon the character of our labor force, upon its training, and upon its security. We are polluting our air and water. The pesticides which we are employing on a mounting scale are a boon to agriculture and a threat to the remainder of our natural resources. We find extreme poverty in the midst of affluence. The problem of the economically deprived citizen, be he black or white, is one of training and education to cope with a highly technological and rapidly changing society.

These are but a few examples. I could cite many more—all too large, too complicated, too sophisticated to be conquered or even arrested by sporadic investigations and isolated research projects. Of course science has generated these problems, and we can be equally confident that science can help us to alleviate and resolve them. But our efforts must now move to a higher plateau. We can no longer afford to nibble away piece by piece at the problems of the modern city, of transportation, of underdeveloped economies, of automation, or of disarmament. We indulge excessively in unco-ordinated conferences, surveys, and studies that on the whole are highly unproductive. Our ailments are vast and complex, and they will yield only to planned, collaborative attacks focused on clear objectives and leading to concerted action.

One of the charges that has been most commonly leveled against science is that progress is leading increasingly to the fragmentation of knowledge and the proliferation of a multitude of specialties. But these great new socio-technical problems and the systems they represent are now also generating strongly countervailing forces toward new unities, bringing together many different resources, and giving rise to a new synthesis of knowledge. For in every instance, success will depend upon the joint contributions of physical and biological scientists, of economists and political scientists, of engineers and architects, of historians and philosophers. The task of articulating or welding together these components of learning into systems of understanding offers the highest intellectual challenge of our time.

As I have reflected on these matters, as I have pondered about how all this is to be accomplished and where, it has seemed to me that there exists nowhere at the present time any one institution or specific kind of organization which is in a position to undertake alone this monumental task. There is to my knowledge no single agency of government which has the necessary diversity of resources and the freedom of action. By their very character these problems lack the motive of profit which is the essence of private enterprise; and because they lead inescapably from the intellectual domain into the field of action, they present definite risks and perils for the university.

And yet it is only within the framework of the modern university that one finds the wide range of interests, a common ground for the exchange of ideas, a forum of discussion for scholars who draw upon the arts and the humanities as well as upon science and engineering. This is particularly true of an institution of the character of M.I.T. I do not believe that we can escape the responsibility of taking part in the solution of problems which touch most deeply upon the total welfare of our society. In the synthesis of knowledge, as well as in the creation of new learning, we must lead the way. And though at times we shall find ourselves drawn more deeply into the main stream of contemporary affairs, we shall continue in the process to educate with relevance to our age. This has indeed been our historic mission.

I have wanted in these few remarks . . . to give you a broader and perhaps a new insight into the changing role of science and technology. The essence of this change lies not so much in the expanding scale of discovery and application; it lies rather in the complete penetration of science and technology into every domain of human affairs.

But principally I want you to understand that these developments have brought a new order of responsibility for the consequences of progress to our society as a whole. Some of this responsibility falls upon our institutions—upon government, upon industry, and upon the university. But in a free society the burden of obligation rests ultimately upon you as individuals. You are in a superlative position to meet the technical challenges of our day. But you owe something more to the common account. You must be ever mindful of your own deepening responsibility, both to the profession you have chosen to follow and to the society which will look to you for positive action. Your life will be productive in proportion to the goals that you achieve; rewarding in proportion to your commitment to all that is of value; and full in the satisfaction that the world will be better for your efforts.

Robert M. Hutchins
SCIENCE, SCIENTISTS, AND POLITICS

. . . It is clear that the behavior of professors is questionable at best. Scientists are worse than other professors because they have special problems. One of these is that their productive lives often end at thirty-five. I knew an astronomer who was contributing to the international journals at the age of eleven. Compare that with the difficulty of contributing at a similar age to an international journal on, let us say, Greek law. A scientist has a limited education. He labors on the topic of

From *Science, Scientists, and Politics* (Santa Barbara, California: Center for the Study of Democratic Institutions, 1963). Reprinted with permission of the Fund for The Republic, Inc., Center for the Study of Democratic Institutions. Dr. Hutchins is president of the Fund for the Republic and former president of the University of Chicago.

his dissertation, wins the Nobel prize by the time he is thirty-five, and suddenly has nothing to do. He has no general ideas, and while he was pursuing his specialization science has gone past him. He has no alternative but to spend the rest of his life making a nuisance of himself.

Scientists are the victims of an education and a way of academic life created by their misinterpreters and propagandists. These misinterpreters have propagandized an entirely inconsecutive chain of consecutive propositions: The pursuit of truth, they say, is the collection of facts. Facts can be experimentally verified. Thus, the only method of seeking truth is the scientific method. The only knowledge is scientific knowledge, and anything else is guesswork or superstition. So Lord Rutherford could say to Samuel Alexander, the great English philosopher, "What is it that you have been saying all your life, Alexander? Hot air. Nothing but hot air."

A recollection I shall always cherish of one of our leading mathematicians, now a professor at Chicago, affords a stunning example of the frame of mind the propagandists have created. He came to Chicago as a graduate student. Toward the close of his first year I asked the chairman of the mathematics department how the boy was doing. "Oh, Mr. Hutchins," he said, "he's a fine mathematician, but I'm sorry to have to tell you, he's crazy." I said, "What do you mean 'crazy'? How does he evidence this unfortunate condition?" And the professor responded, "He's interested in philosophy!"

The misinterpreters' and propagandists' doctrine has paralyzing educational repercussions. According to its tenets, education consists in cramming the student with facts. There is not enough time to stuff in all the facts. Therefore, facts outside a narrow area of specialization must be excluded. One of our Consultants to the Center has described the education in science in the state university from which he graduated as two years of German, two years of military training, and all the rest mathematics, physics, and chemistry.

Seduced by the fact formula, the medical school at the University of Chicago set out on a perfectly sincere, although somewhat misguided, campaign against liberal education. There are countless facts in medicine. A medical school must fill its students with these facts or they will fall behind. This meant that there was no time to teach anything else. The medical school strongly recommended that the whole freshman and sophomore years be abolished—the junior and senior years had already gone—and that the entire curriculum be devoted to science and medicine. I can conscientiously say that any senior in the University of Chicago medical school knew more facts about medicine than any professor in a German university.

The consequences of this line of educational endeavor are clear enough. Everybody specializes. There can be no academic community because scientists cannot talk to one another. The chairman of the anatomy department of the University of Chicago brought this home to me once when we were discussing the great biological symposium that had been held to celebrate the University's fiftieth anniversary. I said, "Tell me, how was it?" He said, "I didn't go." When I asked why not, he replied, "Well, there weren't any papers in my field." Scientists cannot talk to anyone else because there isn't anyone else worth talking to. Hence, university life offers no remedy for the defects of their education.

The propagandists and misinterpreters of science have set the tone for the whole learned world in the United States. Their slogan is, "If you can't count it, it doesn't count." The influence of this slogan is felt in literature, philosophy, languages, and of course in the social sciences. The most striking feature of social science today is the total absence of theory. Its greatest modern achievement is the public opinion poll. Social scientists can count, but cannot comprehend.

Those who live their lives without theory are technicians, or mechanics. As a result there is no significant contemporary social science. Politics is viewed as power because power can be observed and measured. Power is something real. Therefore, using the misinterpreters' logic, it is *all* that is real about politics or political science. The most characteristic book title in social science in the past thirty years is *Politics: Who Gets What, When, How.*

In spite of the misinterpreters' nonsense, science contains elements of sense. Serious scientists know that science is just one very important way of looking at the world. When scientists are actually doing science they are caught in a great tradition. They know they are not simply collecting facts or conducting random experiments. No serious scientist believes that if a million monkeys were put down at a million typewriters one of them would eventually turn out *Hamlet.* Nor does he think the scientific method is the only method. Scientists do not use the scientific method outside of science.

How the propagandists and misinterpreters of science have managed to take over all the academic virtues and label them "scientific" escapes me. I ran across a fascinating study of the scientific attitude by a professor of education. This learned gentleman had written to sixteen eminent scientists and asked them what characterized the scientific attitude. These were the replies:

CHEMIST: *Openmindedness* . . . PHYSIOLOGIST: *Intellectual honesty* . . . BOTANIST: *Openmindedness* . . . ZOOLOGIST: *Observation, inquisitiveness, perseverance and industry, objectivity and critical independent reflection* . . . PHYSICIST: *Objectivity* . . . SOCIOLOGIST: *Objectivity* . . . MICROBIOLOGIST: *Respect observation* . . . MATHEMATICIAN: *Openmindedness* . . . ANTHROPOLOGIST: *Openmindedness*

. . . CHEMIST: *Practiced willingness to label conclusions tentative until supported by reproducible or confirmed data* . . . AGRICULTURIST: *Desire to tolerantly explore ideas* . . . MATHEMATICIAN: *An open mind* . . . PHYSICIST: *A will to know the truth* . . . CHEMIST: *Insistence on critical examination* . . . DIRECTOR OF EDUCATIONAL RESEARCH: *Intellectual curiosity* . . . PSYCHOLOGIST: *An inquiring mind.*

Obviously this study shows that science has a corner on all the rational processes of thought.

But there is not an honest scholar in any field who would not insist on being openminded, honest, and objective, and on considering all the evidence before he reached a conclusion. You can hear Thomas Aquinas laughing.

The propagandists of science say, "Sure, but fellows like Thomas Aquinas had commitments. They all had philosophies and principles that distorted their thinking. Scientists haven't any." The answer to this is that everybody has a metaphysics. Every scientist, for example, has a commitment to the reality of the external world. The distortion comes when the metaphysics is denied instead of being recognized and made as rational as possible.

Understanding science is an indispensable part of a liberal education. To demonstrate my sincerity, I point out that at the University of Chicago one whole half of the first two years of every student's education was natural science. St. John's College, with which I also had something to do, is the only college in the United States that requires four years in the laboratory for every student. An education without science is no education at all. The limitations and possibilities of science cannot be understood without scientific training, and our very existence depends on comprehending these limits and possibilities.

We do not know what science is, and partly as a result we do not know what politics is. Mr. C. P. Snow is wrong about the two cultures. There is only one, and it is pseudo-scientific.

The leading phenomena of our time exhibit a curiously ambiguous character. Technology may blow us up, or it may usher in the paradise of which man has been dreaming ever since Adam and Eve got kicked out of the first one. Bureaucracy may stifle democracy or be the backbone of democratic government. Nationalism may disrupt the world or prove to be the necessary precondition of a world community.

Unfortunately these ambiguities do not lend themselves to scientific procedure. Our essential problem is what kind of people we want to be and what kind of world we want to have. Such questions cannot be solved by experiment and observation. But if we know what justice is, which is not a scientific matter, science and many other disciplines may help us get it.

The problems resulting from these ambiguities are not going to be solved by men of fractional or pseudo-culture. The solution depends on moral and intellectual virtues rather than on specialized knowledge. It is a humbling thought to recall that 25 per cent of the SS guards in Nazi Germany were holders of the doctor's degree.

The solution of these problems must lie in the reorganization of American education and in the redefinition of its purposes. A liberal education, including scientific education, must be established for all, and true intellectual communities must be built where men may overcome the limitations of their fractional cultures. This would require a drastic change in what the nation expects of American education, and an equally drastic alteration in the habits of academic people. I think it will be agreed that this cataclysm is not likely to occur in the lifetime of the youngest person reading this.

The immediate program, then, has to be something else. It must be an attempt to build intellectual communities outside the American educational system and to form widespread connections among the intellectual workers, using these communities as points of interconnection. The hope for the immediate future, as far as we have one, must rest in our capacity to communicate with the adult population. For one thing, unless we do, the rising generation may not have a chance to rise.

It is in centers like the Center for the Study of Democratic Institutions and in the multiplication of meetings like the one that produced these papers that we might get some help with the development of a real culture, and a real understanding of kinds of knowledge and the limits and potential of each kind. The radiation from these points might light the path to a just community for ourselves and for the world.

James D. Finn
THE TECHNOLOGICAL REVOLUTION IN EDUCATION

. . . Each time of change has had its prophets and its individuals who have understood the implications of the process through which they were living and have operated accordingly. In a broad sense, it has always been true that, in time of change, the world belongs to those who can

Reprinted with permission of the author from "The Franks Had the Right Idea," *NEA Journal* (April 1964), pp. 24–27. Dr. Finn is project director of the Instructional Technology and Media Project, University of Southern California.

grasp the nature of that change and fashion their life and culture to make the most of it. . . .

The only danger in applying this generalization to what is happening to education today, particularly in the field of instructional technology, is that we may underestimate the speed and extent of the change which is now taking place. For this revolution is merely a minute reflection of the great force of the scientific and technological revolution that sweeps through Western culture at an ever-accelerating pace and moves now to engage the world.

Man proposes to change human genes and control heredity; to cross the United States in an hour; to redirect human behavior; to land on the moon by 1970. Can the American school teacher honestly believe that the scientific-technological change which permeates the whole culture will stop at the borders of education?

Perhaps at this point, it would be well to bring the micro-revolution that represents the application of science and technology to education into better focus. It might be helpful, for clarity, to list some of the technological developments that are the signs of change. For two-and-a-half years, a project known as the Technological Development Project of the NEA, funded by the U.S. Office of Education, undertook to describe these developments, to predict trends, and to make some kind of assessment of the effect of this developing technology upon education.

A brief summary of trends as analyzed by the Project might prove helpful to this discussion. Central to technological change in education have been developments in both hardware (devices, machines) and materials (films, programed learning materials, etc.). These developments fall into a three-part chronological pattern:

1920–1955

These years marked the development of conventional audiovisual devices and materials; i.e., films, filmstrips, slides, recordings, tape, and the projectors, players, etc., necessary to use them. This phase reached its climax shortly after the end of World War II and leveled off by 1955, at a point much too low to have made a really effective impact upon the educational process. Educational administrators, school boards, and other decision makers did not place a high enough value on these developments.

1955–1965

The years between 1955 and 1961 saw the introduction into the schools of television, language laboratories, and teaching machines and programed learning. As the decade nears its end, 8 mm sound film for individual viewing, large group multimedia presentation devices, classroom communicators, computers, and other advanced devices and materials are appearing on the experimental scene.

This is the decade that has produced the expressions, *new media, educational automation, instructional technology,* and *technological revolution in education.*

With the exception of the language laboratory and, to some extent, television, these devices and the materials and techniques they imply have not yet been applied on any scale. However, since 1958, the amount of audiovisual equipment and materials has been increasing, as a result of Title III of the National Defense Education Act.

1965

The next period promises technological developments even more spectacular than those of the past. The items beginning to show now—computers for educational data processing and as controls of teaching systems, instructional systems themselves, etc.—will be followed by sophisticated information storage and retrieval systems, the communication of visual and other forms of data from computers to people, new forms of long distance communication and control, and machines that can learn.

The foregoing summary presents but one facet of the technological revolution in education. Technology is not just hardware—or even hardware and materials. Technology is a way of organizing, a way of thinking, involving at the center, to be sure, man-machine systems, but including systems of organization, patterns of use, tests of economic feasibility. And in the times in which we live, there is a high-order interacting system between technology and science.

Let us consider some of these other elements in the pattern of educational technological change.

For instance, a whole system of thinking has developed in the field of programed learning which relates a science of learning (behavioristic psychology) to a technology of instruction involving specification of objectives in behavioral terms, frame writing in programed instruction, task analysis as a basis of lesson planning, and the like.

Various staff utilization plans, such as team teaching and other organizational change proposals, lie on the periphery of this technological revolution along with new concepts of school buildings, all of the new curriculum developments (the "new" math, physics, etc.), and even the great interest in studying the problems of educational innovation itself.

Other pieces of this complicated picture include the efforts of the great foundations, the money-power of the National Defense Education Act directed toward the new media and the provision of teaching equipment for the schools, the general interest of researchers in learning and instrumentation, and the press of industry to diversify into the educational market.

So much for the specifics of technological development in education. Before returning to the basic proposition that, in a time of change, success comes to him who grasps the significance of that change, let us take one step further back and examine the socioeconomic-political pressures surrounding the educational system to which this micro-system of educational technological development is a partially realized response. Bear in mind the one brute fact that all of this is occurring in the context of the swiftly accelerating general scientific-technological revolution in our culture, embedded in a setting of world tension and upheaval.

The educational world is faced specifically with two thorny, continuing, and growing problems. One is related to knowledge; the other, to population. A technological culture is a knowledge-generating culture; for reasons of survival (both economic and national), research and development—the information-producing mechanism—is now built into everything we do. This presents the schools with the fantastic problem of deciding what to teach from the exponential growing body of knowledge and how to provide more learning in less time.

The second problem—the problem of extraordinary population growth—continues to fill the schools with more students to be taught, housed, and provided with learning materials. It would appear that the only answer to the pressures on the schools caused by the population and knowledge explosions is to turn to technology, at least in part. . . .

The educational future will belong to those who can grasp the significance of instructional technology. Many years ago William Wrinkle pointed out that the history of the secondary school showed conclusively that when one institution, e.g. the Latin Grammar School, could no longer meet the needs of a society, it was replaced by another, e.g., the Academy. I believe this generalization holds good throughout education today.

Unless present educational workers and their organizations can find the means to deal with problems of knowledge and population growth, and related problems of urbanization, skill demands, etc., within the present school and college context, society will somehow invent other institutions and other means to deal with these problems.

This challenge to the teaching profession requires a creative response for survival and presents unprecedented opportunities for growth and advancement of the profession. In many cases, the response can be related to the equally legitimate welfare demands, for American education has, since its inception, been predicated upon a coolie labor theory. Either the teachers or the children did the work, or it wasn't done.

Certainly no other profession in the United States has put such a low value on its human power. Whether this is the fault of school boards, local control, school administrators, teacher timidity, inadequate pay-as-you-go financing, or combinations of these and other factors is now beside the point. The coolie labor theory of operating the educational system in this country has got to go.

Since 1850 and before, this country has elected to seek technical solutions to its problems of creation and production in order to increase productivity, save manpower, and (to a greater extent than is realized) dignify man and improve the quality of his life. As a result, in many areas of life, the citizen is surrounded by a technological milieu that he takes for granted. This milieu functions as an educator, so that when a new kind of washing machine comes along, the housewife welcomes it.

American education has not yet developed such a technological milieu, and this is as much the fault of teachers and their organizations as of any other group. Schools do not have enough conventional audiovisual equipment or materials, enough books, enough laboratory equipment, let alone the newer devices and materials.

Teachers and administrators are not used to thinking of solving their problems by technological means because so few of their problems are now solved with anything but sweat and, as Anna Hyer has said, "new uses for old coat-hangers."

The best possible example of this is the relatively inexpensive test-grading machine. Such machines, certainly a boon to teachers, have been possible since the middle 1920's. The profession has consistently failed to demand them and has opted for the red pencil, elbow grease, and hours of time. Not until 1962 did such machines become available and not because of teacher demand, even then, and very few schools have them even yet.

The absence of a technological context within the educational system and the general hand-labor orientation of teacher and administrator are, of course, in the process of change because of the pressure mentioned above. However, there is no sign yet of the development of a creative response to this technological revolution on the part of American school teachers, considered either as a group of individuals or as individuals whose will is expressed in the actions of local, state, and national associations.

If the collection of associations, together with the supporting teacher education institutions, can be considered "The Establishment," can the Establishment adjust and make the creative response to the technological revolution in education? Since the Establishment in the long view really expresses the will of its members, will the American teacher creatively respond? . . .

Part Two
Automation:
A Creation of the
New Technology

Automation is the most striking and important creation of the new scientifically based technology. Included under the term "automation" are streamlined production and assembly lines, integrated control systems for the operation of process plants, tape and other control devices to direct operation of machines, and complex electronic data-processing and retrieval systems known as computers. Some consider automation the logical extension of the progressive introduction of machinery, which has been occurring since the late eighteenth century. Others, however, believe automation is an entirely novel development and poses serious problems for our society and its value system.

Automation itself and two problem areas with which it is involved—employment and leisure—are explored in this section. Again we find value conflicts. If masses of people are unable to find employment in our society of affluence, and if those who do work no longer toil in the usual sense of the word, our traditional attitudes toward the means of gaining sustenance surely must change. Leisure has long been considered the reward for useful work, but if a life of comparative leisure is in the offing for the vast majority of people, it seems that our traditional view of leisure, its purposes and its habitual forms, must come under scrutiny.

4
The Nature of Computers and Automation

The selections in this chapter delineate the exact nature of automation: What precisely is meant by the word automation? What is currently being achieved by automation? What does the use of automation imply for the future?

John Diebold views automation not in the sense of "hardware"—electronic computers, transfer machines, or numerical tool controls—but rather as a completely new attitude toward the performance of work. He believes that it offers us the potentiality of doing altogether novel tasks and of achieving previously unattainable goals. He points to the fact that Europe and Soviet Russia are gaining ground in the application of automation, and he believes that the federal government should inaugurate a national policy designed to stimulate the introduction of automation in areas where it can be used to the best advantage.

Richard Bolt describes the uses of the computers of the future and sees machines being drawn into a partnership with man. He details the problems that could be solved and promises that these computers will make man's work more efficient and will give man some new capabilities. Bolt admits that this new power to control nature will increase the power to control man, so that man must have moral responsibility to use these new powers wisely. We must not, therefore, prevent the development of the computers of the future but must learn to live with these new powers.

Both Diebold and Bolt think that the development of automation is beneficial to man. Lewis Mumford is in sharp disagreement. He believes that in many instances the introduction of automation has been destructive. Furthermore, the idea that automation is the prime achievement of our culture, he believes, is short-sighted and dangerous.

Norbert Wiener discusses the type of computer known as the learning machine and points out that if a machine can defeat in a chess game the man who programmed it, the man does not have effective control over the machine. More important, he calls attention to the fact that a man may overlook programing a value. Since the machine works on the basis of its own experience, the omission may lead to destructive results. Wiener also wonders whether man's increasing dependence on machines for decisions might involve a desire to avoid responsibility.

Mortimer Taube argues that it is nonsensical to talk of machines as brains endowed with quasi-human intelligence. He insists that a definite distinction be made between men and machines, no matter how complex the machines. He also attacks the idea that increased automaticity is always desirable. He believes this idea had its root in a naïve concept of the capabilities of computers and warns that it may have grave consequences for our national defense.

Several serious questions, then, arise with respect to automation and computers. Should our federal government stimulate the introduction of automation as Diebold suggests? Must all facets of human life be invaded by computers and must we learn to live with them? How can we ensure that men will possess the moral responsibility to use wisely the new powers achieved by the computers of the future? If computers operate without regard to human values, should important decisions be left to machines? For example, to what extent should the decision to employ our ICBM capability be made by the batteries of computers installed in the Pentagon?

John Diebold
THE NATURE OF AUTOMATION

. . . Throughout the testimony submitted before this Subcommittee, you will come across definitions of automation. Though views will differ, depending on the background of the witness, I think that the concept of automation as a *new* way of analyzing and organizing work will be more heavily stressed than at the original hearings.

. . . I still feel that the concept of the system is most crucial in describing automation. It is the main contribution that automation will make to business organization. If automation means anything at all, it means something more than a mere extension of mechanization. I believe that it marks a break with past trends, a qualitative departure from the more conventional advance of technology that began with jagged pieces of flint and progressed up to the steam engine. It implies a basic change in our attitude toward the manner of performing work. Perhaps because we see things more easily than ideas, this meaning of automation as a way of thinking has been obscured by a fascination with the machines of automation. As a result, when we hear the word "automation" we tend to think of electronic computers, massive transfer machines, numerical tool controls, or perhaps the instrument panel of an oil refinery—machines that new concepts have made possible. Automation, however, is much more than machines, and it is important to understand this if the full social and economic implications are to be understood.

Unquestionably, industrial progress began hundreds of years ago. Great strides were made in the industrial revolution of the eighteenth century. This was the period of mechanization. Mechanization provided power-driven tools, eliminating many manual tasks and freeing labor from much of the physical work required in production. But no matter how small a portion of brute strength was involved in running a machine, a human worker was always needed to operate and control it. Production processes, therefore, were necessarily designed around the human worker as operator. His reaction time, his powers of perception and concentration

Portion of the statement of Mr. John Diebold before the Joint Economic Committee, Sub-Committee on Automation and Energy Resources, 86th Congress, 2nd Session, in *New Views on Automation* (Wash., D.C.). Mr. Diebold is among the top experts in the field of automation.

and discrimination, his height, his power to withstand heat and cold, his two arms and ten fingers and his ability to coordinate them dictated what could and what could not be done.

Now, through systematic application of the principle called feedback, machines can be built which control their own operations, so that production processes do not have to be designed to take into account the human limitations of a human worker. To me, this is one of the distinctive facts about automation. It is no longer necessary to think in terms of individual machines, or even in terms of groups of machines; instead, for the first time, it is practical to look at an entire production or information-handling process as an integrated system and not as a series of individual steps. It is through the new technology of automation that we are now beginning to possess the ability and the tools to build such systems.

Although we are in a position to draw some valid conclusions from an adequate study of today's manifestation of automation, we must remember that automation has not really got off the ground. The concept of automation is what is important. Future machines and hardware will undoubtedly be different from anything that we can presently envisage, but I feel that for a long time to come they will simply be extensions and realizations of the concept of automation.

In the past our limited knowledge of the nature of feedback and control made their application dependent upon the ingenuity of individual inventors who used these principles for the sporadic construction of individual machines or segments of overall systems. Even if we had been inspired by the idea of integrated systems, as some men have certainly been at different times in history, we did not in the past possess the technical knowledge to turn this idea into reality. Today, because of advances in the theory and technology of control, communication, and information, we do possess that knowledge and, equally important, we are beginning to apply it in many fields of endeavor.

Automation is more than a series of new machines and more basic than any particular hardware. It is a way of thinking as much as it is a way of doing. It is a new way of organizing and analyzing production, a concern with the production processes as a system, and a consideration of each element as part of the system. It is something of a conceptual breakthrough, as revolutionary in its way as Henry Ford's concept of the assembly line. Indeed, it may in the end have an even more widespread effect on business and industry, since its technology rests on a firm theoretical foundation rather than on a specific method of organization or particular kind of machine. Automation is, therefore, adaptable to many different kinds of operations—office work as well as factory work—in small concerns as well as large.

I think that a good part of the confusion which has resulted in attempts to describe automation has come about from defining the word in terms of the nature of its applications. Many of the definitions offered in the past have not conflicted with one another as much as they have neglected one another. That is, they have defined only one segment of what can properly be considered automation (this is the difficulty one encounters when a definition is attempted in terms of "hardware," or machinery, instead of concept). . . .

As it has developed in the United States, automation takes many forms and can be classified in several ways.

One such classification is as follows:

Computers.—Automatic handling of information by use of electronic systems.

"Detroit Automation."—Integration of machines; linking together, by means of automatic transfer devices of the machines of production.

Process Control Systems.—Computer and integrated control systems for operation of process (oil, chemical, atomic) plants.

Numerical Control.—The use of tape and other automatic control devices to direct operation of machines and machine systems.

The mechanization of what we already do today is the part of automation that has received the most attention. The automated engine lines in automobile plants, and massive transfer machines are familiar examples of automation. These machines and the jobs they do are important, for they contribute to increases in productivity. But they represent the least significant way in which automation increases productivity.

Eight or ten years ago, I was inclined toward this definition of automation, but with more practical first-hand experience, I soon changed my mind. The more I have been engaged in the actual application of automation to industry and government, the more convinced I am that the fundamental importance of automation is not so much the connecting of machines as it is the ability to create automatic information and control systems. The machines change from year to year, but automation is important as a combination of theoretical understanding, information handling, and of the practical application of this theory to build self-correcting systems.

The truly great gains from automation come when it extends the range of man's capability by permitting him to undertake new tasks and reach hitherto unattainable objectives. It is in this area that man's productivity is multiplied, not a few times, but by many orders of magnitude. And it is here that the greatest difficulties are encountered in determining automation's economic consequences.

For example, the principles of long-range weather forecasting are well understood, but digesting the mass of data necessary to produce accurate long-range forecasts has until now been beyond the reach of man or machine. Just recently, a computer was designed capable of doing more than 100 billion arithmetical computations a day. A giant like this will soon be able to provide accurate long-range forecasts, with repercussions for agriculture, construction, transportation and other industries that are breathtaking to contemplate.

Our experience has shown that the motivations for automating have been very diverse. Apart from the fact that many considered it a band wagon on which they should climb, the overriding factors dictating a decision to automate usually were, and still are, (1) to cut production costs, (2) to reduce labor requirements, (3) to do existing things faster, (4) to do things not possible before, (5) to increase productivity, and (6) to aid in decision-making by providing fuller and faster information.

Probably the most common, and the worst reason for embarking on an automation program is to save labor costs. Office management in particular has been bedeviled for years by rising clerical costs and the difficulty of hiring enough clerks to get the work done. Mindful of claims to the effect that one man can be taken off the payroll for each $5,000 invested in automatic equipment, management has looked on automation as the answer to a nightmare.

At first glance, this looks like a good enough reason. Ordinarily, an automatic machine does reduce labor costs, though seldom as much as management had hoped. Here is a simplified example of the economics of the situation which shows why.

Computer Economics

A computer system with tape, tape printer, and peripheral equipment may rent for about $20,000 a month. In addition, the cost of going from the old to the new system can easily reach $275,000. It may cost more if the old system is particularly antiquated. The new system, therefore, has to relieve enough clerks to pay for the equipment and to yield a return on the investment. For a three year payout on the investment, annual savings above machine costs must be $92,000. To produce this savings from personnel alone, these costs would have to be reduced $332,000 a year. At $5,000 a year per clerk, this means a net reduction of 66 clerks for the investment to be barely justifiable. And this net reduction has to absorb the extra personnel costs for programmers and machine operators.

The main trouble with this approach is not that savings usually fail to match expectations.

When labor saving is the main goal, it automatically demotes to second place what should be the primary aim of any company installing automation equipment; to exploit fully the potentialities of these machines for doing things that cannot be done well, or cannot be done at all, without them. But even so, automation can cut costs in other less obvious directions.

A Department of Labor study of an insurance company, which installed a computer in the classification sections of one of its divisions, reveals where some of these savings lie. The computer reduced personnel in this particular area from 198 to 85 workers and freed more than 15,000 square feet of floor space for other uses. It reduced the number of punched card machines from 125 to 21, and the yearly rental for these machines from $235,000 to $19,000. Monthly punch card requirements have been cut by nearly 2.5 million. Altogether, the computer is expected to cut the classification section's budgets in half.

Indeed, management has often introduced automation largely to reduce labor costs and then finds that it has done the right thing for the wrong reason. One chemical company figured that for every dollar saved by reducing the man-hour content for each unit of product, it saved at least three dollars because it could produce a better product more efficiently and with less waste.

"Detroit" Automation in Practice

Among the first examples of the Detroit type of automation are the two Brooks Park engine plants of the Ford Motor Company, near Cleveland, which since 1951 have been turning out six-cylinder engine blocks from rough castings. The castings which are first produced in an automated foundry, are fed into a broaching machine, which then "just goes 'whoosh' and it is done," as one startled observer described the process. Altogether, 42 automatic machines, linked together by transfer devices that automatically move the blocks through the complete process, perform 530 precision cutting operations and borings. A rough casting goes through the line and emerges as a finished engine block in just 14.6 minutes, as against nine hours in a conventional plant.

From the start to finish along the 1,545 foot line, no operator touches a part. "I don't do nothing but press these two buttons," the operator of the broaching machine on an automated Ford Line at Dearborn remarked. "Sometimes I use my thumbs (to push the buttons), sometimes I use my wrists and sometimes I lay my whole arm across. The only time I sweat on the job any more is when the sun is 100 and something outside."

All too often today the economies expected of automation do not bear fruit in actual practice. The expected savings from high cost installations may turn into unrealized hopes. . . .

Numerical Control

Numerical control automation, which has just recently begun to be applied on a widespread basis, is especially applicable to small shops with short runs of greatly varying products—typical job shops. There are roughly 750 of these tape fed machines in existence today. As I mentioned in earlier testimony, the bulk of U.S. hard-goods production is in lots of less than 25 identical units. But today's plant automation is largely of the "Detroit type"—large transfer machinery, suitable for only a small portion of our national production. The solution of this problem is on hand in the numerically controlled machine tool. The development of smaller versions of this equipment will be of principal importance to the factory in the future. Such machines will be capable of producing a short run of one product and then, with a change of tape, producing a few more units of an entirely different product, all from the same tool.

Process Control

When the material being processed is not a rigid, solid object but something that flows by its very nature—a liquid, a gas, electric energy, a solid in crushed or powdered form—continuous flow is a good deal easier to achieve. Thus, it is not surprising that automation began earlier and has gone much further in the processing industries than in manufacturing, although these industries are still a long way from full automation.

In chemical manufacture and oil refining—the industries that have gone the furthest in automating—entire systems of control instruments regulate the production processes, making it virtually automatic from raw material to finished product, and sometimes to finished by-product as well. A modern oil refinery, oil men estimate, is 80 to 90 percent automatic. In Esso's refinery at Fawley, England, six men on any one shift operate distillation units processing 5.5 million gallons of crude oil a day. In another plant in Iran, one operator in a central control room regulates 50,000 barrels a day, the total output of four wells singlehanded. "A man may work for months on a pipeline, or in a refinery, or even in the production fields and never see or touch oil," an official of the Oil Workers Union has said. . . .

Individual companies adopt automatic control because they expect to benefit from its use by doing existing things better through cutting labor costs, increasing the yield from a facility, reducing in-process inventory, facilitating change in product characteristics or for other reasons. However, the greatest gains in productivity from automation will come from being able to do altogether new tasks and achieve previously unattainable goals. Manufacturers have stated that: using a new numerical controlled machine tool, the total cycle times in the fabrication of an assortment of different parts are reduced from one-half to slightly more than one-tenth the cycle time using under numerical control than comparable tools under manual or tracer control.

Just recently a large manufacturer announced that it already had put into operation seventy-five "program-controlled machines" in the last few years. The company was specifically interested in applying automation to its job shop operations.

The next decade will see the spread of this kind of system in the plant, as the last decade has seen the spread of the computer in the office.

Foreign Aspects of Automation

In the practical application of automation concepts and techniques to industry, the United States leads the world, at the present time. In terms of growth rate in application and absolute number of automated installations we are ahead of any country in the free world. I have not included the communist-block nations because there is no substantial data to estimate their progress accurately.

Qualitatively, we know that they are moving ahead at a fast rate. To the extent that they are employing automation, it is interesting to consider Premier Khrushchev's report to the 21st Congress of the Communist Party of the Soviet Union. He gave some indication of the widespread applications intended for mechanization and automation under the Soviet Seven-Year Plan for Economic Development (1959–1965).

Mr. Khrushchev reported that, "Integrated mechanization and the *automation* of production processes constitute the chief and decisive means for ensuring further technical progress in the economy and, on this basis, a new rise in labour productivity, the lowering of cost prices, and the improvement of the quality of products." This theme is further amplified in Mr. Khrushchev's statement of the "target figures" with regard to level of *automation* to be obtained. Of particular note was the indication of plans for the "establishment of more than 50 experimental model enterprises where the latest patterns of integrated automation will be put into effect."

In a final section, in a discussion of specific provision of the "plan" as it pertains to educational development, it was stated that "the greatest increase in the number of engineers graduated (during the years of the 'plan') will be in the specialties of chemical technology, *automation,* computing engineering, radio-electronics and other branches of new technique." Stress will also be placed upon scientific development and, "in particular the successes of computing mathematics [which] are directly connected with the development of *automation*."

I would suggest that it would be sheer folly to take these words lightly, in view of the Soviet Union's accomplishments in the field of engineering education, and the science of mathematics. Recent reports point to a gap between "theory" and "application" in the field of automation in the Soviet Union. I would not expect this state to last very long (if, indeed, it is an accurate picture of present achievement levels).

It would also be a mistake to take a complacent attitude toward European business. Though we "out-automate" Europe by sheer volume alone, the level of sophistication in automatic techniques is high, especially in factory automation.

My company continually surveys the Western European electronic data processing market. We have found the European attitude to be more cautious of EDP hardware than is true in the United States. The cost factor of automatic equipment is given heavier emphasis. However, we have found that the average European computer user can be expected to make better use of the hardware's capabilities than his American counterpart once it is installed. He has been predisposed by his educational background to more easily accept the theoretical capabilities of the electronic hardware.

Western Europe has a total of over 2,000 computer installations, or about 20% of total United States installations. However, over 90% of this total are small computer system installations. What is most significant is that France and Germany, between themselves, have almost 70% of total European installations. Orders for computer systems number in the hundreds for all Western Europe.

Between the Russians on one hand and Western Europe on the other, we literally "have our hands full." It seems to me that we are in a most tragic plight as a nation when we must worry about the ill-effects of introducing automation—even at a slow rate! . . .

Conclusions

The United States Government should formulate a national policy that will effectively stimulate automation and other technological change.

I find it totally unreasonable—and dangerous—that as a nation we permit the waste of a potent national resource, automation. We are faced with a continuous, economic and political challenge on the international front that demands sizeable outlays for military security, aid to foreign nations, and other international programs. At the same time, we continuously try to raise our material standard of living.

To keep increasing our standard of living and, simultaneously, maintain our economic and political position in the world, we must sustain a high economic growth rate. Real increases in our national output will continue to be heavily influenced by our productivity increases—and productivity increase is a basic result of technological change.

I think we must face up to the fact that we have not made any concerted effort to deal with the problems that retard economic growth. The nation cannot long sustain a high rate of technological advance without coping with these problems; we simply cannot wait for evolutionary forces to solve our internal problems.

The national policy that will foster automation and technological change should be aimed mainly at bettering the environment for change. (For purposes of formulating national policy, automation should be considered as part of general technological change. It is difficult to separate automation out of the mainstream of change and somewhat useless to do so.) This policy should be geared to set in motion two programs simultaneously.

A program for identifying the effects of automation and technological change within our society should be initiated. We must learn how to stimulate automation to best advantage and, at the same time, minimize any harmful effects that may accompany it.

Secondly, mechanisms that can encourage economic and technical growth where such growth has stagnated must be designed. I do not feel that this can be accomplished through the efforts of private enterprise acting alone; the resources of local communities and, of the state governments, are sometimes not sufficient to overcome stagnancy. Individual action by the Federal Government is also insufficient.

A cooperative effort employing the resources of all these sectors of the economy must be brought to bear on these problems if they are to be solved. The government can do much to encourage business through enlightened tax policy and technical aid; communities and states can do more to provide worker training and retraining facilities and assisting in area redevelopment; business can initiate programs to assist employees in adapting to change situations.

A program of continuing study will provide more knowledge on how best to cope with change. It will supply the data needed to influence the social and economic results of the introduction of automation and other technology.

However, no study will be of value if it is an expedient way to avoid taking action on national issues. The extensive knowledge gathered can, perhaps, be best employed in helping to recognize—in advance—where action should be taken to stimulate technological and economic growth.

I also think it is very important that through national policy we encourage the widespread application of basic science to industry. Most of the significant innovations of the post-war period have come about through military research programs. Private industry has been unable to make the fullest use of these advances. The Government can do much to encourage the dissemination of this kind of information to business. Private enterprise can be further stimulated to employ new techniques and equipment through fiscal policy.

The encouragement of innovation in industry must be supported by labor, if we are to achieve its full benefits. Featherbedding in industry has become a valid issue; it is wasteful not only to the individual company in which it occurs but to the entire economy as well. In many instances, labor has shown that it can facilitate change by sponsoring its own retraining programs and by intelligent collective bargaining. The responsibilities of labor in this area will be much greater in the years to come. It remains to be seen whether present labor-management relations, which mainly revolve about periodic collective bargaining sessions, are sufficient to cope with future problems.

These recommendations are far from new. It is vital, however, that they be carried out. I recommend the study of automation at the first congressional hearing, as others have since. Concerted action of government, community and business to make the fullest use of this most important national resource—automation—has been suggested previously, although in vain.

I think it is worth remembering that a national resource, as well as a natural resource, can be lost forever if it is not conserved with intelligence and farsighted planning.

Richard H. Bolt
MAN-MACHINE PARTNERSHIP

. . . Computers were designed to calculate mathematical relations among numbers and perform logical operations using symbols. In the modern world, unless a worker is engaged in manipulation of physical materials he is engaged almost totally in manipulation of symbols.

From Richard H. Bolt, "Man-Machine Partnership in Intellectual Pursuits: A Look Ahead," in National Academy of Sciences, National Research Council, *toward Better Utilization of Scientific and Engineering Talent: A Program for Action* (Washington, D.C., 1964). Reprinted with permission. Dr. Bolt is Chairman of the Board of Bolt, Beranek and Newman, Inc., and Lecturer in Political Science at the Massachusetts Institute of Technology.

Further, computers for the most part have been used to carry out long and tedious but conceptually simple manipulations. The design of high-speed digital computers endows them with an extraordinary ability to perform mathematical and logical manipulations in amounts and at speeds that completely over-shadow man's ability in these respects.

When man thinks and reasons, however, he generally uses words, sentences, and language that do not behave neatly like numbers. Further, the manipulations man performs on linguistic information usually are more subtle and complex than mathematical calculations. Here we are drawing two quite different distinctions between computation of the sort usually done on today's computers and cognition of the sort we shall be able to do in tomorrow's partnership. Today we use mostly numbers; tomorrow we shall use not only numbers but also words—verbal abstractions. Today we perform mostly simple, routine operations; tomorrow we shall perform not only simple operations but also operations that are more complex than any that today's computer systems and programs can handle.

The more important distinction, probably, is the one that concerns complexity. Advancing from numerical to linguistic communication will not be an easy step, but the reward is simply the one we gain from learning a foreign language: now we can communicate where before we could not. Once we have achieved linguistic communication with the machine, however, we then can develop an ever-expanding ability to handle complex processes of thought, and we can apply this ability to all spheres of intellectual endeavor, which, of course, involves a combination of two faculties, memory and association.

The sort of new complexity we can tackle, if we "take a machine into partnership" instead of simply using it from time to time as a one-shot computer, can be explained with the help of an analogy. Solving a problem is like making a journey. There are two distinctly different ways in which we can make a journey—say, from Boston to San Francisco. We can get into an automobile and set off along the highway, following at every intersection the direction-signs that were already in place before this particular journey began. This procedure, of course, depends upon the existence of an elaborate road network and system of signs which exploit and codify the experience of our predecessors, and, to that extent, the element of discovery is taken out of the journey.

At the other extreme, we may travel as the pioneers did, working our way westward toward a goal whose nature is known beforehand only in the most general terms (the Pacific Ocean). In this case, we have no set procedure or highway system: we must make our way from point to point, resetting our course whenever we crest a ridge and come in sight of the next stretch of countryside before us. In such a journey, we are continually being faced with the need to make fresh decisions as we go along, and it is—in the nature of the case—impossible to specify beforehand a detailed set of instructions that will guarantee successful and efficient completion of the journey.

There are two correspondingly different kinds of intellectual problems. There are those in which we can specify explicitly beforehand all the intellectual steps that must be taken if the problem is to be followed successfully through to its solution; and there are those in which, once again, we have to make our way from point to point, repeatedly taking new intellectual decisions in the light of things that are discovered only as we go along. Solving the first, simple, straightforward kind of problem is a standardized and routine operation. All intellectual work involving an element of discovery is of the second, more complex kind, and involves the making of decisions repeatedly and in succession, as the investigation proceeds. Each great discovery made in science, for example, may be viewed as a decision made at an important crossroad.

It is this sort of complexity with which the new generation of machine-aids to cognition is enabling us to deal. The first generation of computing machines was programmed and used largely for routine and standardized operations, comparable to a journey by highway along a route entirely predetermined. Hitherto, that is, machines have been used mainly for "batch processing," in which a completely determinate set of instructions is laid down at the beginning of computation, and there is no opportunity to vary the manner in which the machine deals with the input data in the course of its operation. Although variations are allowed for in some commercial operations, in which the program selects different branches depending upon the inputs received, even in this case all contingencies must be specified in advance.

In order to tackle the more complex kind of intellectual problem, in which we proceed from point to point, making fresh decisions as we go along, we must develop new ways of working with machines, so as to open up the possibility of repeated interactions between the machine and the user in the course of any particular operation. We must replace batch-processing with a more flexible partnership between man and machine, thereby providing for a sequence of decisions to be taken on route. We mean decisions among *unforeseen* alternatives.

The advantages of this new kind of procedure can be explained easily enough by extending our analogy. There are only two ways we can, in advance, lay down precise instructions for making the automobile journey from Boston to San Francisco: (1) by specifying explicitly, before the journey begins, which road is to be taken at every single intersection along the way, or (2) by requiring that at every intersection all the alternative routes are to be explored, one after another. We can follow the first procedure only if all the essentially creative work of exploration and mapping has been done already; the second procedure will no doubt be effective in the long-enough run, but it may be intolerably wasteful, and we shall most likely end up by surveying a great part of the United States before we actually reach the Pacific.[1]

Yet these are, in effect, the only alternatives batch-processing offers us. We can either instruct the computer beforehand precisely how it is to proceed at every step (and this may involve guessing the answers to a lot of difficult questions, about which reliable information would turn up only in the course of solving the problem under investigation), or else we can set the machine to explore every single possibility as it turns up (and this, once again, is a highly wasteful procedure).

The new style of procedures for machine-aided inquiry, involving repeated interaction between the user and the machine, opens up a whole new degree of freedom in the solution of complex intellectual problems, and permits one to escape from the limitations of batch-processing. But we can gain the advantages of a "repeated interaction" only if we can resolve a major economic problem that such interaction poses.

An investigator who was in a position to monopolize a high-grade computing machine could, no doubt, break down any inquiry into a sequence of small steps, and proceed from point to point by orthodox methods—as it were, stopping his car at every intersection to consult his map afresh. But such a use of a computer would in practice be unacceptable: the machine would be effectively used for only a few milliseconds at a time, and would lie inactive after each step for minutes or even hours. An apparatus costing millions of dollars would thus be utilized for only a very small fraction of the time.

If we are to make repeated-interaction procedures economic, we must develop techniques by which *many independent users* or *teams of users* can operate in partnership with a single central machine *at one and the same time*. In a word, the price of repeated-interaction procedures is the development of a "multiple-access" computer. This is the new technical step upon which all machine-aided cognition, as contrasted with simple computing, fundamentally depends.

Progress in Machine Capabilities

The step required has been taken: during the past three years, time-sharing operation of computers has moved from concept, to labora-

---

[1] Whether this second procedure is too wasteful depends, of course, on the speed and cost of the computer used. Also, economy can be increased by programming the machine to remember its successes and failures as it proceeds over any route it has seen before, or to recognize general features of the "map" that may have been described in the program.

tory demonstration, to prototype systems being used simultaneously by many users.

Time-sharing in itself is not a new art: it is used extensively, for example, in telephone switching networks. What is new is the capability to provide man-machine partnership simultaneously to several users of one computer. Especially relevant is the multiple access to the computer's memory, as is reflected in the expression *memory-sharing* now coming into use. The key step has been the development of special programs that control the access to the computer.

An example of a large, multiple-access system now operating is the Project MAC system at the Massachusetts Institute of Technology. This system includes some 40 Teletypewriters (Model 35), which have access to an IBM 7094 computer in Project MAC and also to another computer of the same type located in the M.I.T. Computation Center. Placed in offices and laboratories throughout the campus, these Teletypewriters offer access to the system simply by dialing through the M.I.T. telephone exchange. Professors and students in many departments are using the system to carry on research on such diverse topics as solving mathematical equations, proving theorems, designing mechanical structures and systems, and making decisions in industrial management.

The system is connected to the TELEX network of the Western Union Company, and within months will be connected to the TWX network of the American Telephone and Telegraph Company. Access thereby offered to persons throughout the United States and in Europe enables the carrying out of several experiments, to provide experience in long-distance operation of time-sharing systems for machine-aided cognition. Already one scientist in Europe has used the system at M.I.T. through a trans-Atlantic telephone connection.

How many other time-sharing computers are in operation now? Perhaps five or ten, but the number is uncertain because experiments with new uses of computers are springing up faster than news about them can get around.

Most of the progress achieved thus far has come from the development of new programs for the computers. Some of the advances have appeared in the form of new devices, such as visual displays, that help give man an easier, more natural way of interacting with the computer. Not many changes specifically to aid machine-aided cognition have as yet shown up in the design and construction of the basic computer itself, although more such changes will find their way into computers in the future. Perhaps more relevant is the change in the balance among types of "hardware" used; proportionately more of it will be input-output equipment used in linking man and machine.

Advances made in computer programs, now usually called the

"software," have been aimed at serving functions of several kinds. One function, mentioned earlier in this paper, is the provision of new language that enables the user to communicate more easily with the machine. Another function is the rapid switching needed to provide multiple access; any one user is hooked in for only a very short interval at a time, but the intervals recur so often that the user, in effect, has continuous access to the computer. Other programs manage the handling of data stored in the computer, call up bodies of information as needed, or assist a programmer in preparing still more programs.

Let us now look, in somewhat more detail, at a few representative systems (perhaps we should say sub-systems) that have been put together to serve man-machine cognition in certain ways. Although for the most part these systems are experimental ones, they already have led to practical results through use in activities such as planning, engineering design, research, and teaching.

First we mention two systems, developed independently, that link a computer to a designer engaged in planning. *Sketchpad*, developed at M.I.T.'s Lincoln Laboratory, puts before the designer a cathode-ray screen, like the face of a television set, flanked by a set of control buttons. With a light-sensitive pointer or "light pen" in one hand, the designer sketches a diagram, which may, for example, represent a small machine part or a complete office building. With the other hand on the control panel, he gives the computer the additional information needed to interpret the meaning of the lines he is sketching. The computer can help the designer in a number of ways: it can rotate the figure, change its size, display different cross sections, or combine it with other pieces drawn previously.

In doing its work, *Sketchpad* can put individual pieces together to form an assembly; combine several such assemblies together as sub-assemblies to form a higher assembly; and so on, until the entire structure is put together. Eventually the designer completes his first rough sketch. At this point the computer, using specific dimensions and scales specified by the user, takes over and produces on the screen an accurately scaled drawing with all relevant dimensions indicated. Then the designer can continue to interact with the computer in order to modify and improve his design.

Coplanner, a somewhat different system, is being developed by my colleagues for use in architectural planning. In designing a new hospital, for example, the architect might start by giving the system some relevant statistical data concerning operations in a number of existing hospitals, such as the number of patients served per day, the number of trips that doctors make between various parts of hte hospital, and the flow of visitor traffic.

On its screen, *Coplanner* can display the data in any of several forms, such as graphs, tables, or bar charts. With the use of a light pen, the designer can modify the statistical distributions to make them apply more specifically to the particular hospital under consideration, or to project future requirements. Then the designer sketches a possible plan of the hospital, and instructs the computer, using the statistical data, to evaluate the hospital layout in terms of objective design criteria, such as communications efficiency, delays in serving patients, the number of doctors and support personnel needed, and so on. Working together, *Coplanner* simulates the assumed operations in the hospital and the designer modifies the layout, back and forth, until a suitable plan emerges.

Next we cite the use of computer-based systems in engineering design. New roads being built in Sweden, Norway, Finland, and Germany have been designed by engineers interacting with programmed aids developed by AB Nordisk ADB and the Swedish Board of Roads. Aids provided include computer-made movies that let you see "from the driver's seat" what it would be like to drive along roads you have designed. Recently this movie technique has received further development at the Bell Telephone Laboratories.

Stress, a computer program for use in the analysis of structures, is being developed in the Civil Engineering Department at M.I.T. *Stress* converses with the engineer in his own language; helps him analyze a large variety of structures; and carries on a dialogue resulting in successive modifications and improvements to the original design concept.

Machine-aided cognition is starting to play a role in fundamental research. At Thompson Ramo Wooldridge (now Bunker-Ramo), Culler and Fried have developed a system to help the scientist carry out mathematical computations. Seated at a console that includes display scopes and keyboards, the user develops his mathematics on a symbolic level, using any new symbols and operations he may need in exploring the mathematical problem at hand. When he embarks, the scientist may have no clear-cut idea as to how he can solve the problem. At any point along the road, he can ask the machine to display the partial results found up to that point. Then the scientist may continue to follow the route he has chosen or he may go back and try another approach. In actual use, this system has enabled the solution of some complex, previously unsolved problems in contemporary physics.

As we can see, some of these systems resemble a fast, tireless laboratory assistant with an unlimited memory. And some of the systems being conceived or demonstrated promise to bring truly revolutionary capabilities to bear upon intellectual tasks carried out by planners, managers, physicians, lawyers, educators, writers, scientists, and engineers.

Although very large (and costly) computers serve as the central processors of information for many of the systems being developed, some of the new aids to cognition, such as *Coplanner*, operate in connection with small or medium sized computers. Each size has its advantages and disadvantages, which are being studied in several different organizations using computers of different size and kind. Larger machines can more readily provide multiple access by users in large numbers, and this more widespread use can help in defraying the high costs associated with the development of the auxiliary equipment and with the complex programs needed. Smaller machines, on the other hand, can be set up more cheaply and quickly to explore new approaches in early stages of conception; and can be enlarged later. As we have already noted, the future will see the evolution of computers specially adapted, in size, speed, and all other characteristics, to the special needs of machine-aided cognition.

Future Impacts upon Utilization of Manpower

We turn now to speculations based upon the evidence sketched in preceding sections and elaborated in many publications including those cited in the references. We try to visualize ways in which machine-aided cognition in future decades may affect the utilization of manpower, particularly scientists and engineers. Any or all of the impacts suggested could occur, but we shall not try to guess which ones will prove to be the more important or when the impacts will show up. Some of the impacts will be felt as benefits; others, as difficulties to be overcome. All the impacts will compel us from time to time to reassess the patterns of utilization.

Machine-aided cognition will increase the effective *supply* of manpower in research and, at the same time, will increase the *demand* for such manpower. The research scientist or engineer working in partnership with the machine will be able to carry out a given intellectual task in less time than he would take working alone. Parts of his task automated, and thus speeded, will include searching the literature for information relevant to his research problem, checking the information for reliability and consistency, combining the information with new facts that he (in partnership) has found, plotting graphs and combining graphical data from several sources, and recording all the results. Helping the man carry out these relatively routine chores will not be the most significant contributions the machine will make, but it will save him a great deal of time. The time thus saved converts into an increase in the effective supply of research manpower.

What seems quite likely, in view of the motivational nature of highly creative people, is that the man will go on and do more research, make additional discoveries, and uncover yet more problems that merit research. He will increase the *demand* for more research personnel and for more assistants to help investigators work on the new problems.

More significantly, machine-aided cognition will give men some fresh *capabilities,* beyond those they possess when working alone: notably, in the study of complex processes, involving enormous numbers of variables and interrelationships. To return to our analogy of a cross-country journey, such extremely complex processes present one with many "crossroads," points at which one must make choices among alternatives that could not be foreseen except in the vicinity of the new choice-point. In such cases, man-machine partnership, with its continuous, on-line interaction, will bring its greatest rewards, and the analytical power of this partnership will gain in strength as we discover how the responsibilities may most effectively be divided between the man and the machine.

As a result, the ways in which scientists and engineers tackle their work will be greatly changed. The relative amounts of time they spend on different tasks, the kinds of problems they attack, the patterns of machine-aided collaboration among different persons: the whole *pattern of endeavor* in science and technology will be altered by revolutionary new equipments and environments.

Here the main effect will be an indirect one: machine-aided cognition amplifies the role of automation, such as machine tools, and the automation then replaces skilled and semi-skilled labor in large numbers. For example, certain systems, such as aircraft, already are being designed in part through the use of computers and automated instruments, which are replacing rooms full of draftsmen and months of routine handwork in the shop. In many cases, too, simulation based on the use of computer-based models enables one to dispense with the making and testing of large-scale, physical models of the system. Thus the net impact upon the pattern of endeavor will be a shift away from the more routine tasks and toward the more creative ones. . . .

These new capabilities will, of course, carry with them grave responsibilities, and the moral issues so raised may be as difficult in their own way as those highlighted by the development of nuclear weapons. By his very nature, man will continue to expand his intellectual horizons and venture into the unknown. His new power to control nature will increase his power to control and to encroach upon the privacy of his fellow man. Every such new intellectual advance will carry with it a moral responsibility to use the new powers wisely. This applies to the development of machine-aided cognition as much as to any other new development. Man cannot resolve this issue of possible abuse of his new powers simply by preventing their development; instead, he must learn to live with these powers, to use them properly and so to grow in wisdom and moral sense. The new man-machine partnership will increase the rate at which scientific and technical information accumulates, and thereby will create added demands for *storage, dissemination, and retrieval of information*. At the same time, systems for man-machine cognition will automatically— we might say necessarily—contain the seeds of solution for the problems associated with the "information explosion."

Through linkage among all the machine systems involved, all recorded information, including the contents of all libraries, will become accessible to all users, no matter where they are. The word "accessible" here refers to the full power of the system to search, check, correlate, and display all relevant information to the human user. The system would, of course, contain such aids to information retrieval as automated card catalogues, aids to bibliographic search, display and print-out capabilities, and all the other appurtenances of the automated library of the future.

Two particular possibilities merit comment here. First, through the use of associative memory, the system will retrieve items of information related to a specified topic but expressed in different ways— specialized jargons—used by workers in different fields. The computer memory is organized in such a way as to associate all items that resemble each other in specified, substantive respects no matter how they are put into language. Second, the system will seek out the user instead of waiting to be consulted. If Scientist A is interested in a certain topic, the information system will recognize the relevance of a new contribution reported by Scientist B, and will relay it directly to Scientist A. Both of these new capabilities, associating similar items and initiating the dissemination of new information, will also find valuable uses outside of science—for example in business management, in which decision makers often require up-to-date information from many unrelated sources.

Improving our ability to retrieve information, in the several ways mentioned, might alone justify all the investments of men and dollars now being made or contemplated in the development of man-machine systems to aid cognitive processes. But again we must emphasize that these relatively "mechanical" gains, speeding and expanding the search for information, are not the contributions that will in the long run be most significant for man's progress. Even more significant will be the creation of entirely new capabilities to deal with complex problems and those that enlarge our conceptual outlooks. . . .

Lewis Mumford
AUTOMATION

. . . Let me first challenge the notion that automation is in any sense a final good, so unqualifiedly beneficial in every aspect that the process must be hastened and extended relentlessly into every field. If the human organism had developed on that principle, the reflexes and the autonomic nervous system would have absorbed all the functions of the brain, and man would have been left without a thought in his head. Organic systems are infinitely more complex than automatic systems; and what makes them so is the margin of choice, the freedom to commit and correct errors, to explore unfrequented paths, to incorporate unpredictable accidents with self defined purposes, to anticipate the unexpected and to plan the ". . . impossible—all traits . . ." that no efficient automatic system can countenance.

Already most of us have witnessed the often comical embarassments of automation, as currently employed in industry, education, and government today; too well we know its sad inability to function in situations that do not conform to its own rigid code of operation. But despite these limitations most people still regard the whole process of automation as a highly desirable one or if not actually desirable, then inevitable and inescapable. Though we have had twenty years' experience of the devastating effects of reducing our complex efficient system of pre-1940 transportation with its many public and private choices, to the technologically primitive organization we labor under today, they strangely cling to their naive faith in monotransportation by private motor car. This method successfully absorbs the automatic production of motor cars only at the price of turning our cities into disorderly parking lots and our countryside into a mere refuse dump for metropolitan populations, serving neither urban nor rural purposes.

But in spite of this classic demonstration of destructive automation our fellow citizens, unless they are threatened with the loss of their jobs, are not ready to question the inevitability of eventual total automation. Not only do they look forward, as all reasonable men should, to the transference of much burdensome servile labor to the machine but they

From Lewis Mumford, "The Automation of Knowledge," *Vital Speeches of the Day*, 30 (May 1, 1964), 441–446. Reprinted by permission.

are equally eager to turn as many other human functions as possible over to machines, fascinated, indeed hypnotized, by their superior accuracy, their fantastic rapidity, their staggering productivity.

In other words, many of us have now come to regard automation as the climax stage of human culture. For the sake of achieving this climax, our leaders are eagerly turning over to our great mechanical collectives—industrial, financial, military, and not least educational—the remaining functions of life, wiping out, with no sense of the colossal loss, all natural richness and diversity, all ecological complexity, all independent human selectivity and purposefulness, though these are the basic conditions of human creativity in every department—not least, of course, in science and technology.

While the pace of mechanization and automation has accelerated during the past half century now that the method itself has been perfected, we have yet to achieve a dispassionate evaluation of the results. Yet these results were accurately anticipated a full century ago by the English satirist Samuel Butler who as a young sheep rancher in New Zealand found himself with plenty of time to ruminate profitably, as no incipient Ph.D. would dare to ruminate today, on the Future of Man. Already Butler plainly saw, in a letter now printed in his notebooks, that mechanical life was displacing organic life: that because people then were already feeding their life into automatic systems, machines were taking on more of the attributes of living organisms, becoming self-operating, self-regulating, and self-directing; while man, on the other hand, was adapting himself with pathetic docility, to the limitations of the machine. In short, man and the machine were exchanging roles.

But what has proved worse, we have now found out, is that as our system of automation becomes more perfect, the less possible it is to intervene in the process, to alter its pace, to change its direction, to limit its further extension, or to reorient its goal. Automation has a colossal qualitative defect that springs directly from its quantitative virtues; it increases probability and decreases possibility. Though the individual component of an automatic system may be programed like a punch card on a motor assembly line to deal with variety, the system itself is so fixed and rigid that it seems in fact little more than a neat mechanical model of a compulsion neurosis. This system can operate in fact with only one set of goals, purely quantitative goals unrelated to organic, capacity or human need—faster and faster, further and further, bigger and bigger, more and more.

When our translation of organic and human aptitudes into their system-controlled mechanical counterparts has fully taken place, man will have lost the full use of even his physical organs. There are areas in this country today where people have already lost the free use of their legs; in many California cities pedestrians are arrested on sight by the police. The next step will be to imprison anyone who uses his own voice to sing instead of turning on his transistor radio; even the possibility of indulging in autonomous daydreams has already been largely taken over by centrally directed television and radio stations whose final advance will be to extend their operations to sleep.

Why this massive translation of all organic aptitudes into mechanical counterfeits should be hailed as an improvement, I have yet to discover. Many people, for example, express pride over the fact that we have devised computers intelligent enough to play chess; but what will happen to human pride, or to the game of chess for that matter, when computers become so intelligent that they will deign to play only with other computers? If man's own life is indeed so utterly worthless, what new value does it acquire by being turned over to a machine? And if the Brave New World we have put together with the aid of science, is, by definition, a world without values, on what strange logical principle can we assign value to science or automation? When you empty out the proper life of man, all that's left is emptiness. . . .

Norbert Wiener
"THE MONKEY'S PAW"

I think we have been talking a good deal about computing machines on the basis of rather a shady account of what these machines are, and an even shadier account of what these machines are going to be.

I shall not confine my remarks to computing machines; I am going to talk about control apparatus in general. The difference between the two from our point of view is not very great. The computing machine is a general-purpose device that can be programmed to do very specific jobs, and it may be at the heart of the control apparatus for certain applications. But let us talk in general about control and communication machines, rather than specifically about computing machines.

. . . We are starting to hear about a class of machines just coming into being—the learning machine. I want to say something more about the

Reprinted from Martin Greenberger, ed., *Management and the Computer of the Future*, by permission of the M.I.T. Press. (c) 1962. The late Dr. Wiener was an authority on "cybernetics," a term that he coined.

learning machine, because I think that both the greatest part of the difficulties which we have been discussing and the greatest part of the possibilities for relieving these difficulties lie in this machine.

Take the learning machine as it now exists. One form of it is a machine for playing checkers. Now, it is possible to play checkers with machines that are not learning machines. It is possible to write down at any stage of a game all the successive moves that are legally possible for the next stage; to rank them on a scale of values involving loss of pieces, mobility, control, and many other factors (I believe about fifteen factors have been considered in one game); and then to give these factors certain weightings, established at the beginning. This procedure leads to a machine that is a checker-playing machine to a limited extent, but not a learning machine. If you were to play against this machine, it would feel like a rigid personality. (By the way, if you play correspondence checkers or chess, whether with a machine or a person, you do acquire a feeling for the personality opposed to you.) When a rigid personality makes a blunder, it always repeats the same blunder in the same situation.

A machine with a less rigid personality can be achieved as follows. The machine plays as before, but now keeps a record of all plays made and all games played. At intervals it is run in a different way. Instead of evaluating moves in terms of a fixed scale of evaluation, it evaluates the scale of evaluation in terms of the games played. It determines which scale of evaluation would have led to wins more assuredly than any other. There are various tricks of accomplishing this which I need not describe here; they are not perfect, but they are valid. The machine, having determined which scale of evaluation would have been most conducive to winning, adopts it for further play. That is learning.

Such a machine, if you use it for playing checkers, as it has been used, would have a more flexible personality. The tricks that once worked against it might fail with its increasing experience and its re-evaluation of various considerations. Such a machine has been developed by Samuel of IBM. At first the machine was able to defeat Samuel fairly consistently. Later on he learned a little more checkers and was able to defeat the machine more often. Nevertheless, the fact is that the machine can go beyond the person who programmed it. Even though Samuel caught up, there is always the possibility that the machine may catch up again later with more sophisticated programming.

The fact that a machine can defeat the man who programmed it means that having made such a machine does not give him completely effective control over it. If he had that, he would not let it beat him. Now, this is very important. Such a machine could be very useful in certain decision situations. It could be used to play games other than checkers:

the business game, the war game, and the game of determining when to press the button for Armageddon—for the thermonuclear war.

How are you going to program such a machine? Well, you cannot program it based on prior thermonuclear wars. You would have to play the game according to a set of postulates which you constructed. You could make the machine learn to be more successful within the framework of these postulates. However, you receive no indication from this whether your postulates have the right values. Such a machine, in other words, can beg the question very badly and can be very dangerous.

What you have here is a situation not unlike that found in the folk tale "The Monkey's Paw." "The Monkey's Paw" is a story told by W. W. Jacobs of England at the beginning of the century. An old soldier returns from India to visit a friend. He has with him a talisman that he says has the ability to grant three wishes to each of three people. The first owner of the talisman had taken the first set of three wishes, two unknown to the soldier, but the third one for death. That is how the soldier became owner. The soldier took the second set of wishes for himself, but declines to talk about them. His experiences were too terrible. One set of wishes remains. With considerable reluctance the soldier yields to his friend's request for the talisman. The friend's first wish is for £200, and an official of the company where his son is employed comes in to tell him that his son has been crushed in the machinery. As a solatium, but without any admission of responsibility, the company has granted the father £200. The next wish is that the boy be back, and his mutilated ghost appears knocking at the door; the third wish is that the ghost go away.

The point is that magic is terrible literal-minded. It will give you what you ask for, not what you should have asked for, nor necessarily what you want. This will most certainly be true about learning machines. If you do not put into the programming the important restriction that you do not want £200 at the cost of having your son ground up in the machinery, you cannot expect the machine itself to think of this restriction.

"The Monkey's Paw" suggests a very real danger of the learning machine. The danger of these machines is greater than that of the simple computing machine, because you do not set down for it the tactics of the policy but only the strategy. You let the tactics work themselves out from the experience of the machine. The machine acquires a nature based on its experience.

So there are real dangers here. Is there any way of partially overcoming these dangers? The importance of learning machines is not how they act as pure machines, but how they interact with society. We thus are led to the concept of a system involving both human actions and machines. Is there any way in such a system to transfer values from the human being to the machine?

In a general, imperfect sense there is. Suppose you build a machine to translate a language. The value of the translation is a human value. The value depends upon whether people reading the translation will interpret it with the same meaning as the original. It is conceivable that you might attain a value system by having a complete logical code of translations, a superperfect grammar; but this would not be a really profitable way to proceed. Instead, you would have the machine do exercises, just as a human pupil does exercises. These exercises would be marked by a teacher who possesses human values. The machine would modify itself based on these marks, just as the checker-playing machine modifies itself based on its prior wins. It is at least theoretically possible to transfer values from the human being to the machine in such man-machine organizations. I think that the possibility of reproducing human values is of great importance, but in itself has dangers too.

The last thing I want to discuss is the temptation of gadgets. What are the tempting things about gadgets? What are the tempting things about machines? What are the tempting things about an organization with great compartmentation and high secrecy? These are the human questions that arise.

I am reminded here of the game of Russian roulette. At various times, in remote barracks and posts, officers have played this game of putting one bullet into their revolvers, spinning the chamber, and pulling the trigger, either at themselves or somebody else. This is obviously a means of expressing aggressive impulses either against oneself or against one's opponent. It is obviously a form of masochism or sadism. It is permissible, however, because one man has removed final responsibility for the act from himself, put it in the machine, and left it to chance. If he kills the other man, he has provided himself with a way (in his mind) of reducing his responsibility from what we ordinarily associate with murder to what we associate with manslaughter. He can blame chance.

This is very much like the game that is often played when a prisoner is taken before a firing squad. Each man in the firing squad has his rifle loaded with several blank cartridges and a single bullet. The result is that the men are more willing to fire because of the overwhelming likelihood that they will not kill the prisoner. This a way of avoiding responsibility.

I am certain that a great deal of the use of gadgets for decisions, as it exists now and as it may exist even more in the future, is motivated by this desire to avoid direct responsibility. I am sure that a lot of the subdivision of effort in secret projects and highly compartmented projects has the same motive. The subordinate does not know enough about the project to feel responsibility, and the man in charge can place responsibility with the system. I believe that one of the greatest dangers at the present time has to do with the attempt to avoid responsibility in order to avoid the feeling of guilt. . . .

There is a real possibility that changes in our environment have exceeded our capacity to adapt. The real dangers at the present time—the danger of thermonuclear war, the computing-machine sort of danger, the population-explosion danger, the danger of the improvement of medicine (to the extent that we shall very soon have to face not letting people live as part of the policy of letting them live)—all of these dangers make one wonder whether we have not changed the environment beyond our capacity to adjust to it, and whether we may not be biologically on the way out. We may not be, but this is not at all clear. . . .

Mortimer Taube
COMPUTERS AND COMMON SENSE

. . . It is a fact of considerable importance that the literature on machine learning is almost exclusively concerned with learning to play games like Turing's game, checkers, or chess. This is certainly curious. If machines can learn, why restrict their efforts to learning games which are not likely to have significant social implications? Even human chess and checker players are less important socially than football players. Why should multimillion dollar machines be used in pastimes which the machines certainly do not enjoy (or do they)?

The justification for teaching machines to play chess or checkers is usually presented in the following terms. Chess, it is said, is an excellent example of a human activity which is definitely intellectual; and yet which is sufficiently separable or definable to permit limited experiments which will not involve unspecifiable background conditions. This, at first glance, seems an eminently reasonable justification. It is with certain ambiguities in the notion of learning to play a game that the balance of this chapter is concerned.

Let us consider first the game of football. It will readily be

Mortimer Taube, *Computers and Common Sense* (New York, Columbia University Press, 1961), pp. 47–52, 83–86. Reprinted by permission. The late Dr. Taube was chairman of the board of Documentation, Inc., an information handling concern, and was a lecturer in documentation at the University of Chicago and Columbia University.

admitted that knowing the rules of football is not equivalent to an ability to play football. In other words, concerning football at least, the statements, "John knows the rules of football" and "John can play football" are not equivalent. It may be said here that the reason for this nonequivalence lies in the fact that football is intellectual with respect to the rules, and physical with respect to the ability to play it; but it will be seen that this same distinction holds with reference to games which do not involve physical ability. Consider the game of poker. The rules of poker are very simple. A man could teach his wife the rules of poker in fifteen minutes. On the other hand, knowing the rules of poker and being able to *play* poker are two different things. Bridge, as contrasted with poker, has a much more elaborate system of rules; but here again, it is only after people learn the rules of bridge that they can begin to learn to *play* it. If we go from cards to checkers or chess, the typical computer games, the distinction between knowing the rules of a game and knowing how to play the game still stands. Anyone can learn the rules of chess in fifteen minutes, but one cannot learn to *play* chess in fifteen minutes.

It can readily be admitted in this case, as in the case of mechanical translation, that any operation which can be formalized, that is, described by a set of rules, can be handled by a mechanical device. To the extent that a game has formal rules, including not only rules of play, but rules to evaluate the results of play, the game can be played by a machine.

On the other hand, we have it on Claude E. Shannon's authority that the game of chess can be completely formalized. Unfortunately, a computer playing a completely formal game, with the ability to consider 1,000,000 moves per second, would require 10^{95} years to make its first move. In other words, chess is formalized by making every move an instruction according to a rule, and in a forty-move chess game there would be 10^{120} such possible instructions. Since humans can play good chess and can plan long sequences of moves, it seems clear that they do not play formal chess, any more than they play formal poker or translate formally. Hence, it must be insisted that the common-sense distinction between the informal process of learning to play a game and the formal process of learning its rules is valid.

In more general terms, this distinction is, of course, the distinction between learning by precept or rule and learning by experience. The insistence upon "learning by doing" in modern education is an insistence that learning is not a formal process of memorizing and behaving according to rules.

There should be no need, at this point, to reiterate that experience is a conscious process and that human learning based on experience is also a conscious process. But it is still necessary to meet the following type of objection. It will be said that man knows that he learns, but not "how" he learns. "Man can solve problems without knowing how he solves them. This simple fact sets the condition for all attempts to rationalize and understand human decision making and problem solving."

The truism expressed in this and similar statements is that man can do something or other without knowing the exact physiology of what he does. He can move his fingers without knowing how the nerves control the muscles; he can see without understanding how messages are coded and transmitted from the environment to his brain. He can also digest food without knowing how his stomach and intestines operate.

So far as he is interested in "how," any man can study physiology, which is apparently more than the computer experts are prepared to do. But even without studying physiology he can notice a significant difference between seeing or moving his arm, and digesting his food. To see is to be conscious; it is to have a conscious experience whatever the underlying physiology of the process; and a man can move his arm or not as he wills. But he is not conscious of his digestion and he cannot control it by willing. The fact that a man solves problems without, in many cases, understanding the physiology of the solution may be an interesting fact to the metaphysician; it is of no importance to either a man interested in solving any given problem or, for that matter, to the physiologist. The gambit disclosed by such comments is the following: If man doesn't know the underlying physiology of his actions, maybe it is all right to suppose these actions resemble the actions of a computer. Such an argument makes as much sense as supposing that if a man understands bicycles and doesn't understand airplanes, he can assert that "airplanes are bicycles."

Turing considers in some detail the "alleged fact" that humans are conscious and machines are not, as constituting a fundamental distinction between the thinking or learning ability of men and machines. He attempts to argue against this distinction on the grounds that anyone who uses this argument must be a solipsist, that is, must assert that only his own consciousness exists. There is no way to answer Turing on this point, any more than one can make a reasonable reply to a string of nonsense syllables. Like Uttley's deduction of machines from a hopelessly confused statement of set theory, Turing's argument for solipsism is incredibly jejune. He may have been a creative mathematician but he was an amateur in philosophy. He illustrates here a common form of scientific aberration, namely, the tendency of computer experts to be pontifical about subjects in which they have no competence. Most of the time the incompetence is in the field of physiology, as in discussions of human learning and conditioned reflexes by mathematicians and electrical engineers. This point cannot be too strongly emphasized.

In three different passages Bar-Hillel notes that what he calls

FAHQMT (fully automatic high quality mechanical translation) is not possible unless learning machines ". . . can be built and programs written for them which will endow these machines with quasi-human intelligence, knowledge and knowledgeability." Such a statement is no more scientific, and certainly less meaningful, than a statement by a theologian who says we will never attain peace until and unless Christ comes again. It would be more sensible to devote the nation's monetary resources to research looking toward the Second Coming than it would be to support research to solve the problems of FAHQMT by attempting to build learning-machines with intelligence, knowledge, and knowledgeability.

In the final analysis, our electrical engineers and computer enthusiasts should stop talking this way or face the serious charge that they are writing science fiction to titillate the public and to make an easy dollar or a synthetic reputation. . . .

. . . The general view that increased automaticity and decreased human participation in systems is *always* desirable is here being denied. It will be shown that this doctrine is not only false but that it may have deleterious effects on our national defense. It will be shown further that this doctrine has its origin in a naïve and superficial concept of both machine capability and human nature. Speculation about "thinking machines" is in itself a harmless exercise and has been indulged in since the time Lucretius described the mind and thinking as composed of tiny, round, small atoms which moved very rapidly, as compared to the heavier, slower moving corporeal atoms. However, when such speculation ceases to be a metaphysical exercise and becomes a guiding principle of a major segment of the defense effort, it is serious enough to warrant detailed examination. Out of this examination, there should emerge serious and not fanciful concepts of the role of man and machine in any man-machine system. The view being advanced here, in contradistinction to the prevalent view, is that there are radical and basic discontinuities between digital computers and living organisms; that the essential characteristics of living organisms cannot be simulated, copied, imitated, or surpassed by machines. It is also true that the essential characteristics of machines cannot be profitably copied, simulated, or imitated by living organisms.

Unless one has carefully followed the literature being produced by some of the major laboratories concerned with computers and their development, it is perhaps difficult to realize how prevalent has become the doctrine of man-machine identity. Not only are serious technical journals full of articles on thinking-machines, learning-machines, perceiving-machines, decision-making machines, and the like, but even the popular press has learned to follow the fashion and to report on such marvels without even the faintest suggestions of tongue-in-cheek. It appears that the "sputnik," as the latest practical realization of Buck Rogers's speculations, has made it unfashionable to think that anything is impossible or even impractical. Today, it is the mark of sound scientific perspective to accept the wildest speculation as describing tomorrow's operating gadget. Thus, *Time* in reporting on an international conference on "The Mechanization of Thought Processes" held at Britain's National Physical Laboratory, noted that Dr. Minsky, a representative of Massachusetts Institute of Technology, "felt that the problem is unduly complicated by irrational human reverence for human intelligence. . . . Dr. Minsky is convinced that there is nothing special about intelligence or creativity." During the same week, *The New Yorker* reported on an interview with Dr. Frank Rosenblatt, the designer of the *Perceptron,* a machine which demonstrates that "a non-biological organism will achieve an organization of its environment in a meaningful way . . . our machine (is) a self-organizing system (and) that's precisely what any brain is."

And once again we can add to these sources a passage from our favorite scholarly (*sic*) work, the *Automata Studies:*

> Human beings learn, they remember, and their behavior is modified by experience in various ways. They ingeniously solve problems, compose symphonies, create works of art and literature and engineering, and pursue various goals. They seem to exhibit extremely complex behavior. . . . In this section, we will describe a general method for designing robots with any specified behavioral properties whatsoever. They can be designed to do *any* desired physically possible thing under any given circumstance and past experience, and certainly any naturally given "robot" such as Smith or Jones can do no more.

In examining the existing literature to discover the reasons for this inordinate optimism concerning what digital computers and similar machines may one day accomplish, one is struck by the paucity of real evidence and accomplishment. Most of it reads like exercises in imaginative extrapolation. Von Neumann has considered this process of imaginative extrapolation and found it completely unwarranted in fact and in logic; but his warnings have, in general, been unheeded. The prevalent notion that nothing is impossible in science seems to justify the most extreme claims of wonders to come; and the more extreme, the better.

It is perhaps worthwhile to point out that many of the truly momentous scientific advances have been demonstrations that certain things are impossible—that certain lines of investigation are sterile and can lead to no significant results. From the second law of thermodynamics, the *impossibility* of perpetual-motion machines can be demonstrated; from the Heisenberg principle of indeterminism, the *impossibility* of determining the exact position and velocity of an electron can be deduced; from the theory of relativity, the *impossibility* of determining simultaneity at different places can be deduced; and Goedel's theorem holds that it is *impossible* to state a set of axioms of arithmetic that is both complete and consistent. Goedel's theorem has a direct bearing on the limitations of computers which have been noted by Turing, Church, Nagel and others; although these limitations, like those pointed out by Von Neumann, have been, in general, overlooked. . . .

5
Automation and Society:
The Problem of Employment

Although the gross national product of the United States has in each year, during the 1960s, mounted to new record levels, and although the total employment figure has also shown a yearly increase, chronic unemployment continues to exist. For seven years, an average of about 5 percent to 5½ percent of the work force has been unemployed. In 1963, for example, during each month about 4,200,000 persons were unemployed. In an economy of abundance, this is a staggering figure. On the personal and family level, this amount of unemployment means discouragement, poverty, hardship, and necessity for government relief.

To what extent does the increasing introduction of automation contribute to this high level of unemployment? Will the situation get worse with the passage of time? Does industry or society have a responsibility to those individuals who have lost their jobs as a result of automation? What steps should the federal or state governments take to alleviate this situation? The selections in this chapter demonstrate that authorities disagree widely in their answers to these questions.

Ben B. Seligman argues that automation is a major cause of unemployment. Automation, he says, has increased productivity, but production has not increased rapidly enough to provide jobs for our growing population. A larger output cannot be achieved without an adequate market for goods produced, but at the same time the market is adversely affected by the high rate of unemployment. He points out that despite the large increase in the gross national product, the number of full-time jobs created by private industry has been very small. He views aid to depressed areas and retraining programs as helpful, but in no way does he consider them solutions to the problem. In the long run, he states, automation means that we will need fewer workers, and we should prepare for this eventuality now. We should amplify our retraining programs and pay the cost of moving workers to areas where their skills are in demand. We should reduce the work week; we should plan substantial public-works programs; we should give sufficient retirement funds to those who are unlikely ever to work again. Above all, we should rid ourselves of the archaic ethic that he who does not work shall not eat.

Donald Michael also views pessimistically the effects of automation (or, as he terms it, cybernation) on employment. Going wider afield in his analysis than Seligman, Michael believes that automation will decrease employment in the service industries, in the middle-management area, and in certain professional categories and that it will reduce employment opportunities for adolescents. He thinks also that retraining programs or huge public-works projects will be of little benefit in alleviating the situation.

William H. Peterson rejects completely the notion that automation destroys more jobs than it creates. Automation may make some jobs or skills obsolete, but the advance of technology serves to allocate labor more efficiently. He believes that the current high level of unemployment is the result of labor having overpriced itself (with the help of the federal government) through collective bargaining and minimum-wage laws. What is needed, he believes, is less government interference in the labor market.

Insufficient total demand, according to John M. Culbertson, is the main problem. If the demand for goods is created, technological progress will not be a problem. Sufficient demand, itself, will create jobs for all, although there may be a need for greater mobility of labor. This problem could be handled by a government program.

Yale Brozen admits that automation is different from the technological innovations of the past but feels that it is not completely novel. He points out that the accumulation and employment of capital is the necessary prerequisite for the creation of jobs. If wages increase, then not enough capital will be available to create new jobs and the unemployment level will rise. Modernization of all U.S. industry to the level of plants built in the 1950s, he calculates, would take about fifty years at the present rate of spending for new plants and equipment. Two centuries would be necessary to automate industry completely. In the long run, he concludes, technological change has created far more jobs than it has destroyed, so that we should welcome rather than fear automation.

The views of a number of businessmen are presented by Duns. These men feel that the effects of automation have been greatly exaggerated, although they agree that there have been some temporary dislocations. Not all of them agree that industry has an obligation to workers displaced by automation, and few of those interviewed were prepared to make specific suggestions concerning the immediate future of the unemployed. One remarked that we are powerless to resist change and can only adapt ourselves to it, a statement that is reminiscent of Werner Siemens' thoughts, expressed in the first chapter.

Is this latter course the best approach to the problem? Should we proceed on the assumption that automation is indeed nothing new, that it is in fact he same kind of technological change that has contributed so greatly to our economic growth in the past? But, meanwhile, what about those currently unemployed? Should the government undertake extensive public-works programs and increase its efforts to retrain workers? Should industry assume some of the burden of retraining workers displaced by automation? Or should the government offer only temporary aid to the unemployed and leave their future employment subject to the demands of the labor market?

Ben B. Seligman
AUTOMATION AND THE STATE

In 1944, MARK I—an electromechanical digital computer with over 760,000 parts and 500 miles of wire—was completed. It was a rather slow machine: addition or subtraction took one-third of a second and computing a logarithm to twenty decimal places took an unconscionable one-and-one-half seconds (as compared with today's speed of several

Commentary, 37 (June 1964), 49–54. Reprinted from *Commentary* by permission; copyright © 1964 by the American Jewish Committee. Mr. Seligman is Director of the Department of Education and Research of the Retail Clerks International Association and the author of *Main Currents in Modern Economics*.

millionths of a second). Pressured by the needs of ballistic science, MARK
I soon begat ENIAC, the world's first electronic computer. ENIAC made
MARK I as archaic as a water wheel. Yet there were drawbacks even in
ENIAC, for its memory capacity was small, and it was necessary to rewire
afresh for each new problem. And so, with the help of the work of John
von Neumann, ENIAC begat EDVAC, a computer with a larger memory and
employing the binary number system. EDVAC in turn begat EDSAC, which
was able to place both instructions and data into the memory unit. Then
came RAYDAC, a second cousin to UNIVAC I; SEAC, BIZMAC, FLAC, MIDAC,
and DYSEAC quickly followed, all utilizing the basic EDVAC storage idea.
MARK III was born in 1950, while OARAC, a close relation, arrived three
years later. Some of the immediate descendants of these machines had no
names, only numbers, but after ORDVAC came AVIDAC and after ILLIAC came
MANIAC I. Finally, a third generation of computers was born surpassing the
older vacuum-tube and solid-state systems with magnetic thin film memo-
ries and microminiaturization.

By 1963 the number of computers in use in the United States had
reached 20,000, and another 5,000 will be added by 1965. The Bureau of
Labor Statistics estimates that this technological advance resulted in the
loss of over one million jobs in manufacturing industries alone between
1953 and 1959, with prospects for the future looking even gloomier. There
are, however, those who dispute the idea that automation has been
destroying jobs, and in quarreling with the Bureau of Labor Statistics'
estimate, they point to the 1964 Manpower Report which shows a 4.3
million growth in "nonfarm employment" in the years 1957 to 1963. But
hidden in the report was a table on the sources of that growth: direct
employment by federal, state, and local governments accounted for 46 percent; government "procurement" programs for 19 percent; non-profit
institutions for 16 percent; part-time jobs generated by private demand
for 14 percent; and *full-time jobs created by industry's own efforts for
only 5 percent.* Lost in the industrial and technological shuffle each year,
then, were 200,000 jobs; and this figure does not include the file clerks and
accountants whose positions evaporate every time a computer enters an
office.

There is little consolation for the factory worker in the expansion
of government employment (which has resulted primarily from the
assumption of more tasks), since he does not possess the requisite
transferable skills. In any event, according to a recent joint report by the
Departments of Labor and Commerce, further growth in the number of
federal jobs seems doubtful. To make matters worse, employment is also
expected to drop because of technology in eighteen major industries
which have up to now enjoyed high volume—automobiles, iron and steel,
electric power, etc. In fourteen other industries, moreover—including

trade, banking, insurance, transport, electronics, and synthetics—only increased demand can, in the opinion of the report, overcome the effects of spreading labor-saving devices.

The fundamental economic relationships involved are very simple: as productivity (i.e., the power to produce) increases, there must be a concomitant increase in output or jobs are bound to disappear. Technology, in part a child of the state, has given a fillip to productivity, but production has not been increasing fast enough to provide all the jobs we need for an ever growing population. Here are the facts: from 1909 to 1947, the average annual increase in productivity was 2 percent; from 1947 to 1960, it was about 3 percent; and from 1960 to 1963, it rose 3.6 percent each year. With such an annual rise in productivity, and with 60 million people in the private labor force, 2.1 million new jobs would have to be created every year just to keep unemployment from going up—and another 1.5 million a year to take care of the young people just coming into the work force. Now, while output has indeed been on the increase, the pace of the increase has been too sluggish to compensate for the enhanced productivity stemming from automation, mechanization, cybernation—that is, from the new technology.

The answer, then, would appear to be simple—just increase output. That, however, is more easily said than done, for there is no way of bringing about greater output (at least in the private sector) when there is no market, and there is no market when there are no jobs. One possible solution—which is indeed on the verge of adoption by default—is to allow Disraeli's Two Nations to develop once again and let the poor go hang. Another solution—advanced by those who believe that fiscal policy alone can cure the affliction of unemployment, no matter what its etiology may be—is to create additional output by such means as the recent tax cut, which is expected to generate an additional thirty billion dollars worth of demand. But the real likelihood is that not even an expanded demand of this magnitude could do much for footloose miners, unemployed packing-house workers, displaced auto workers, laid-off railroad workers, and all the others whose skills have suddenly become unnecessary and unwanted. To be sure, the Council of Economic Advisers argued before the Senate Labor Committee last year that there is a "proven capacity for a free labor market to reconcile discrepancies between particular labor supplies and particular labor demand." Yet in recent years the Gross National Product has grown as much as 6 percent per annum, and no new jobs have come into being for those who need them most bitterly—the displaced, the young, the unskilled. The industries in which displacement has been occurring are mature ones—autos, steel, food-processing, clothing—and it seems highly improbable that they will expand their sales sufficiently to replace the jobs that have been dispensed with. Automation has accelerated productivity in these industries just enough for them to keep pace with normal market growth while getting along with fewer workers.

Despite the grudging recognition the Council of Economic Advisers sometimes gives to the structural distortions stemming from technology, its position is that added investment and greater consumer demand will do more than anything else to ease the burden placed on those who must find new sources of income. The Council insists, too (citing the imperatives of national defense), that the encouragement of innovation—this means automation as well as ordinary industrial change—is a direct responsibility of government. Hence, research and development—for which government paid two-thirds of the $16 billion spent in 1962–63 and which mostly goes to aircraft, missiles, electronics, chemicals, and machinery—needs to be continued. But what of those who, like the handloom weavers of yore and the coal miners of today, are unable to enjoy "the fruits of technology"? Collective bargaining in meat-packing, printing, autos, steel, and on the docks has not been overly successful in dealing with automation. In fact, such schemes as profit-sharing, cost-savings sharing, severance pay, interplant transfers, or early retirement are of help only to the worker who is still on the inside. They do nothing for the worker who was displaced last year, or the year before, or the year before that—nor for the young worker just out of school and looking for a job.

From the point of view of the state—which wants technology unlimited—many of these schemes are really not "practicable" in that they "cannot provide complete worker protection without unduly slowing the pace of technical advance," as the CEA has so bluntly put it. It seems that ways must therefore be found to help the victims of material advancement, not because they are people, but because they are potential Luddites. This curious view was faintly hinted at back in 1955 when the Joint Economic Committee expressed an earlier optimism about automation. Several years later President Kennedy's Labor-Management Committee's report on automation, echoing the concern he had voiced for young people seeking jobs and for displaced older workers, recognized that the net effect of technology has been increasing unemployment and suggested that something might have to be done. (Henry Ford II and Arthur F. Burns, who had been Eisenhower's chief economist, dissented and would not support the majority, for it seemed to them that any sort of government action might be oppressive to free enterprise.) Then, last July, it was bruited about that the President might appoint a high-level Commission on Automation: the administration seemed disturbed that if the impact of automation were not softened, resistance would arise and the introduction of new machines slowed down. (Nothing, however, has yet come of the Commission idea despite a revival of Congressional talk about it: it is currently rumored that Johnson may set up an Interdepartmental Committee, an elegant way of burying any controversial issue.)

There are some who say that precedent for government action was provided by the Full Employment Act of 1946. But this statute does not even offer a rough blueprint. Failing to define what "full employment" goals ought to be in an economy that undergoes perpetual change, the Act, which directs the Council of Economic Advisers merely to study conditions and write reports remains what it was intended to be—a superb example of legislative rhetoric. If one looks at the debates in Congress preceding its passage, one finds much talk on fiscal and monetary policy and how the Federal Reserve System might stimulate investment by manipulating interest rates and member bank reserves and by buying and selling securities in the open market. Unfortunately, the Federal Reserve System is still a quasi-independent agency, and it has not always pursued policies that would benefit the rest of us. The Full Employment Act, therefore, is of little help in an age of automation.

The pressures on government to do something, however, continued and they finally did boil over in 1961 into the first major piece of legislation to deal with structural unemployment—the Area Redevelopment Act, which authorized the spending of $375 million to stimulate economic activity in depressed areas. Most of the money was earmarked for long-term loans, and some of it for grants to local communities. Since the measure was not intended to deal specifically with the aftermath of automation, only a modest sum was allocated for teaching the unemployed new skills.

By the end of 1963, over $200 million had been committed, presumably enough to create 20,000 new jobs in areas long afflicted by joblessness. Additional funds were refused last summer, however, and the ARA will probably expire in futility in mid-1965. Indeed, the overly modest nature of the program suggests that Congress intended it merely as a gesture. Even so, there was a basic defect in the conception of the Act. Although the idea behind it was to plant seed capital in depressed areas to attract new ventures, the very restriction of the loans to companies that were poor risks at the bank in the first place made it unlikely that much good could be done. For the fact is that within the context of the present social and economic order, a depressed area needs the kind of lift that can only be generated by successful firms; marginal companies continue to stagger no matter how much financial blood is pumped into them.

Senator Paul Douglas, who designed a bill to aid depressed areas as far back as 1955, thought of helping just a few of the hardest hit localities as demonstration projects: he wanted to show what could be really done for areas devastated by time and technology. However, as the ARA bill went through one session of Congress after another, through committee and subcommittee hearings, through drafts, redrafts, and rewrites, a pork-barrel sentiment developed. In response to pressures from mayors and governors all over the country, the ARA's geographic responsibility was widened and its possible effectiveness thereby diluted. As Dr. Sar A. Levitan argues in *Federal Aid to Depressed Areas*,[1] the program, considering its limited size, ought to have focused on *declining* areas— communities which were losing population and whose social capital (homes, schools, churches, businesses) was being left to waste away. Instead, by the time all the baker's dozens of Congressmen and state and local officials got through, there were enough *growing* towns in the program to convert it into a travesty. Of course, unemployment in a town whose population is on the upswing is just as serious as unemployment in a town whose young people are running off to other places. But ARA was not designed to cope with both situations: its objective was supposed to be to encourage new industries—new to the community—to move into *depressed* areas to provide jobs.

Yet even if ARA had stuck to this objective, it is doubtful whether the program as conceived could have worked properly. ARA assumed that bolstering existing social capital and social overhead would make a sick town with decrepit shells of abandoned factories attractive enough to draw in a new auto assembly plant or automated abattoir. This "trickle down" theory may have seemed plausible on paper but, in the event, it proved difficult to convince Ford or Armour to invest in a town on the downgrade. In short, it was evident that contemporary politics and economics had alike shown themselves inadequate to cope with the needs engendered by the new technology.

One might think that the huge volume of defense contracts could be employed to help depressed areas. But the Department of Defense may not by statute give awards to businesses in the poorer areas if a lower cost can be arranged elsewhere. This statute is based on normal accounting procedures. From a social standpoint, however, unemployment surely ought to be included in any calculus of cost, as it is in West Germany and Britain, where efforts are made to locate plants in areas that need jobs; in Sweden, similarly, investment tax credits are utilized to locate factories where they can be most helpful. Unfortunately, such ideas are much too suggestive of economic planning to be fully acceptable to American policy-makers; even Senator Douglas did not appear overly enthusiastic with the limited planning provisions urged by some proponents of the Area Redevelopment Act.

Among the other things the ARA experience has revealed is the urgent need for a viable manpower policy. It is a need that arises not only

---

[1] Johns Hopkins University Press, 227 pp.

from the high unemployment rates which persist despite prosperity and from the monthly influx of thousands of teen-agers into the labor market, but from the dislocations created by automation as well. Of course, the employment situation is complicated; disentangling in statistically precise ways the variety of elements involved is almost impossible. While some unemployment may be attributed to lagging effective demand, computer technology and rapid obsolescence of older methods of making goods have destroyed numerous skills while creating other more esoteric occupations *which themselves require fewer bodies to fill.* Hence no amount of heat emanating from a warmed-up fiscal policy will melt the icebergs of hard-core unemployment: existing measures such as the tax cut are like trying to light a match to Antarctica. But what of the other measures that have been adopted—vocational education, retraining, and programs to improve labor mobility? How have they been faring?

To begin with labor mobility: there are some 1,900 public employment service offices in the nation, operated jointly, as it were, by the Department of Labor and the states. The effectiveness of these offices varies from state to state, for administrators have been apt to think of the unemployment insurance program in which they are involved as primary and of placement, counseling, and information as secondary and not very urgent responsibilities. It took the chiding of President Kennedy and the continual prodding of the Labor Department to get the local offices to do more placement work last year. But for all the chiding and prodding and for all the appropriations—$160 million by the federal government alone in 1963—"new hires" through state employment offices still run around a mere 15 percent of the total number of new jobs acquired.

In 1962, the United States Employment Service installed an "early warning system" to identify in advance groups of workers who might be threatened by technological displacement or mass layoff. This was an excellent idea, except that not all employers were willing to say what they were planning far enough ahead for the system to do much good: after all, to announce a layoff months in advance might have a harmful effect on a corporation's stock prices. When Studebaker closed its South Bend operations in December 1963, it gave exactly one week's notice; with the sudden shutdown, 7,000 workers were stranded, over 7 percent of the South Bend work force: the shock to the community was a stunning one. Perhaps voluntary "early warning" should be reinforced by some legislative sanction. Certainly at the very least, employers should be persuaded to register all job vacancies. Legislative action, which hitherto has run afoul of the private employment agency lobby, might begin rather modestly by offering firms an adjustment in unemployment insurance rates in return for registering job vacancies at the USES. The President's Executive Order prohibiting discrimination in government contracts could also be broadened to include the same registration requirement. For as Dr. Levitan has argued, people should not have to pay a fee in order to obtain a job in a firm that does business with the government.

While placement by itself cannot create new jobs, it can reduce unemployment by directing those with proper skills to such openings as do exist. The key term, of course, is "proper skills" and here an effective retraining program is essential. By now, there seems little doubt that large numbers of the unemployed lack the skills that would qualify them to fill whatever jobs are available. In Washington, for example, there were recently several hundred empty jobs in the printing trades with no one around to do the work—and no program in operation to train unemployed individuals for these posts. As for the young, two-thirds of the new entrants into the labor force have no specific training of *any* kind: even possession of a high school diploma does not qualify them for work. What is being done to provide all these people with the skills they need if they are ever to obtain jobs?

There has, of course, been a federal program in existence for vocational education since 1917, when the Smith-Hughes Act provided for sharing costs with the states. But in the ensuing forty-six years, federal support of these traditional efforts has only averaged about $1.2 million a year, or 7 percent of state and local outlays. An additional deficiency is that some two-thirds of the approximately four million youngsters receiving vocational education today are being taught home economics and farming, which is hardly likely to prepare them for the age of automation. Probably the situation will be altered somewhat by the Morse-Perkins Act of last year which more than doubled federal allotments to the states and authorized a jump in federal contributions to an annual $226 million by 1967. Occupations other than cookery and farming have also finally been allowed into the program, and part of the new federal money may be used to build vocational schools, to sponsor research, and to engage in such experiments as work-study programs.

Some training was provided for unemployed persons under the ARA in 1961, but it was not until a year later that a more hopeful start was made. The Manpower Development and Training Act, passed in 1962 after much legislative travail, provides allowances for giving unemployed heads of families up to fifty-two weeks of training. At first, lesser allowances were extended to youths between the ages of nineteen and twenty-two, and the proportion of expenditures for such newcomers to the labor market was limited to 5 percent of the total to be spent on training. The demand for youth training, however, was so great that the law had to be liberalized in 1963. This is all to the good, and would be even better if the training courses were only blessed with more imagination. Stenography, typing, automobile mechanics, nursing, and welding account for half of the program. An effort has also been made to reach farm workers in New Jersey, Arkansas, Oklahoma, and Texas with a course in farm equipment mechanics. (It is good to note that twenty of the twenty-five New Jersey trainees successfully secured new jobs.) In addition, ambitious courses were attempted to train Indians in New Mexico and Arizona as electronic solderers, but when the graduates went to work in the Los Angeles area for an average of $1.76 an hour, well below union rates, organized labor objected. (The Bureau of Indian Affairs would nevertheless like to see the course repeated, since $1.76 an hour is still a good deal more than can be earned on the reservation.) Other courses—the sort of training projects that are said to be necessary to reach the so-called hardcore unemployed—have up-graded janitorial work into a custodial occupation (the latter requires more skill than swabbing a floor with a mop, for maintenance of a modern building requires a knowledge of appliances, detergents, insecticides, and waxes). Finally, there is a modest on-the-job training program and several special demonstration projects aimed at "functional" illiterates and school dropouts.

Yet training programs are not a solution to unemployment. As one economist has remarked, they are rather a salvaging operation to help a few individuals acquire marketable skills. The fact remains that most of the unemployed could not fill the jobs for which there may be openings even if they got a whole decade's training. Most of those in charge of the training programs acknowledge this, and motivated by an understandable bureaucratic desire for success, they have had to impose high admission standards, select the courses carefully, and concentrate on younger people. Consequently, older persons and women have by and large been overlooked (while 10 percent of all MDTA programs involve persons over the age of forty-five, more than a quarter of the unemployed fall into this age bracket).

How successful has the training effort been thus far? Labor Department officials say that 88 percent of those who completed their courses got jobs. This sounds impressive until one translates it back into the actual numbers: in 1963 only 27,500 unemployed persons (out of a total of 65,000 who originally enrolled) received training, and of these only 17,000 were able to put it to use successfully. Obviously, much more needs to be done if training is to have any sort of impact. MDTA officials may believe that they have an unqualified success on their hands, but 27,500 graduates a year will not meet Congress's hope for 400,000 retrained workers within three years. At best, it is a useful start; at worst, a piece of misleading showmanship.

Our economy is changing in ways that suggest a far lesser need for workers than has been the case in the past. The old pyramid, in which a large base of employed supported a narrower apex of non-workers, is revolving about its center, so that soon, perhaps in a decade or two, a relative few will provide the material requirements of the many. To prepare for that contingency—which would indeed make automation meaningful—we should start now to reduce the work force. Of course, retraining is necessary to make square pegs round enough to fit into their proper holes. But in addition, a wage system that functioned well enough and at high enough levels to obviate the need for moonlighting and multiple-jobholders would contribute enormously toward alleviating the strains of automation. A variegated works program, geared to rebuilding the neglected "social overhead" in the public realm—roads, parking space, school buildings, urban transport, housing, and parks—would not only give jobs to several million untutored, but also, over the long haul, provide them with minimal work skills. And for those unlikely ever to work again, of which there must be at least a million or more (aside from the aged), why not simply give them enough money to carry on with some measure of decency?

Interestingly enough, other nations have initiated many of these measures precisely as a response to technology. The Swedish Labor Market Board attempts to locate redundant workers and grants travel subsidies and money allowances to help them move to localities where they may be in demand. Financing for new construction is provided in towns where pockets of unemployment develop. By such devices, unemployment in Sweden has been kept down to 1.5 percent of the labor force—an extraordinary achievement. Last January the Canadian government introduced legislation to establish similar labor mobility schemes. The Dominion authorities proposed to pay half the cost that any province or industry would incur in moving idle workers and their families to places where jobs might be available. Further, unions and management are encouraged to investigate adjustment plans well in advance of changes stemming from automation.

But the centuries-old habit of American politics intrude on our dreams. An archaic ethic which insists that he who does not work shall not eat; a Congressional structure virtually unchanged since colonial days; a federalism that fails to come to grips with the complexities of regional economies; an apathetic response from the affluent; and the American posture of make-do and sudden crash programs—all these raise almost insuperable barriers to the formulation of a reasonable program to deal with automation and its consequences.

Meanwhile, the technology of our age—fostered by the state, which at the same time has responded with such pathetic inadequacy to the problems it has created—continues to spread with undiminished force, altering traditional work relationships and dispossessing hundreds of thousands of people with every passing year.

Donald N. Michael
THE PROBLEMS OF CYBERNATION

. . . Insight into the problem of declining employment for the blue-collar worker comes from union statements to the effect that the number of these employees in manufacturing has been reduced by 1,500,000 in the last six years. As one example from the service industries, automatic elevators have already displaced 40,000 operators in New York.

Another disturbing aspect of the blue-collar displacement problem is its impact on employment opportunities for Negroes. There is already an increasingly lopsided Negro-to-white unemployment ratio as the dock, factory, and mine operations where Negroes have hitherto found their steadiest employment are cybernated. This, plus the handicaps of bias in hiring and lack of educational opportunity, leaves Negroes very few chances to gain new skills and new jobs. Continued widespread and disproportionate firings of Negroes, if accompanied by ineffectual re-employment methods, may well produce a situation that will increase disenchantment abroad and encourage discontent and violence here.

. . . It is commonly argued that, with the growth of population, there will always be more need for people in the service industries. The assumption is that these industries will be able to absorb the displaced, retrained blue-collar labor force; that automation will not seriously displace people who perform service functions; and that the demand for engineers and scientists will be so great as to provide employment for any number of the young people who graduate with engineering training. (Indeed, some of this demand is expected to arise from the needs of cybernetic systems themselves.)

It is all very well to speak glowingly of the coming growth in the service industries and the vast opportunities for well-paid jobs and job-upgrading that these activities will provide as blue-collar opportunities

From Donald N. Michael, *Cybernation: The Silent Conquest* (Santa Barbara, Calif.: Center for the Study of Democratic Institutions, 1962). Reprinted with permission of the Fund for the Republic, Inc., Center for the Study of Democratic Institutions. Dr. Michael, a social scientist and author, is associated with the Institute for Policy Studies, Washington, D.C.

diminish. But is the future as bright and as simple as this speculation implies? In the first place, service activities will also tend to displace workers by becoming self-service, by becoming cybernated, and by being eliminated. Consider the following data: The U.S. Census Bureau was able to use fifty statisticians in 1960 to do the tabulations that required 4,100 in 1950. Even where people are not being fired, service industries can now carry on a vastly greater amount of business without hiring additional personnel; for example, a 50 percent increase in the Bell System's volume of calls in the last ten years with only a 10 percent increase in personnel.

Automation frequently permits the mass production of both cheap items and items of adequate to superior quality. It frequently uses methods of fabrication that make replacement of part or all of the item more efficient or less bother than repairing it. As automation results in more leisure time, certainly some of this time will be used by more and more do-it-yourselfers to replace worn-out or faulty components in home appliances that are now repaired by paid service personnel. Nor is it clear that repairing computers will be big business. Computer design is in the direction of microminiaturized components: when there is a failure in the system, the malfunctioning part is simply unplugged or pulled out, much as a drawer from a bureau, and replaced by a new unit. Routine procedures determine which component is malfunctioning, so routine that the larger computers now indicate where their own troubles are, so routine that small computers could be built to troubleshoot others. This does not mean that clever maintenance and repair people will be completely unnecessary, but it does mean that a much more careful estimate is required of the probable need for these skills in home-repair work or in computer-repair work.

Drip-dry clothes, synthetic fabrics, plus self-service dry and wet cleaning facilities, probably will outmode this type of service activity.

Identification by fingerprints, instantly checked against an up-to-date nation-wide credit rating (performed by a central computer facility), could eliminate all service activities associated with processing based on identification (for example, bank tellers). A computer that can identify fingerprints does not yet exist, but there is no reason to believe it will not be invented in the next two decades.

If people cost more than machines—either in money or because of the managerial effort involved—there will be growing incentives to replace them in one way or another in most service activities where they perform routine, predefined tasks. It is possible, of course, that eventually people will not cost more than machines, because there may be so many of them competing for jobs, including a growing number of working women. But will service people be this cheap? As union strength is weakened or threatened through reductions in blue-collar membership, unions will try, as they have already begun to do, to organize the white-collar worker and other service personnel more completely in order to help them to protect their jobs from managements willing to hire those who, having no other work to turn to, would work for less money. Former blue-collar workers who, through retraining, will join the ranks of the service group may help to produce an atomosphere conducive to such unionizing. But how many service organizations will accept the complications of union negotiations, strikes, personnel services, and higher wages in preference to investing in cybernation?

It is possible that as automation and computers are applied more widely an attitude of indifference to personalized service will gradually develop. People will not demand it and organizations will not provide it. The family doctor is disappearing; clerks of all sorts in stores of all sorts are disappearing as well. . . .

People either get used to this or, as in the case of the self-service supermarket, seem to prefer it.

It is already the rare sales clerk who knows the "real" differences between functionally similar items; indeed, in most stores, sales clerks as such are rare. Thus, the customer is almost forced to do much of his own selecting and to know at least as much about or to be at least as casual about the differences between competing items as the clerk. As automation increases, the utility of the sales clerk will further diminish. With some products, automation will permit extensive variation in design and utility. With others, especially if our society follows its present course, automation will encourage the endless proliferation of items only marginally different from one other. In either event there is no reason to believe that the clerk or salesman will become more knowledgeable about an even larger variety of competing items. Finally, it is obvious that the remaining tasks of the clerk, such as recording the sale and insuring that the item is paid for, can be cybernated without difficulty.

The greater the indifference to personalized service by both buyers and sellers, the greater the opportunity, of course, to remove human judgments from the system. Cybernation may well encourage acceptance of such depersonalization, and this, in turn, would encourage further reductions in opportunities for service jobs.

. . . The blue-collar worker and the relatively menial service worker will not be the only employment victims of cybernation. . . . As cybernation moves into the areas now dominated by middle management in government and in business—and this move is already beginning—growing numbers of middle managers will find themselves displaced. Perhaps the bulk of displaced members of the blue-collar and service work force might be trained "up" or "over" to other jobs with, generally speaking, little or no decline in status. But the middle manager presents a special and poignant problem. Where can he go? To firms that are not as yet assigning routine liaison, analysis, and minor executive tasks to machines? This may take care of some of the best of the displaced managers and junior executives, but if these firms are to have a future, the chances are that they will have to computerize eventually in order to compete. To the government? Again, some could join it, but the style and format of governmental operations may require readjustments that many junior executives would be unable to make. And, in any case, government too, as we have seen, is turning to computers, and it is entirely possible that much of the work of *its* middle management will also be absorbed by the computers. Up into top management? A few, of course, but necessarily only a few. Into the service end of the organization, such as sales? Some here, certainly, if they have the talent for such work. If computers and automation lead to an even greater efflorescence of marginally differentiated articles and services, there will be a correspondingly greater emphasis on sales in an effort to compete successfully. But can this be an outlet for a truly significant portion of the displaced? And at what salary? Overseas appointments in nations not yet using cybernation at the management level? Again, for a few, but only for those with the special ability to fit into a different culture at the corresponding level from which they came.

Middle management is the group in the society with the most intensive emotional drive for success and status. Their family and social life is molded by these needs, as the endless literature on life in suburbia and exurbia demonstrate. They stand to be deeply disturbed by the threat and fact of their replacement by machines. One wonders what the threat will do to the ambitions of those who will still be students and who, as followers of one of the pervasive American dreams, will have aspired to the role of middle manager "on the way up."

With the demise or downgrading of this group, changes in consumption levels and patterns can also be expected. These people, although they are not the only consumers of products of the sort advertised in *The New Yorker, Holiday*, and the like, are certainly among the largest of such consumers. They are the style-setters, the innovators, and the experimenters with new, quality products. With their loss of status and the loss of their buying power, one can imagine changes in advertising, or at least changes in the "taste" that this advertising tries to generate. It is possible that the new middle élite, the engineers, operations researchers, and systems analysts, will simply absorb the standards of the group they will have replaced. But they may be different enough in outlook and motives to have different styles in consumption.

. . . There are service jobs, of course, that require judgments about people by people. (We are not including here the "personalized service" type of salesmanship.) The shortage of people with these talents is evidenced by the 60-hour and more work-weeks of many professionals. But these people are the products of special education, special motives, and special attitudes that are not shared to any great degree by those who turn to blue-collar or routine service tasks. Increasing the proportion of citizens with this sort of professional competence would require systematic changes in attitudes, motives, and levels of education, not to mention more teachers, a professional service already in short supply. Alterations of this magnitude cannot be carried out overnight or by casual advertising campaigns or minor government appropriations. It is doubtful indeed, in our present operating context, that they can be done fast enough to make a significant difference in the employment picture for professional services in the next decade or two. Values become imbedded early in life. They are subject to change, to be sure, but we are not, as a democratic society, adept at or inclined to change them deliberately and systematically.

Even if the teachers and the appropriate attitudes already existed, service needs at the professional level might not be great enough to absorb a large share of the potentially unemployed. Much of the work that now takes up the time of many professionals, such as doctors and lawyers, could be done by computers—just as much of the time of teachers is now taken up by teaching what could be done as well by machines.

The development of procedures for medical diagnosis by machine is proceeding well. A completely automatic analysis of data can produce just as good a diagnosis of brain malfunction as that done by a highly trained doctor. Cybernated diagnosis will be used in conjunction with improved multi-purpose antibiotics and with microminiaturized, highly sensitive, and accurate telemetering equipment (which can be swallowed, imbedded in the body, or affixed to it) in order to detect, perhaps at a distance, significant symptoms. All of these developments are likely to change the nature of a doctor's time-consuming tasks. In the field of law successful codification, so that searches and evaluations can be automatic, as well as changes in legal procedures, will probably make the lawyer's work substantially different from what it is today, at least in terms of how he allocates his time.

Computers probably will perform tasks like these because the shortage of professionals will be more acute at the time the computers acquire the necessary capabilities. By then, speeded-up data processing and interpretation will be necessary if professional services are to be rendered with any adequacy. Once the computers are in operation, the need for additional professional people may be only moderate, and those who are needed will have to be of very high calibre indeed. Probably only a small percentage of the population will have the natural endowments to meet such high requirements. A tour of the strongholds of science and engineering and conversations with productive scientists and engineers already lead to the conclusion that much of what now appears to be creative, barrier-breaking "research and development" is in fact routine work done by mediocre scientists and engineers. We lose sight of the fact that not everybody with dirty hands or a white coat is an Einstein or a Steinmetz. Many first-class scientists in universities will testify that one consequence of the increasingly large federal funds for research is that many more mediocre scientists doing mediocre work are being supported. No doubt for some time to come good use can be made by good professionals of battalions of mediocre professionals. But battalions are not armies. And sooner or later one general of science or engineering will be able to fight this war for knowledge more effectively with more pushbuttons than with more intellectual foot-soldiers. . . .

The Labor Department estimates that 26,000,000 adolescents will seek work in the Sixties. If present performance is any indicator, in the decade ahead 30 percent of adolescents will continue to drop out before completing high school and many who could go to college won't. The unemployment rate for such drop-outs is about 30 percent now. Robert E. Iffert, of the Department of Health, Education, and Welfare, concluded in a 1958 study that approximately one-fourth of the students who enter college leave after their freshman year never to return. Figures compiled since then lead him to conclude that there has been no significant change, in spite of the National Defense Education Act, which was supposed to help reduce this figure.

If some figures recently given by James B. Conant turn out to be typical, at least one situation is much more serious than the average would imply. He found that in one of our largest cities, in an almost exclusively Negro slum of 125,000, 70 percent of the boys and girls between 16 and 21 were out of school and unemployed. In another city, in an almost exclusively Negro slum, in the same age group, 48 percent of the high school graduates were unemployed and 63 percent of the high school drop-outs were unemployed. These adolescents would in the normal course join the untrained or poorly trained work force, a work force that will be more and more the repository of untrainable or untrained people displaced from their jobs by cybernation. These adolescents will have the following choices: they can stay in school, for which they are unsuited either by motivation or by intelligence; they can seek training that will raise them out of the untrained work force; they can compete in the growing manpower pool of those seeking relatively unskilled jobs; or they can loaf.

If they loaf, almost inevitably they are going to become delinquent. Thus, without adequate occupational outlets for these youths, cybernation may contribute substantially to further social disruption.

Threatened institutions often try forcibly to repress groups demanding changes in the *status quo*. Imagine the incentives to use force that would exist in a nation beset by national and international frustrations and bedeviled by anarchic unemployed-youth movements. Imagine, too, the incentives to use force in view of the reserves of volunteer "police" made up of adults who can vent their own unemployment-based hostility in a socially approved way by punishing or disciplining these "children."

A constructive alternative, of course, is to provide appropriate training for these young people in tasks that are not about to be automated. But this implies an elaborate, costly program of research and planning to recruit teachers, to apply advanced teaching machine methods as a supplement to teachers, and to stimulate presently unmotivated youngsters to learn. The program would also require intensive cooperation among business, labor, education, local social service agencies, and the government. And all this must begin *now* in order for it to be ready when it will be needed.

None of this is easily met. Persuading drop-outs to stay in school will not be easy. Teachers will not be easy to recruit unless they are well paid. There is already a shortage of teachers. And let no one suggest that an easy source of teachers would be displaced workers. There is no reason to believe that they have the verbal and social facility to teach, and most of them would have nothing to teach but skills that have become obsolete. Some, of course, might be taught to teach, though this would add obvious complications to the whole effort.

Knowing what to teach will depend on knowing what types of jobs are likely to exist when the student finishes his training. This will require knowledge about the trends and plans of local industry, if that is where the youths are to work (and if that is where industry plans to stay!), and of industries in other localities, if the youths are willing to move. Such knowledge often does not exist in a rapidly changing world or, if it exists, may not be forthcoming from businesses more concerned with competition than with the frustrated "delinquents" of their community. As of now, in the words of Dr. Conant, "unemployment of youth is literally nobody's affair."

. . . Retraining is often proposed as if it were also the cure-all for coping with adults displaced by cybernation as well as young people. In some circumstances it has worked well for some people, especially with office personnel who have been displaced by data-processing computers and have learned other office jobs, including servicing the computers. But in other cases, especially with poorly educated blue-collar workers, retraining has not always been successful, nor have new jobs based on that retraining been available. . . .

Moreover, management has not always been willing to institute retraining programs. People are either fired outright in some cases or, more often, simply are not rehired after a layoff. . . .

The problem of retraining blue-collar workers is formidable enough. But, in view of the coming role of cybernation in the service industries, the retraining problem for service personnel seems insuperable. No one has seriously proposed what service tasks this working group could be retrained *for*—to say nothing of training them for jobs that would pay high enough wages to make them good consumers of the cornucopia of products manufactured by automation.

Another proposal for coping with the unemployment-via-cybernation problem is shorter hours for the same pay. This approach is intended to maintain the ability of workers to consume the products of cybernation and, in the case of blue-collar workers, to maintain the strength of unions. This would retain the consumer purchasing capacity for x workers in those situations where the nature of the cybernation process is such that x men would do essentially the same work as x plus y men used to do. But when the task itself is eliminated or new tasks are developed that need different talents, shorter shifts clearly will not solve the problem. The latter conditions are the more likely ones as cybernation becomes more sophisticated.

Proponents of cybernation claim that it should reduce the price of products by removing much of the cost of labor and increasing consumer demand. Whether the price of beef, or milk, or rent will be reduced in phase with the displaced worker's lowered paycheck remains to be seen. So far this has not happened. Whether the price of TV sets, cars, refrigerators, etc., will be reduced substantially depends in part on how much product cost goes into larger advertising budgets aimed at differentiating the product from the essentially same one produced last year or from the practically identical one produced on some other firm's automated production line.

An obvious solution to unemployment is a public works program. If our understanding of the direction of cybernation is correct, the government will probably be faced for the indefinite future with the need to support part of the population through public works. There is no dearth of public work to be done, and it is not impossible that so much would continue to be needed that an appropriately organized public works program could stimulate the economy to the point that a substantial portion of the work force could be re-absorbed into the private sector. That is, although the proportion of workers needed for any particular task will be reduced through the use of cybernation, the total number of tasks that need to be done could equal or exceed the absolute number of people available to do them. It is not known whether this situation would obtain for enough tasks in enough places so that the portion of the population working on public projects would be relatively small. However, if it should turn out that this felicitous state of affairs could be realized in principle, clearly it could only be realized and sustained if there were to be considerable and continuous centralized planning and control over financing, the choice of public projects, and the places where they were to be done. If, for whatever reasons, this situation could not be achieved, the public works payroll would remain very large indeed.

What would be the effects on the attitudes and aspirations of a society, and particularly of its leadership, when a significant part of it is overtly supported by governmental public works programs? ("Overtly" is used because much of the aerospace industry in particular and of the weapons systems industry in general is subsidized by the government right now: they literally live off cost plus fixed fee contracts, and there is no other comparable market for their products.) Whatever else the attitudes might be, they certainly would not be conducive to maintaining the spirit of a capitalistic economy. This shift in perspective may or may not be desirable, but those who think it would be undesirable should realize that encouraging the extension of cybernation, in the interests of free enterprise and better profits, may be self-defeating.

The inherent flexibility of cybernated systems, which permits great latitude in their geographic location, is the inspiration for the proposal that if jobs are lost through cybernation, the unemployed could be moved to another area where jobs exist. It is said that a governmental agency similar to the Agricultural Resettlement Administration, which moved farmers from the Dust Bowl to cities, could be used. However, two important differences between that situation and this one would complicate this effort: the contemporary cause of the unemployment would not be the result of an act of God; and it is not immediately evident that these unemployed people could find jobs in other areas, which might be suffering from a similar plethora of useless workers.

Herbert Striner has suggested that a more extreme approach would be to export blue-collar and white-collar workers and their families to nations needing their talents. The problem of whether or how the salary differential might be made up is one of several difficulties with this proposal. Yet, if such emigration could be carried out, it might be a better solution than letting the workers atrophy here. The economic history of former colonial powers and their colonization techniques indicate that "dumping" of excess personnel into foreign lands would not be a radically new innovation.

Another possible long-run approach might be curtailment of the birth rate. In times of depression the rate falls off naturally—which may be the way the process would be accomplished here if enough people become unemployed or marginally employed (although the effects of the lowered birth rate would only follow after the economic and social changes had been made). Of course, the government could encourage birth control by reducing the income tax dependency deduction or by other tax means.

Finally, there is the proposal to reduce the working population by increasing the incentives for early retirement. Government could do this by reducing the retirement age for social security, and unions and management could use their collective ingenuity to provide special retirement incentives. Naturally, this would increase the already large percentage of retired elderly people. Along with the other familiar problems associated with this group is the poignant one: how are all these people to be kept happily occupied in their leisure?

Whether any of these proposed solutions is adequate to the challenge of unemployment is not known to us or, we gather, to those who have proposed one solution or another. But even if, in principle, some combination of them would be adequate, in order to put them into effect a considerable change would be necessary in the attitudes and voting behavior of Congress and our tax-paying citizens. Preconceptions about the virtues and vices of work, inflation, the national debt, and government control run deep and shift slowly.

Not all of these dire threats would come to pass, of course, if cybernation reduced consumer buying power through unemployment and, thereby, the financial capability of industry and business to introduce or profit from cybernation. In this way we might all be saved from the adverse effects of unemployment from this source. But the economy would still be faced with those threats to its well-being which, as were pointed out earlier, make the need to cybernate so compelling.

Cybernation is by nature the sort of process that will be introduced selectively by organization, industry, and locality. The ill-effects will be felt at first only locally and, as a result, will not be recognized by those who introduce it—and perhaps not even by the government—as a *national* problem with many serious implications for the whole social system. Also, because one of the chief effects of cybernation on employment is not to hire rather than to fire, the economic-social consequences will be delayed and will at any time be exacerbated or ameliorated by other economic and social factors such as the condition of our foreign markets, which also are being changed and challenged by European and

Russian cybernation. By the time the adverse effects of cybernation are sufficiently noticeable to be ascribed to cybernation, the equipment will be in and operating.

Once this happens, the costs of backtracking may be too great for private enterprise to sustain. For, in addition to the costs of removing the equipment, there will be the costs of building a pre-cybernation system of operations. But which firms will voluntarily undertake such a job if they are unsure whether their competitors are suffering the same setback—or indeed if their competitors are going to decybernate at all? And, if not voluntarily, how would the government enforce, control, and pay for the change-over? . . .

William H. Peterson

AUTOMATION AND UNEMPLOYMENT —A MYTH REVIVED

The United States is advancing rapidly into a national economy in which there will not be enough jobs of the conventional kind to go around. The acceleration of technology is responsible. A social and political crisis will be the result . . ."

The Olympian words are those of W. H. Ferry, vice president of the Fund for the Republic and author of the study, *Caught on the Horn of Plenty*, published by the Fund for the Republic's Center for the Study of Democratic Institutions. And just to be sure everyone gets the point about technological unemployment, the Fund—which lists as directors and consultants such names as Robert M. Hutchins, Paul G. Hoffman, Herbert H. Lehman, Henry R. Luce, William O. Douglas, Reinhold Niebuhr, A. A. Berle, Jr., and Elmo Roper—also has published "Cybernation: The Silent Conquest," by Donald N. Michael director of planning and programs for the Peace Research Institute in Washington and former consultant to UNESCO. Mr. Michael paints a pretty grim picture of America's future under automation. He predicts that jobs will be destroyed by the millions. The Michael answer to automation ties in with that of Mr. Ferry: national planning and control.

Messrs, Ferry and Michael are not just two stray voices crying in

William H. Peterson, "Automation and Unemployment—A Myth Revived," *Christian Economics*, 15 (February 1963), 1–2. Reprinted with permission. Dr. Peterson is Associate Professor of Economics at New York University.

the wilderness. A kind of technophobia seems to be overtaking the nation. A recent Gallup poll disclosed that, next to communism, most people were worried about technological unemployment, in particular about the new bogey, "automation."

The late Eleanor Roosevelt epitomized these fears when she wrote in her column: "We have reached a point today where labor-saving devices are good only if they do not throw the worker out of a job."

So one of man's oldest economic delusions rises to blind him again—namely, the notion that machines, technology, science and invention destroy more jobs than they create, that hand-in-hand with the march of science must go the shuffle of the unemployed. To be sure, a flood of books and studies advancing this theory in the past has been proved false. But now it seems these dire predictions, clothed in the new scare words "automation" and "cybernation," are somehow about to become true.

If rigorously applied to economic history, however, this belief leads to absurd conclusions. The primitive who invented the wheel, the caveman who discovered fire, the aborigine who made the first flint axe, the long-ago boatman who discovered that wind pocketed in a sail could do away with muscle power applied to an oar—all these early technologists would then be malefactors of mankind, crassly stealing jobs and livelihoods from their fellow men for millennia to come.

Or so working people have frequently thought. From 1811 to 1816, for example, the Luddites—mostly displaced hand-loom weavers from Lancashire and landless croppers from Yorkshire—rioted in public squares, burned down factories and systematically wrecked machinery which, they agreed, was wiping out jobs—a charge which overlooked the more likely source of unemployment stemming from the Enclosure Laws and the inflation-induced depression of the time.

The ways of the twentieth century are more sophisticated than in the time of the Luddites. Inventors nowadays need not tremble in their laboratories: arson is infrequently resorted to; yet the attempted muzzling of technology persists. Automation becomes the excuse by which the government moves into the "retraining" business. Electricians in New York seek to nullify the efficiencies of automation by enforcing a 25-hour week. "Firemen" still grace railroad Diesel cabs.

Most if not all of these restrictive practices are granted social respectability by influential writers, politicians and social commentators. Thus the waste of restrictionism persists because the public either believes that the unions and their intellectual and political supporters are right, or is too baffled to understand why they are wrong.

Clearly what believers in the technological theory of unemployment fail to take into account is that technology does not in any sense destroy labor, even if it may destroy obsolete jobs and skills. Technology, in other words, serves to allocate labor to its most efficient use. Indeed, not only does technology not destroy labor, but also in a sense it creates labor; technology, when linked to capital formation, actually permits the expansion of population and hence the working force. It is inconceivable that England—Shakespeare's "tight little island"—could have expanded its population from 11 million in 1801 to more than 50 million today were it not for massive capital accumulation and the advance of technology.

To be sure, machines can lead to a reduction in the work-week. But the division of increased output between more goods or shorter hours—and the ratio in which productivity gains should be distributed—ought to be decided by a free market and not arrived at under any form of union or government coercion. For a reduction of hours clearly involves a diminution in production and a lowering of real income. The choice boils down to greater leisure or more goods, or some combination of the two—a linkage which capitalism has abundantly achieved.

But to W. H. Ferry and Donald N. Michael, authors of the Fund's automation studies calling for national planning, the choice is recast in the old bogey of technology versus jobs. Mr. Ferry writes: "For generations the dictum that Machines Make Jobs was demonstrably valid. Now the dictum is losing its force and generality."

To be sure, the United States economy has been experiencing some persistent unemployment in the past few years. But this Ferry-Michael "proof" of growing technological unemployment does not stand up under scrutiny. For years union and government labor-pricing practices, through collective bargaining and minimum wage laws, have tended to price labor out of the market place, with the twin consequences of inflation and unemployment. Since World War II expecially, wage rates have raced ahead of productivity.

Again, apparently both Ferry and Michael, like Marx, believe in the lump-of-work theory—the idea that there is only so much work to be done, and that it had to be allocated, rationed, spread around. Actually, the work to be done is without limit. Man's needs are practically insatiable—all experience clearly indicates this—and technology, which contributes to an increase of production at lower cost, will always find willing customers for the greater values and the higher living standards it spins off.

The U.S. economy has been prodigious in its ability to open up millions of job opportunities, even with an excessively costly industrial wage structure. It already has far surpassed Henry A. Wallace's wartime dream of 60 million jobs. To be sure, there has been a so-called "hard core" of unemployment ever since the 1958 recession. But the unanswered question is: how much of the problem is due to automation, and how much to the overpricing of labor?

In sum, the U.S. requires not less productivity but more: not fewer hours in the workweek but greater assiduity and superior workmanship; not less savings and investment but more—more machines, computers, automation, and, yes, even more "cybernation." At the same time, the country needs not more government omnipotence, but less. Labor leaders must see the Marxist fallacy of capital supposedly exploiting labor, for the exact opposite is true: labor exploits capital. Hence, the greater the capital, the higher the wages and the greater the job opportunities.

The Ferry-Michael studies are a throwback to the blind world of the Mercantilists and Luddites, of Veblen and Marx. As Henry Ford once said: "There is no conflict, in a machine economy, between low costs and high wages." Mr. Ford might have added there isn't any conflict between machines and high employment either.

John Matthew Culbertson

AUTOMATION AND STRUCTURAL UNEMPLOYMENT

As surely as night follows day, a period of unemployment gives rise to lamentations about machines replacing workers, which are nowadays focused about the exciting word "automation." Doubtless we can find examples of this sort of thing as far back as history takes us. In the Great Depression of the 1930s, the machine was widely attacked as the cause of unemployment, even though it should have been perfectly clear that the problem was deflation and deficiency of total demands and that technological improvement was not markedly more rapid than at other times. Because they are ignorant of the theory of total demand and are naïvely trusting that their troubles did not stem from government policy, people are wont to attribute them to some immediately tangible factor such as the machine or, nowadays, the computer. Those who for ideological reasons will not raise questions about the adequacy of total demand and the role of government policy also may find the machine a convenient explanation of unemployment.

In a reasonable analysis, technological progress, whether automated or otherwise, plays two roles. In the first place, more rapid

John Matthew Culbertson, *Full Employment or Stagnation?* (New York: McGraw-Hill, 1964), pp. 55–58. Reprinted with permission. Dr. Culbertson is professor of economics and commerce at the University of Wisconsin.

technological progress leading to more rapid growth in efficiency and real output would mean that a more rapid increase in total demand would be required to take the full-employment output of the economy off the market. This is simply our usual problem of sufficient total demand, and the presumption is that an alert use of conventional policy instruments could always solve it.

The other aspect of rapid technological advance is that it may require more mobility of labor, more movement or retraining. Other things being equal, it could thus tend temporarily to push the wage-price function upward. Insofar as this happens, it can be combated by the programs for labor mobility mentioned above. Neither of the two aspects of the matter, then, is mysterious or beyond our potential control. In developing policy, we can ignore technological progress as such and attend to doing a good job of assuring sufficient total demand and promoting sufficient mobility in the labor force.

On this basis, in an economy that does not have worrisome inflation but does have excessive unemployment, there is only one possible diagnosis: deficient total demand. Unless additional total demand is provided to buy their output, additional workers cannot be put back to work, regardless of any structural problems. If, when total demand is moved toward the full-employment amount, wages and prices begin to rise because of problems of worker location and training, then—and only then—these problems can be identified and steps taken to solve them.

To put the argument the other way around, if there is inadequate total demand and high unemployment, it is inevitable that the unemployment will not be equally distributed among regions and industries. It never is. As Keynes observed, people will be wont to explain their plight in terms of particular factors that they feel they know something about rather than in terms of the general operation of the economic system, of which they are sadly ignorant. In the past, when an increase in total demand reduced unemployment, talk of technological unemployment and structural problems gradually melted away. When areas of genuine labor shortage developed, workers in areas of labor surplus packed up and moved to the jobs. When genuine shortages developed in certain skills, employers looked harder for people who could do the job, took the initiative to train people, or redesigned the jobs to suit the available workers. If one assumed that the United States economy lacks such flexibility, he could not possibly explain what has been achieved in the past.

Since, as we argue below, the United States economy in 1963 has excessive unemployment but does not have significant inflation, its difficulty can only be diagnosed as deficiency of total demand, a deficiency, specifically, of at least $25 billion. Automation and "structural unemployment" seem to be serving largely as scapegoats to be pointed to by those who are not of a mind to do what has to be done to restore full-employment levels of total demand.

Unemployment calls for a two-pronged attack. Whenever there is excessive unemployment, the presumption is that additional total demand will reduce it. The first step toward full employment is the generation of a sufficient increase in demand by monetary, fiscal, and debt management policies. If prices have a tendency to rise, or if it is feared that they will rise as employment is increased, an attack can be launched to lower the wage-price function of the economy. As employment does increase and the monotony of unrelieved labor surplus is broken by some areas of shortage, there will be a tangible basis for efforts to improve labor mobility by getting the unemployed workers where the jobs are. There will be some jobs to get them to.

To sit stagnant, pontificating over automation and halfheartedly training workers for jobs that do not exist—this is not a hopeful course.

Yale Brozen
THE PACE OF AUTOMATION

Technology is felt to have moved at a sedate pace in the past compared with the recent rate of advance. In the 1930's, it was fashionable to argue that the country was stagnant because, among other factors, technology was not producing the great new techniques it formerly did. For this reason, it was said, there was little use for additional capital. Unemployment then was attributed to the lack of technological advance and the resultant lack of outlets for the application of new capital.

Too much technological change, however, may be as bad as too little. In the late 1940's, we were told that automation was coming with such speed that factories would be fully automated in 10 to 20 years and that we were faced with "a decade or more of ruin and despair." It is more than 12 years since that forecast was made by Norbert Wiener, the popularizer of the term "Cybernetics" and one of the developers of the

Yale Brozen, *Automation: Impact of Technological Change* (Washington, D.C.: American Enterprise Institute for Public Policy Research, 1963), pp. 3–9. Reprinted with permission. Dr. Brozen is Professor of Business Economics at the University of Chicago.

mathematics of communication which underlies much of the new control technology. Yet, we still employ over 12 million production workers in factories, about the same number as at the time of Wiener's prediction. Total employment in manufacturing industries has grown by more than a million men since 1950.

How rapidly we automate depends upon the availability of capital and the rapidity of the rise in real wage rates. Present rates of capital formation are not much higher than the amount required to equip additions to the work force with the same quantity of capital as that used by the presently employed work force. If we add 1,300,000 workers a year to our labor force, the rate forecast for the next decade, nearly $20 billion a year will be needed to equip them sufficiently to be productive enough to be employable at current wage rates. If wage rates increase, a larger amount of capital will be required. If a larger amount does not become available in this situation, unemployment will grow.

Total spending on business plant and equipment is less than $40 billion a year. Almost half of this amount is required to replace plant and equipment worn out by use, rendered economically obsolete, and destroyed by fire or other catastrophe. There is very little left to increase the quantity of capital per man employed after providing for additions to the work force. In these circumstances, the spread of automation will be slow.

Automation is spreading somewhat more rapidly than is indicated by these figures because of the overpricing of labor in some industries. Increases in wage rates make it economic to automate when it otherwise would not be so. The cost of the new equipment required to replace a man is about $35,000. If the annual wage of a man is less than $7,000, it does not pay to replace him at this cost since property and corporate earnings taxes, insurance, depreciation, and interest costs amount to about $7,000 on $35,000 worth of equipment. If annual employment costs rise above $7,000, it then pays to replace a few men. The rate at which men will be released by an industry to other occupations or to the manning of additional capacity depends upon how rapidly wage rates rise. (If they rise too rapidly, men will not be completely absorbed by expanding occupations and unemployment will rise.)

As men are replaced, it becomes increasingly expensive to replace additional men. In the late 1940's, when coal mining employment exceeded 400,000, the cost of replacing a man was about $20,000. Now that coal mining employment has dropped below 170,000, the cost of replacing a man is close to $50,000.

To automate as completely as possible with present technology, only one major segment of the American economy, manufacturing, would require an expenditure of well over $2.5 trillion, assuming output is not increased. Even to modernize manufacturing to the levels of the new plants built in the 1950's would require over $500 billion. Since total spending on new plant and equipment in manufacturing amounts to about $15 billion per year, American manufacturing could not be modernized even to the level of the technology of the 1950's for over 30 years. And this is under the extreme assumption that all the expenditure is used for modernization and none for expansion. With the current division of capital outlays between modernization and expansion, modernization to the level of new plants of the variety built in the 1950's would require about 50 years.

To automate completely manufacturing industry with no increase in total output would require two centuries at current rates of modernization. If we expand output at the rate necessary to keep up with population growth, however, present rates of capital formation will never result in complete automation of manufacturing unless the cost of automation is reduced to less than one-sixth of its present expense. That is unlikely to occur within the foreseeable future.

Judging by changes in productivity, the recent pace of technological change is no greater than in the past and is slowing. In manufacturing, output per man-hour rose by 2.9 percent per year from 1947 through 1961. The rise was more rapid in the earlier part of the period than in the latter. It averaged 3.2 percent per year from 1947 through 1953. Since 1953, the average rate of rise has dropped to 2.7 percent.

Output per man-hour in manufacturing rose much more rapidly in the 1920's than in the last decade. The rate of increase was 5.3 percent per year, a rate almost double that of the 1950 decade. Automation is proceeding more slowly, in terms of its effect on productivity, than earlier technological change.

There are observers who argue that automation or cybernation is something more than the latest stage in the long evolution of technology. Automation is said to be so different in degree that it is profoundly different in its effect. Automated machines controlled by computers do not simply augment muscle power, but replace and outperform human intelligence. In the future, machines will not only run machines; they will repair machines, program production, run governments, and even rule men. Union leaders will collect no dues and business will have no customers because, presumably, there will be no production workers required. Human beings will be made as obsolete by these superior machines as horses were by the tractor and the automobile.

Although we may grant that automation differs from other kinds of technology, we should not blind ourselves to history to the point of saying it is completely new. Perhaps the earliest automated device was the pressure cooker invented by Denis Papin in 1680. He originated a pressure control, which is still one of the simplest and most widely used regulators today.

During the 18th century, several types of automatic regulators were applied to windmills. An automatic, card-programmed loom was devised by Jacquard over 150 years ago. An automatic flour mill was built in 1784. Automatic silk looms were designed by Jacques Vaucanson in 1741. Eighteenth century steam engines were controlled by governors which had the sensing, feedback, and resetting characteristics which are the hallmark of automation. And despite increasing automation in the last two centuries, employment continually rose.

In terms of a very recent type of automation, the use of electronic data processing equipment, a United States Department of Labor study of large firms which introduced such equipment concluded that:

> Despite the reduction in labor requirements for the tasks performed by the computers, total employment of the offices as a whole rose. Over the 4 years from December 1953 to December 1957, total office employment at 17 of the offices studied increased an average of 7 percent. This increase, however, was less than the 15 percent rise reported for clerical and kindred workers in the Nation as a whole. In 6 of the 17 offices, the increase was greater than 15 percent; in 7, less; and in 4 there was a decrease. Although the immediate effect of electronic data processing suggests some retardation in the growth of office employment, particularly part-time work, the experience of some offices suggests the possibility of expanding employment in new areas of office activity to handle information which had previously been uneconomical to acquire.

We know from experience that automation in the factory turns machine operators into machine tenders and maintainers. This has already occurred in the textile industry, to name one example. Upon walking into the loom room of a modern mill, the first impression is that of a vast space filled with busy machinery and no people in sight. Yet employment in textile mill products exceeds 900,000. The chemical and petroleum refining industries use automatically controlled, continuous processes. They, too, provide employment on large scale amounting to more than one million jobs.

The effect of automation has been to increase the relative number of maintenance men, engineers, office employees, production control specialists, and other non-machine operators that are required. This is simply a continuation of a trend which has been going on for decades. In 1899, less than 7 percent of the manufacturing industry labor force consisted of persons other than production workers. Today, 25 percent of manufacturing employees are indirect workers. Since 1940, production worker employment in manufacturing has increased by 52 percent while other workers increased by over 100 percent.

The primary effect of automation is not a reduction in the number of jobs available. Rather, it makes it possible for us to do many things which otherwise could not and would not be done. It will, in the future, literally make it possible to travel to the moon. It has, through the aid it gives doctors, saved lives that otherwise would be lost. By controlling traffic signals in response to traffic flows and reducing traffic congestion, it has added hours to the free time of commuters every week. It has helped scientists, with the aid of high-speed indicators, to develop new knowledge that would not have been available in our lifetimes. We are increasing the scale of educational activities because mechanization, automation, cybernation, or whatever we choose to call our new technology, makes it possible to do more than we could formerly. With the coming of automation, men are able to do more and have more. Both sublime and mundane activities are being enlarged.

Those who fear a great rise in unemployment think in terms of a given list of goods to be produced. If a man helped by an automatic machine can turn out twice as many widgets per hour, then, presumably, only half as many hours of work will be available for each man to do or only half as many jobs. The President of the United States has said "that approximately 1.8 million persons holding jobs are replaced every year by machines." Presumably, 18 million persons lost their jobs in the 1950's because of machines; yet, total employment rose by seven million.

Using the above logic, there would be more jobs now if productivity had not increased. It would take nearly two million more men to turn out our present production if our productivity were at the 1961 level. Reducing this to absurdity, if we froze productivity at the 1952 level, it would take 17 million more men to produce our present output. Unemployment then, would be minus 13 million, obviously an impossibility.

Technological change enables us to do more than we could otherwise. It enables us to pay men more and, at the same time, provide more jobs. It enables us to improve our housing, enrich our diets, provide better medical services, educate ourselves to higher levels, as well as making it possible to explore space.

Those who are concerned about unemployment should welcome rather than fear automation. If it were not for the technical advances of the past decade, unemployment, at present wage levels, would be above the astronomical levels of the early 1930's. Alternatively, if real wage rates were at levels consistent with full employment under the same technology as that practiced in 1950, wage rates would be about $10.00 per week lower than they are now.

Technological change has created more jobs than it has destroyed. The number of civilians at work in 1961 was seven million higher than ten years before. Technological change and the growth in our stock of capital (in the form of plant and equipment and in the form of investment in raising the educational level of our population) created over 20 million jobs in the fifties, and about 13 million jobs were destroyed by various causes. The 20 million new jobs created and the 13 million jobs destroyed left a net gain of seven million positions.

THE OTHER SIDE OF AUTOMATION

Over the past year, automation abruptly has taken the form of a lowering black cloud. Economists have written learned monographs on its effects. Labor leaders have fought its inexorable march. And President Kennedy has called it "the major domestic challenge of the 1960s," one that will require finding 25,000 new jobs during every week of the next ten years for workers who have been replaced by machines.

But is the specter quite that grim? Surprisingly, the question has never really been asked of the men who should know: the business executives who are buying, installing and operating that labor-saving machinery. Sociologists have been interviewed, yes, and even the man-in-the-street in newspaper surveys. Businessmen have not, to any wide extent.

So *Dun's Review*, in what may be the first major poll of its type, has attempted to plumb the feelings of the overlooked experts on automation by polling the 300 presidents and chairmen of its Presidents' Panel. The men who are responsible for the vast change even now are computing the capital investment and payrolls they will face over the next ten years.

What do they, these overlooked experts, think about automation? Do they believe that machines will drastically reduce the nation's workforce? And if they do, what provision are they making to meet the mass unemployment that will result?

Their answers are disarmingly simple. Almost to a man, they believe that the issue of automation has been wildly exaggerated. Neither the economy nor the fabric of U.S. society, they say, faces radical changes from the march of the machines.

Looked at coldly and dispassionately, of course, the replies might

Reprinted by special permission from *Dun's Review & Modern Industry*, May 1962. Copyright, 1965, Dun & Bradstreet Publications Corp.

be considered as a kind of cover-up for an industrial complex which is bent on automating at any price. The panelists, however, were asked to back up their statement with facts. And, as one of them cogently points out, the industrialists of the nation really stand to lose as much through mass unemployment as the workers—for they would be crippling the very customers who buy their wares.

The panelists readily admit that automation will not be without its problems. This point is summed up by the president of one huge metal company. "Automation," he says, "may cause some temporary dislocation of the workforce. But over the long run, the more efficient utilization of resources that automation promises will benefit everyone."

To this chief executive, a very simple equation proves that point. "Man's material welfare," says he, "equals natural resources plus human energy, multiplied by tools." And he adds: "The whole subject of automation has been built up out of all proportion to what its effect will be on the economy."

In this lies the key to the feelings of the vast majority of panelists on the issue of automation. Almost all of them believe there is a widespread misunderstanding of the effects of automation. Malcolm P. Ferguson, president of Bendix Corp., approaches the problem with the analytical mind of the engineer he is. "The changes that will take place will not be radical ones," Ferguson notes, "but will be the same orderly and logical progression that has characterized the previous stages of the Industrial Revolution. These have always resulted in temporary dislocation, but eventually in a better situation for all mankind. Resistance to change is a normal, human reaction. But if anything is to be learned from the past it is that we are powerless to resist change and that our energies are much better spent adapting ourselves to it."

And the corporate chief of a giant international company says: "The public has been receiving much misinformation about automation. The changes that it may soon bring to industry are nothing to be alarmed about; in fact, they represent the key to our national prosperity in the face of world competition. It is true that technological change means shifts in employment from one industry to another and from one community to another. But this is nothing new."

It may well be that exaggeration of automation's probable effects stems from a basic confusion over just what "automation" means. Webster says it means "the automatically controlled operation of an apparatus, process or system."

But to many businessmen in many industries it means many different things. To some it means simply one further step in the mechanization of production lines. To others it means something even simpler; a soft-drink bottler, for instance, regards his soda-pop dispensing machines as automated systems. And to still others it implies vast and enormously expensive plants that operate under the supervision of only small teams of maintenance men.

There can, perhaps, be no single definition of automation simply because the meaning of the word inevitably varies from one industry to another. What is automation to the meat-packing industry looks to a coal mining engineer as nothing more than a belated step in mechanization. And to the petroleum engineer, the coal industry itself seems like a center of wasteful, low-productive practices.

Just how far the confusion and misunderstanding reaches became clear shortly after President Kennedy spoke out about automation a couple of months ago. For just a few hours after the words from the White House, the President's own Under Secretary of Labor Willard Wirtz said that the challenge was far greater than the President had indicated. Indeed, Wirtz added, the figure of 25,000 new jobs a week cited by the President was too low by at least 10,000 and possibly more.

And another load of explosive material has been dumped into the debate with the recent publication by the Fund for the Republic of the book, *Cybernation, The Silent Conquest,* which forecasts that millions of workers will lose their jobs as automation proceeds through industry and that mass unemployment, reaching from the ranks of unskilled laborers to those of middle management, will be the result—unless there is some form of national planning and control.

Such prognostications, say the vast majority of the *Dun's Review* panelists, are far wide of the mark. Nothing in the history of technological change or in the record so far of automation, they insist, has led to widespread or truly long-lasting unemployment. What unemployment there is, they say, will be short-lived and certainly will not be massive.

"Automation is not a major cause of payroll reductions at our company," insists Lloyd B. Smith, president of the A. O. Smith Corp. "The business cycle, increased competition, product obsolescence, shifting population, governmental regulations and policies and high labor costs all have a far greater effect on employment."

Leeds & Northrup Co.'s President I. Melville Stein carries the same idea a step further. "It is my belief," he says, "that more unemployment will be caused by failure to automate than by doing so." Adds Motec Industries' President William F. Foss: "You need only look at the record of the past. Where one blacksmith served a village a century ago, today there are half a dozen garages and filling stations and countless auxiliary transportation services in addition to the huge automotive, automobile and petroleum industries. . . . New jobs will be created in the manufacture and use of automated equipment, just as has been the case in each era of the Industrial Revolution."

Yet most of the *Dun's Review* panelists do agree that there is almost certain to be some short-term dislocation as automation in industry increases. Few chief executives should be in a better position to estimate the extent and effect of this than President A. L. Williams of IBM Corp. "In the past," says Williams, "technological advance destroyed some jobs while creating others. The net result has been that it has created many more jobs than it destroyed. However, technological unemployment *is* a reality in the short run, both for the individual and the nation; it is a problem that cannot be ignored and it must be faced with the urgency that it deserves. I do not believe, however, that in the long run widespread unemployment will result from technological change."

How, then, should industry face up to the problem? Only a very small fraction of the panelists are ready to make specific suggestions. But Rayonier Inc.'s Russell F. Erickson does say: "In the long term, as productivity increases, we may face the necessity of spreading available work by reducing the workday or workweek to create sufficient jobs."

Retraining of workers threatened with displacement by new machinery seems to far more of the panelists a more plausible way for industry to ease its employees through the period of transition when short-term unemployment is likely to crop up. And retraining schemes are being considered by a few industry groups, several top officials in the Federal Government and even some individual managements. So far, though, these retraining plans have developed sluggishly.

The scheme that started with greatest fanfare called for retraining of displaced workers in the meat-packing industry. But it has failed to live up to the first high hopes, chiefly because the meat packers have found few acceptable answers to the question: What jobs should we retrain these men for?

This is the problem that many of the panel presidents foresee. Says the head of a building materials company: "If you assume that retraining is socially desirable and that, of course, someone must pay for it, then I agree that industry does have some obligation to foot at least part of the bill for retraining. But the big question remains: What do you retrain people for?"

By no means are all the panelists ready to assume that industry does have any obligation toward the retraining of displaced workers. Indeed, the presidents are split about fifty-fifty on this question. And many of those who do agree with the idea believe that their companies' obligation is strictly limited to retraining men for employment elsewhere in their own companies, or at most within the same industry. But as one major supplier to the auto industry puts it: "No law and no amount of money can repeal the adage that 'the man must seek the job because the job won't seek him.'"

Will this disruption—even though it might be short-term—reach far up the corporate ladder? Some of the pessimists have been saying that lower and middle management men will suffer hard as a result not only of automation of production but of office procedures. And it seems from the responses of several panel presidents that some management people might get hurt.

Who and how many will suffer depends on the nature of the industry in which they work. In the steel industry there may be no great problem at all. Inland Steel Co.'s President John F. Smith Jr., for one, says: "I believe that the developments we will see in the next three or four years will tend to *increase* the need for lower and middle management men." And Joel Hunter of Crucible Steel Co. of America, looking to the record of automation in his company, says: "Middle management men are not likely to be displaced, though there are some lower management positions that eventually may not be required."

In the oil industry, on the other hand, there is a strong chance that management men will begin feeling the effects of technological advances. "In the next three or four years," says Sinclair Oil's Edward L. Steiniger, "we expect to reduce our personnel by another 10% to 12%. The lower and middle management people who are now employed working out answers to innumerable questions will tend to be replaced more and more by computers. And the computer operators won't number as many as the managerial people they replace."

Men who are low on the corporate totem pole in transportation companies are also likely to feel the pressure of automation. Several other railroad chiefs echo the New York Central's President Alfred E. Perlman when he says: "We expect automation may cause the displacement of men in lower and middle management in the next few years." Nor will the airlines be immune from the pressure if one executive is correct in his estimate that "our automated reservations system will displace men in our lower and middle management in the next few years. This has already been taken into account in our plans."

If the small man in the big company faces an increasing element of risk these days, what of the big man in the small company? Some pessimists who have sought to forecast the effects of increasing automation have charged that it will redound chiefly to the benefit of the big company, because only big business can afford the huge outlays needed for large-scale, automated production systems. The small businessman, they claim, will be put under ever more severe pressure as the big keep getting bigger.

But the majority of the panel presidents certainly do not see it this way. Most of them maintain that small businesses, well run, stand to benefit just as much from new technological breakthroughs as big companies. And this is for the simple reason that as Walter J. Tuohy of the Chesapeake & Ohio Railway puts it, "Most small businesses do not compete directly with big companies. They supplement them in many different ways. In addition, small businesses can take advantage of automation through cooperative arrangements of ownership and use of computers."

IBM's Williams, one top businessman who could hardly be closer to the subject, sees it in another light: "High volume," he points out, "*is* one of the factors which lends itself to automated techniques. As a result larger businesses have tended to adopt automated techniques more rapidly than smaller businesses. But small companies usually are more specialized and are thus able to concentrate their efforts for improvement. They have displayed great creativity in the past in using the newest and most advanced techniques to meet their problems. And today, lower cost and more diversified automation equipment is becoming available, and smaller businesses should benefit increasingly from these."

Certainly not all the panel presidents are as sanguine about the prospects for small business as Williams is. A few say quite determinedly that the small businessman faces little but tougher times. American Bosch Arma Corp.'s President Charles W. Perelle observes: "It's true that small business will be at a disadvantage. For large capital investment is required to automate and the risk is high. So naturally, a well-financed company will benefit most from automated production systems."

Yet the panel presidents, by a ratio of 10 to 1, believe that small companies, given good management and the specialization and flexibility that come with it, are not likely to be put at a disadvantage by the long strides in automation being made by the nation's big producers. This claim, too, they say, is simply one more specter growing out of the confusion and misunderstanding over what automation means to industry.

The president of one major paper company sums it up. "It may be a bit old-fashioned," he says, "but at times I get extremely irritated about the wide publicity on how many people are going to starve to death due to so-called automation. Automation in the broad sense has made our standard of living what it is today." And Standard Pressed Steel's President E. Thomas Hallowell Jr. adds another thought. "The best way I know to really increase employment" he quips, "would be to pass a law making it illegal to use a wheel in any form. Then everyone would be more than fully employed carrying things on his back. But we would also have an amazingly low standard of living."

6
Automation and Society: The Problem of Leisure

One of the goals of our society is to achieve full employment, with each individual working forty hours a week. In a statement appended to the Labor-Management Policy Committee Report on Automation in 1962, however, several prominent labor leaders warned that if unemployment were not reduced substantially in the near future, it would be necessary to resort to a general shortening of the work period through collective bargaining. They pointed out that a reduction of the basic work period has historically been one of the means of man's sharing the fruits of technological progress. It is taken for granted, of course, that a worker's real purchasing power would not be reduced by such a step; he would receive the same salary or wages for the reduced work period. But another problem arises in the event that this policy becomes necessary. How and for what purpose will people use the spare time thus put at their disposal? Are there alternative solutions to a shortening of the work period? The two long selections in this chapter explore the problems of work and leisure.

John K. Galbraith believes that the necessity for reduced work hours is not the result of increased productivity but is instead, the result of a marginal urgency for goods. If this is the case, why should work not be made more agreeable; why should not a man work less hard? If we can do without the young and the old in the work force, then we should be able to afford to educate the former and provide an adequate retirement income for the latter. He makes a crucial point in distinguishing kinds of work. We have customarily considered the work of the business executive, the college professor, and the machinist as "work" in the same sense of the word. This fallacy prevents us from realizing what has been occurring for some time, the emergence of what he calls the "New Class." The New Class does not toil for pay. Pay is not unimportant, but work is performed for the rewards of enjoyment and prestige. Galbraith believes that the rapid expansion of the New Class should be a major social goal. The expanding investment in education he views as a distinct advance in this direction. Automation, in the long run, will thus be a boon in minimizing the number of people who must toil without pleasure. We need worry only that it will proceed so fast that it will create a surplus of those who do have to toil.

Taking a somewhat shorter-range and less optimistic view, David Riesman feels many people are unprepared for leisure in our mass culture. He points out that there is comparatively little information in the sociology of leisure. There is a great deal of TV viewing; in the upper social strata there is some studying and partying. In the lower-income groups, there is some do-it-yourself work and much just driving around to kill time. Some people take additional jobs to fill their spare time. Among those whose work period has already been shortened, there was no display of eagerness for the extra day off. Riesman agrees that education would be the most beneficial leisure activity.

To provide creative and challenging work for all, it appears, should be a goal of our society. How can this be accomplished? And in our society, where increased leisure is in the offing for the majority of people, should provisions be made to ensure that this time be spent creatively? Should programs be created by state and local governments to work toward this goal?

John K. Galbraith
LABOR, LEISURE, AND THE NEW CLASS

In a society of high and increasing affluence there are three plausible tendencies as regards toil. As the production of goods comes to

From *The Affluent Society* (Cambridge, Mass.: The Riverside Press, 1958), pp. 334–348. Reprinted by permission. Dr. Galbraith is Professor of Economics at Harvard University and former Ambassador to India.

seem less urgent, and as individuals are less urgently in need of income for the purchase of goods, they will work fewer hours or days in the week. Or they will work less hard. Or, as a final possibility, it may be that fewer people will work all the time.

In the last century a drastic decline has occurred in the work week. In 1850 it is estimated to have averaged just under seventy hours, the equivalent of seven ten-hour days a week or roughly six at from six in the morning to six at night. A hundred years later the average was 40.0 hours or five eight-hour days.

This decline reflects a tacit but unmistakable acceptance of the declining marginal urgency of goods. There is no other explanation. However, such is the hold of production on our minds that this explanation is rarely offered. The importance and rewards of leisure are urged, almost never the unimportance of goods. Or, since production per hour has been increasing as the work week has declined, it is said that we are able to reduce the work because more is produced in less time. No mention is made of the fact that even more would be produced in more time. Or, finally, the decline is related to the feeling that steps must be taken to share the available work as productivity per worker rises. This also implies that the marginal urgency of production is low or negligible, but again the point remains unmade.

A reduction in the work week is an exceedingly plausible reaction to the declining marginal urgency of product. Over the span of man's history, although a phenomenal amount of education, persuasion, indoctrination, and incantation have been devoted to the effort, ordinary people have never been quite persuaded that toil is as agreeable as its alternatives. Thus to take increased well-being partly in the form of more goods and partly in the form of more leisure is unquestionably rational. In addition, the institution of overtime enables the worker to go far to adjust work and income to his own taste and requirements. It breaks with the barbarous uniformity of the weekly wage with its assumption that all families have the same tastes, needs, and requirements. Few things enlarge the liberty of the individual more substantially than to grant him a measure of control over the amount of his income.

Unfortunately in the conventional wisdom the reduction in hours has emerged as the only legitimate response to increasing affluence. This is at least partly because the issue has never been faced in terms of the increasing unimportance of goods. Accordingly, though we have attributed value to leisure, a ban still lies on other courses which seem to be more directly in conflict with established attitudes on productive efficiency. In a society rationally concerned with its own happiness these alternatives have a strong claim to consideration.

II

The first of these is that work can be made easier and more pleasant.

The present-day industrial establishment is a great distance removed from that of the last century or even of twenty-five years ago. This improvement has been the result of a variety of forces—government standards and factory inspection; general technological and architectural advance; the fact that productivity could be often increased by substituting machine power for heavy or repetitive manual labor; the need to compete for a labor force; and union intervention to improve working conditions in addition to wages and hours.

However, except where the improvement contributed to increased productivity, the effort to make work more pleasant has had to support a large burden of proof. It was permissible to seek the elimination of hazardous, unsanitary, unhealthful, or otherwise objectionable conditions of work. The speed-up might be resisted—to a point. But the test was not what was agreeable but what was unhealthful or, at a minimum, excessively fatiguing. The trend toward increased leisure is not reprehensible, but we resist vigorously the notion that a man should work less hard while on the job. Here older attitudes are involved. We are gravely suspicious of any tendency to expend less than the maximum effort, for this has long been a prime economic virtue.

In strict logic there is as much to be said for making work pleasant and agreeable as for shortening hours. On the whole it is probably as important for a wage earner to have pleasant working conditions as a pleasant home. To a degree, he can escape the latter but not the former—though no doubt the line between an agreeable tempo and what is flagrant featherbedding is difficult to draw. Moreover, it is a commonplace of the industrial scene that the dreariest and most burdensome tasks, requiring as they do a minimum of thought and skill, frequently have the largest numbers of takers. The solution to this problem lies, as we shall see presently, in drying up the supply of crude manpower at the bottom of the ladder. Nonetheless the basic point remains: the case for more leisure is not stronger on purely *prima facie* grounds than the case for making labor-time itself more agreeable. The test, it is worth repeating, is not the effect on productivity. It is not seriously argued that the shorter work week increases productivity—that men produce more in fewer hours than they would in more. Rather it is whether fewer hours are always to be preferred to more but more pleasant ones.

III

The third of the obvious possibilities with increasing affluence is for fewer people to work. This tendency has also been operating for many years although in a remarkably diverse form. Since 1890, when one boy in four and one girl in ten between the ages of ten and fifteen were gainfully employed, large numbers of juveniles have been retired from the labor force and their number now is negligible. At the same time a large number of women have been added. In 1890 19.5 percent of the female population ten years and over was in the labor force and by 1953 this proportion had risen to 29.7 percent. However, this change reflects in considerable measure the shift of tasks—food preparation, clothing manufacture, even child-rearing—out of the home. Women who previously performed them have gone along to other work. The woman who takes charge of a day nursery has joined the labor force, as have the women whose children she cares for.

For seventy-five years the proportion of the male population in the labor force has been constant at around seventy-five percent of those over ten years of age. There are a smaller percentage of the very young and of those over sixty-five, but this has been offset by the increase in population in the ages between twenty and sixty-five where the proportion of workers to the total is very high.

With diminishing marginal urgency of goods it is logical that the first to be spared should be old and young. We have yet, however, to view this tendency consistently and comprehensively. We are able to dispense with the labor of those who have reached retiring age because the goods they add are a low order of urgency, whereas a poor society must extract the last ounce of labor effort from all. But we have ordinarily subjected those who retire to a drastic reduction in income and living standards. Obviously, if the retirement can be afforded because the product is no longer urgent, a satisfactory—meaning for most purposes the customary— living standard can be accorded to the retired employee for the same reason. Similarly we have excluded youngsters from the labor market, partly on the ground that labor at too early an age is unduly painful and injurious to health, and partly to make way for educational opportunity. But while we have felt it possible to dispense with the goods that the youngsters produce, we have yet to provide them, at least in full and satisfactory measure, with the education that their exemption from labor was designed to make possible. If we are affluent enough to dispense with the product of juvenile labor, it again follows that we are affluent enough to provide the education that takes its place.

In addition to releasing the old and young, it may be that we need not use all of the labor force at all times. . . . If the marginal urgency of goods is low, then so is the urgency of employing the last man or the last million men in the labor force. By allowing ourselves such slack, in turn, we reduce the standards of economic performance to a level more nearly consonant with the controls available for its management. And in so widening the band of what is deemed tolerable performance lies our best hope of minimizing the threat of inflation with its further and persistent threat to social balance.

Such a step requires much more adequate provision than now for those who are temporarily unemployed. . . . Such measures are possible and, indeed, have a vital stabilizing effect. And again such compensation accords with the logic of the situation. If our need for production is of such a low order of urgency that we can afford some unemployment in the interest of stability—a proposition, incidentally, of impeccably conservative antecedents—then we can afford to give those who are unemployed the goods that enable them to sustain their accustomed standard of living. If we don't need what the employed do not make, we can obviously afford them what they customarily eat and wear.

IV

However, the greatest prospect that we face—indeed what must now be counted one of the central economic goals of our society—is to eliminate toil as a required economic institution. This is not a utopian vision. We are already well on the way. Only an extraordinarily elaborate exercise in social camouflage has kept us from seeing what has been happening.

Nearly all societies at nearly all times have had a leisure class—a class of persons who were exempt from toil. In modern times and especially in the United States the leisure class, at least in any identifiable phenomenon, has disappeared. To be idle is no longer considered rewarding or even entirely respectable.

But we have barely noticed that the leisure class has been replaced by another and much larger class to which work has none of the older connotation of pain, fatigue, or other mental or physical discomfort. We have failed to appreciate the emergence of this New Class, as it may be simply called, largely as the result of one of the oldest and most effective obfuscations in the field of social science. This is the effort to assert that all work—physical, mental, artistic, or managerial—is essentially the same.

This effort to proclaim the grand homogeneity of work has commanded, for different reasons, the support of remarkably numerous and diverse groups. To economists it has seemed a harmless and, indeed, an indispensable simplification. It has enabled them to deal homogeneously with all of the different kinds of productive effort and to elaborate a general theory of wages applying to all who receive an income for services. Doubts have arisen from time to time, but they have been suppressed or considered to concern special cases. The identity of all classes of labor is one thing on which capitalist and communist doctrine wholly agree. The president of the corporation is pleased to think that his handsomely appointed office is the scene of the same kind of toil as the assembly line and that only the greater demands in talent and intensity justify his wage differential. The Communist officeholder cannot afford to have it supposed that his labor differs in any significant respect from that of the comrade at the lathe or on the collective farm with whom he is ideologically one. In both societies it serves the democratic conscience of the more favored groups to identify themselves with those who do hard physical labor. A lurking sense of guilt over a more pleasant, agreeable, and remunerative life can often be assuaged by the observation "I am a worker too" or, more audaciously, by the statement that "mental labor is far more taxing than physical labor." Since the man who does physical labor is intellectually disqualified from comparing his toil with that of the brainworker, the proposition is uniquely unassailable.

In fact the differences in what labor means to different people could not be greater. For some, and probably a majority, it remains a stint to be performed. It may be preferable, especially in the context of social attitudes toward production, to doing nothing. Nevertheless it is fatiguing or monotonous or, at a minimum, a source of no particular pleasure. The reward rests not in the task but in the pay.

For others work, as it continues to be called, is an entirely different matter. It is taken for granted that it will be enjoyable. If it is not, this is a source of deep dissatisfaction or frustration. No one regards it as remarkable that the advertising man, tycoon, poet, or professor who suddenly finds his work unrewarding should seek the counsel of a psychiatrist. One insults the business executive or the scientist by suggesting that his principal motivation in life is the pay he receives. Pay is not unimportant. Among other things it is a prime index of prestige. Prestige—the respect, regard, and esteem of others—is in turn one of the more important sources of satisfaction associated with this kind of work. But, in general, those who do this kind of work expect to contribute their best regardless of compensation. They would be disturbed by any suggestion to the contrary.

Such is the labor of the New Class. No aristocrat ever contemplated the loss of feudal privileges with more sorrow than a member of this class would regard his descent into ordinary labor where the reward was only the pay. In the years following World War II a certain number of grade school teachers left their posts for substantially higher paid factory work. The action made headlines because it represented an unprece-dented desertion of an occupation which was assumed to confer the dignity of the New Class. The college professor, who is more securely a member of the New Class than the schoolteacher, would never contem-plate such a change even as an exercise in eccentricity and no matter how inadequate he might consider his income.

In keeping with all past class behavior, the New Class seeks energetically to perpetuate itself. Offspring are not expected to plan their lives in order to make a large amount of money. (Those who go into business are something of an exception at least partly because income, in business, is uniquely an index of prestige.) But from their earliest years the children are carefully indoctrinated in the importance of finding an occupation from which they will derive satisfaction—one which will involve not toil but enjoyment. One of the principal sources of sorrow and frustration in the New Class is the son who fails to make the grade—who drops down into some tedious and unrewarding occupation. The individ-ual who meets with this misfortune—the son of the surgeon who becomes a garage hand—is regarded by the community with pity not unmixed with horror. But the New Class has considerable protective powers. The son of the surgeon rarely does become a garage hand. However inadequate, he can usually manage to survive, perhaps somewhat exiguously, on the edge of his caste. And even if, as a salesman or an investment counselor, he finds little pleasure in his work, he will be expected to assert the contrary in order to affirm his membership in the New Class.

v

The New Class is not exclusive. While virtually no one leaves it, thousands join it every year. Overwhelmingly the qualification is educa-tion. Any individual whose adolescent situation is such that sufficient time and money is invested in his preparation, and who has at least the talents to carry him through the formal academic routine, can be a member. There is a hierarchy within the class. The son of the factory worker who becomes an electrical engineer is on the lower edge; his son who does graduate work and becomes a university physicist moves to the higher echelons; but opportunity for education is, in either case, the open sesame.

There can be little question that in the last hundred years, and even in the last few decades, the New Class has increased enormously in size. In early nineteenth century England or the United States, excluding the leisure class and considering the New Class as a group that lived on what it has carefully called earned income, it consisted only of a handful of educators and clerics, with, in addition, a trifling number of writers, journalists, and artists. In the United States of the eighteen-fifties it could not have numbered more than a few thousand individuals. Now the number whose primary identification is with their job, rather than the income it returns, is undoubtedly in the millions.

Some of the attractiveness of membership in the New Class, to be sure, derives from a vicarious feeling of superiority—another manifestation of class attitudes. However, membership in the class unquestionably has other and more important rewards. Exemption from manual toil; escape from boredom and confining and severe routine; the chance to spend one's life in clean and physically comfortable surroundings; and some opportunity for applying one's thoughts to the day's work, are regarded as unimportant only by those who take them completely for granted. For these reasons it has been possible to expand the New Class greatly without visibly reducing its attractiveness.

This being so, there is every reason to conclude that the further and rapid expansion of this class should be a major, and perhaps next to peaceful survival itself, *the* major social goal of the society. Since education is the operative factor in expanding the class, investment in education, assessed qualitatively as well as quantitatively, becomes very close to being the basic index of social progress. It enables people to realize a dominant aspiration. It is an internally consistent course of development.

Recent experience has shown that the demand for individuals in the occupations generally identified with the New Class increases much more proportionately with increased income and well-being. Were the expansion of the New Class a deliberate objective of the society this, with its emphasis on education and its ultimate effect on intellectual, literary, cultural, and artistic demands, would greatly broaden the opportunities for membership. At the same time the shrinking in the number of those who engage in work *qua* work is something to be regarded not alone with equanimity but with positive approval. For one of the inevitable outlets for the intellectual energies and inventiveness of the New Class will be in finding substitutes for routine and repetitive manual labor. To the extent that such labor is made scarce and more expensive, this tendency will, of course, be acclerated. To minimize the number of people doing such work is the counterpart of the goal of expanding the New Class.

It is a measure of how little we need worry about the danger from reducing the number of people engaged in work *qua* work that, as matters now stand, our concern is not that we will have too few available for toil but too many. We worry lest such technical advances as automation, an already realized dividend of the expansion of the New Class, will proceed so rapidly as to leave a surplus of those who still work. This, indeed, could be the greater danger.

VI

I venture to suggest that the unprofessional reader will find rather reasonable and rational the ideas here offered. Why should men struggle to maximize income when the price is many dull and dark hours of labor? Why especially should they do so as goods become more plentiful and less urgent? Why should they not seek instead to maximize the rewards of all the hours of their days? And since this is the plain and obvious aspiration of a great and growing number of the most perceptive people, why should it not be the central goal of the society? And now to complete the case, we have a design for progress. It is education or, more broadly, investment in human as distinct from material capital.

But in the more sophisticated levels of the conventional wisdom, including, regrettably, some professional economists, any such goal will seem exceedingly undesirable. The production of material goods, urgent or otherwise, is the accepted measure of our progress. Investment in material capital is our basic engine of progress. Both this product and the means for increasing it are measurable and tangible. What is measurable is better. To talk of transferring increasing numbers of people from lives spent mostly in classical toil to lives which, for the most part, are spent pleasantly has less quantitative precision. Since investment in individuals, unlike investment in a blast furnace, provides a product that can be neither seen nor valued, it is inferior. And here the conventional wisdom unleashes its epithet of last resort. Since these achievements are not easily measured, as a goal they are "fuzzy." This is widely deemed to be a fatal condemnation. The precise, to be sure, is usually the old and familiar. Because it is old and familiar it has been defined and measured. Thus does insistence on precision become another of the tautological devices by which the conventional wisdom protects itself. Nor should one doubt its power.

Yet anyone who finds this analysis and these proposals sensible should not be entirely discouraged. We are here in one of the contexts where circumstance has marched far beyond the conventional wisdom. We have seen how general are the efforts to join the New Class and how rapid is its expansion. We are not here establishing a new economic and social goal but identifying one that is already widely if but tacitly accepted. In this situation the conventional wisdom cannot resist indefinitely. The economist of impeccable credentials in the conventional wisdom, who believes that there is no goal in life of comparable urgency with the maximization of total and individual real income, would never think of applying such a standard to himself. In his own life he is an exponent of all the aspirations of the New Class. He educates and indoctrinates his children with but one thing in mind. It is not that they should maximize their income. This is abhorrent. He wants above all that they will have an occupation that is interesting and rewarding. On this he hopes, indeed, that they will take their learned parent as their model.

David Riesman
LEISURE AND WORK IN POST-INDUSTRIAL SOCIETY

To the rest of the world, the American has characteristically appeared as someone who could not stand being idle or alone, someone who rushes about, whether in work or play, and is preternaturally restless. Tocqueville for instance observed, "No men are less addicted to reverie than the citizens of a democracy." It is important to recall this pre-industrial image of America lest we assume that industrialization, the automobile, or television are responsible for what Clifton Fadiman deplores as "the decline of attention": the "American" way preceded the inventions which gave that way added scope. Like Tocqueville, Lewis Mumford, in his remarkable book *The Transformations of Man*, discusses these changes from Old World to New World life, suggesting that the Americans, released by social and geographic space from age-old limits and norms, have exhibited from the beginning an exuberance and vitality, a romantic strenuousness, that in their respective ways both Emerson and Whitman represented and celebrated.

Mass Leisure: The End of Sumptuary Traditions

At the present time, two processes are going on simultaneously. On the one hand, a decline of exuberance is just barely noticeable in America, making itself felt particularly among the more highly educated and the well-to-do in a loss of appetite for work and perhaps even for leisure. On the other hand, the spread of industrialization and of the mass media are bringing both the residual pockets of traditionalism within this

Reprinted with permission of The Free Press from *Mass Leisure* by Eric Larrabee and Rolf Meyersohn, eds. Copyright 1958 by The Free Press, a Corporation. Drawn from an article, "Abundance for What?" in *Problems of U.S. Economic Development*, Vol. I (N.Y., Committee on Economic Development, 1958), pp. 223–234. Dr. Riesman is a professor in the Department of Social Relations at Harvard University.

country and the great areas of it outside into a more "American" pattern. Whatever a nation's political or religious ideology, mass culture continues to spread, even ahead of industrialization, bringing the disruption of old ways and the lure of a new hedonism (as most dramatically seen in the cargo cults of the Pacific islanders which combine a nativist revival with the belief that the white man's goods can be obtained, without the white man himself, by appropriate rituals).

I recently saw a documentary film focused on a family living in the hills of Tennessee in the 1930s—a family with many children and many dogs, eking out a bare existence. Despite efforts to insure minimal schooling, knowledge of the outside world scarcely percolated. Today, despite remaining pockets of abysmal misery, many of the very Tennessee shacks where, before the coming of the TVA, life resembled that in other peasant and pre-industrial cultures, are equipped with television aerials that now bring in not only the local boys who made good with a guitar, like Elvis Presley, but all the insignia of making good which pass as currency in the nation at large: cars, clothes, washers (which are often put on the front porch), and general styles of life and leisure. Some of the farms even in this area have become nearly as over-mechanized, and hence engaged in "conspicuous production," as the richer agricultural areas of the North; horses and mules are disappearing, and the South is catching up with the rest of the country in per capita ownership of automobiles. (In that sense, the North is finally winning the Civil War, whatever resistances can be focused around racism—a theme that W. J. Cash already foresaw in his prophetic book *The Mind of the South*.)

Indeed, Southerners coming North, white or Negro, Caribbean or native, have replaced the immigrants from Southern Europe as fodder, not for the machines of production so much as for those of consumption; for coming from a pre-industrial culture they lack sales resistance, let alone consumer sophistication: entering, if not the high-wage economy, at least the high-credit one, they are being "processed" as consumers, while escaping, because of their late arrival, some of the drill and exhausting hours that met earlier pre-industrial cadres entering the work force of industrial society.

They enter a society which has over the past eighty years taken in the form of leisure or free time approximately a third of the gains in productivity which industrialism and organization have achieved. (The average work-week now hovers around forty hours, as contrasted with seventy hours in 1850 and, in many industries and on the farms, nearly as much as that as late as 1920.) When the Bantu who works, let us say, in Johannesburg, has attained an increment over his old standard of living, he is likely to quit and return to the reservation; few of these Americans have a reservation to return to, consequently, the Americans remain rather steadily at work while having time enough left on their hands for learning how to spend money in accordance with, and just beyond, their new wages.

This injection at the bottom is, I believe, responsible for much of the American economy of leisure, and more than makes up for the withdrawal of those people in the educated strata (whose attitudes we shall discuss more fully later) who no longer find in the purchase of possessions a sufficient agenda for living. (There still remain in America some more or less permanently underprivileged enclaves, principally among the old, the infirm, and among the less agile and mobile Negroes and poor whites in the South.)

But it is those who have recently been released from underprivilege by mass production and mass leisure who have gained, along with an often meaningless political vote, an often influential voice in the direction of consumption and hence of production. It is, for instance, the very millions whom Henry Ford helped release from drudgery who eventually defeated his ascetic and still rural canons of taste; it is they who like borax furniture or juke-box culture; their aesthetic is akin to that of all deracinated peasants whose folk culture crumbles at the first exposure to mass-produced commodities.

Even in countries formerly run by an elite or presently run by a dictatorship, the same democratization and vulgarization of taste make themselves felt. The British mass press and the Butlin Holiday Camps are more than the equal of our Hearst papers and our own vacation "culture." Likewise, although the newly urbanized in the Soviet Union may read a few more books and go to fewer movies, and will surely spend less time aimlessly driving about, their Parks of Culture and Rest are hardly more elevating than Coney Island; their privileged youth appears to be even more bored and delinquent; and the documentary realism of their art and its general lack of subtlety are being steadily outgrown in America. What distinguishes the Soviet Union is that it still has the goal of catching up with America and still possesses millions of unsatiated and eager buyers.

Technological Overprivilege

As many thoughtful people have recognized, our society offers little in the way of re-education for those who have been torn away from their traditional culture and suddenly exposed to all the blandishments of mass culture—even the churches which follow the hillbillies to the city often make use of the same "hard sell" that the advertisers and politicians do. In the past, the relatively voluntary nature of the immigration to this country, and the belief in progress of natives and immigrants alike, have tended to blind us to the casualties of transplantation. There are a few exceptions. For example, in the 1930s I admired the Rust brothers, inventors of the cotton picker, who hesitated to market their invention because they were worried about technological unemployment among Southern workers. (They were as unconvinced of the gospel of progress as were the members of the Advisory Committee which recommended under Oppenheimer's leadership against proceeding with the H-bomb.) It is ironical to reflect that this invention came along just in time to save some Southern fields from utter desertion—not only because Negroes and poor whites were leaving for the cities in the North but also because the cotton picking machine, as a form of conspicuous production, frees its operator from work which has long been considered dirty work and thus raises the status of the operator: it is the counterpart on the production side of today's Tennessee shack, electrified and gadget-filled. Even so, I think that the Rusts' scruples were well taken: people should not be ruthlessly torn away even from their incapacities and given the industrial bends: this country is rich enough and inventive enough to make social provision for a moratorium and retraining in those instances where uprooting is inescapable.

For many people today, the sudden onrush of leisure is a version of technological unemployment: their education has not prepared them for it and the creation of new wants at their expense moves faster than their ability to order and assimilate these wants.

The Conservative Belief in Progress

In the mercantilist era, and even today in the countries of grinding poverty, the creation of new wants has been a first step towards a better life and wider horizons of choice. But in the United States today, the belief that one cannot stop invention, cannot stop technological progress, has itself become tradition, indeed a form of realistic insanity, or what C. Wright Mills calls "crackpot realism." Although adult Americans, contrary to European impression, are not dazzled by machines as such—but simply want to have those appurtenances that betoken an appropriate style of life—we are nevertheless half-willing slaves of the machine process itself. Even big business, thanks to the anti-trust laws and to the potential competition of small business, does not quite have sufficient control of the market to plan to its own liking the sequence of applied technology. A fortiori, it seems inconceivable to Americans that we could reduce the aggression our technology keeps up against our traditions and the texture of our lives—and we can always use the competition of the Russians to counter any tendency within ourselves to relax the rate of growth or to question the belief in growth as a value per se.

To be sure, the optimism of the booster was once much stronger in America than it is now. The ideal of manifest destiny, which took us across the continent and held the South bound to the Union in the Civil War, infects now only those perpetually adolescent males who are eager to conquer space or the planet Venus. But the booster psychology has for so long been built into our culture and into our patterns of individual and group achievement that we tend to take for granted the notion that growth in population, in assets, in national income, is inevitable if not always desirable. Imagine the outcry, for instance, and not only from Catholics, against any suggestion that people be encouraged in this country to practice birth control, let us say, by removing the tax concession for child dependents or by instituting a sales tax on children's toys and clothes, or even by pointing out forcefully to people some of the less happy consequences of an exploding population. For most Americans still believe that the future can take care of itself, or at any rate that we are not required to do anything to make it easier, less crowded, less full of friction, for our descendants. (In the same way, on a far smaller and simpler and less controversial issue, it seems almost impossible to cut down the growth of our autos in size and horsepower, let alone to forbid them from entering our downtown areas without good cause shown. Instead, everything else has to adjust to the auto: our central cities must tear down homes and tear up parks to provide those highways that, as Mumford has often pointed out, only brings more cars in an endless vicious spiral.)

In other words, we have become a conservative country, despite our world-wide reputation for seeking novelty, in that we are unable to envisage alternative futures for ourselves. In an illuminating essay, John Kouwenhoven has suggested that a certain style of extrapolative thinking and designing is characteristically American. He referred there to the way we have laid out our cities in gridiron blocks, to our assembly lines and consecutive sections, to our skyscrapers in serried stories. He pointed to our continuous flow of comic strips, movies, the stanzas of our popular music; he might have added our football cheers, and our seriatim credits and terms as one passes through the educational plant. Though no one of these is unique to America, it can be argued that our way of thinking tends to be extrapolative: we add one story to another, one thing to another, one frame to another: we think in terms of additives.

The Abyss of Leisure

So, too, it has been until recent years in the field of leisure time— so much so that my collaborators and I in *The Lonely Crowd* took it for granted that it was impossible to reverse the trend towards automation; we assumed that the current efforts to make work more meaningful—

which by and large succeeded only in making it more time-consuming and gregarious but not more challenging—might as well be given up, with the meaning of life to be sought henceforth in the creative use of leisure. We failed to see, in the famous Marxist phrase, that "quantity changes into quality" and that there would come a point where additional increments of leisure would prove more stultifying than satisfying and that the mass of men would be incapable of absorbing any more.

The situation confronting Americans—and, as already indicated, in due course the rest of the industrially advanced countries also—is historically unprecedented. In pre-industrial cultures leisure is scarcely a burden or a "problem" because it is built into the ritual and groundplan of life for which people are conditioned in childhood; often they possess a relatively timeless attitude towards events. Likewise, the tiny leisure classes of the past would sometimes be able to absorb what seems like an overdose of leisure because they lived in an era when work itself was thought demeaning and when free citizens engaged in physical and intellectual self-cultivation and in the arts of war and government—they, so to speak, exercised their leisure on behalf of the whole society. During this era, which lasted throughout most of history, it was inconceivable that the mass of men could support a large and growing leisure class, let alone join such a class themselves. Yet today we live in such a world. The rich and leisured are no longer drastically set apart, but seek for the sake of their souls as well as their public relations to work with relative sobriety and consume with relative modesty and inconspicuousness; thus, they no longer set an example for either good or ill.

At the present time, the closest thing we have to the traditional ideology of the leisure class is a group of artists and intellectuals who regard their work as play and their play as work. For such people, and for the larger group of professional people whom we shall discuss later, work frequently provides the central focus of life without necessarily being compartmentalized from the rest of life either by its drudgery and severity or by its precariousness. At best, the painter may always be seeing and the poet and writer always envisaging, although with greater or lesser intensity and concentration.

Work as a Psychological Stabilizer

Such considerations and reconsiderations led the Center for the Study of Leisure to decide in 1957 to examine the prospects of the four-day week in manufacturing industry and to initiate conversations with union officials concerning the bearing of such a pattern of work on the leisure activities of the workers. At that time Walter Reuther and the UAW were contemplating such a week and other union leaders were also interested in it as a possibility. We were curious about the effects on employees of receiving an unexpected and unplanned-for dividend of leisure. Accordingly, when a small aircraft parts manufacturer in Southern California unilaterally decided to give its employees a four-day week at the beginning of each month, with Monday off (to be made up by working one Saturday at the end of the week), Rolf Meyersohn, Research Director of the Center, went to the spot and began to question workers concerning their reactions to the new plan. The periodic interviewing of these employees is presently under way; and *in medias re* it is, of course, not possible to say just what the research will turn up. But, so far, it would seem that the employees have accepted the idea of a four-day week readily enough and without Puritan inhibitions or misgivings; the only major problems appear to arise from the fact that the rest of the family is not as yet on a similar schedule. One could argue indeed that Southern California can absorb increments of leisure more readily than can other parts of the country: many of the employees have camps in the hills or boats in the water.

In fact, in a Roper Poll taken in the summer of 1957 concerning attitudes towards a possible four-day week, it turned out that there were some distinct regional differences as well as differences among people of different age and economic levels (although differences in education were the most pronounced). Strikingly enough, in the Far West a third of the respondents would use an additional day to take another job—in part apparently to get still more money to spend in the remaining time off or in a later stage of the life cycle. Contrastingly, the Southerners were least able to come up with ideas about what they would do with the extra day: do-it-yourself was less in evidence, as were hobbies, sports, and trips. College graduates incidentally were the most trip-prone: 47% would take trips as against 19% who had had only a grade school education; likewise, the college graduate also had a far greater interest in participant sports. Older people (who are also people of lesser education) were somewhat more worried about the possibility that people would get soft and lazy while younger people were somewhat more likely (27% to 19%) to believe that with the extra time people would relax more, enjoy themselves more, and be happier.

On the whole, this survey did not turn up great eagerness for an extra day (nor did a somewhat comparable Gallup survey). In our own more limited inquiries we have discovered many wives who are aghast at the thought of having their husbands around the house for a still-longer "lost weekend"—and not a few husbands who are not notably eager for what they term "honey-do" days; that is, days at home when their wives ask them, "Honey, do this!" and "Honey, do that!"

An informal poll of a union local (conducted by James Carper) found that the leaders did want a shorter work week whereas the rank and file did not. This was interpreted as suggesting that the leaders, better educated and more enterprising, feel cramped for time to do everything they want to—to read more books, to see more of their families, to take more adult education courses. Such men already had many hobbies, including being union leaders. But the less active members (no doubt including many who might tell the union leaders that they "lack time to go to meetings") had no similar feeling of wanting the days to be longer. Such men, asked what they would do with an extra day, sometimes say, "sleep"; others could use it in hunting season—and already did so to the dismay of the foreman.

Union leaders have pointed out to me that a lack of any experience with extensive leisure may be responsible for the frequent breakdown and anomic reactions among men forced to retire, regardless of the medical and recreational facilities that may be provided for the retired. Moreover, these officials have envisaged the impact of automation on their industry as well-nigh complete, and they have described to me what was already occurring: namely, the creation of many jobs which consist of little more than half-attentive dial watching of nearly self-corrective automatic machinery—machinery which, if it does break down, requires the services of specialists. Envisaging a continuing decline in working hours, either through a four-day week or the six-hour day of the rubber workers, these thoughtful men have felt that leisure has to take up the slack in work, providing both the challenges and the variations of monotony that can no longer be found in work.

Certainly, there is plenty of evidence that even as things stand, unskilled industrial workers do not like their work, although some enjoy the companionship it provides. In a study by Nancy Morse and Robert Weiss, some 80% of such workers stated that they, in effect, kept on working for lack of alternatives, not for positive satisfactions. These workers were asked whether they would go on working even if there were no financial need to do so, and they said they would, although also indicating that the job itself (and in many cases any job they could imagine) was boring and without meaning in its own terms. This clinging to the job is not simply a legacy of the Puritan ethic: it is rather a legacy of industrialism itself, of the old structures it has destroyed and the new structures it has created. Nor, in Mr. Weiss's opinion, is it merely the feeling of shame in not having a job which is involved (although this is certainly an element). Work may not be an active presence in the life of these workers, but its absence would be an active absence. Or, more accurately, it is not so much "work" that would be missed as having a job: it doesn't have to be, and should preferably not be, hard work, nor need it even be gregarious work, but rather the self-definition (these data refer only to male workers) that comes from holding a job and the punctuations of life provided by regular employment. Putting together the still incomplete data from the four-day week studies and from the study by Nancy Morse and Robert Weiss, it would seem that there is a difference in kind between a four-day or three-day week and a no-day week—a difference which leisure in its present versions and for people of this level of education cannot possibly fill. These workers, in other words, are too intelligent and too well educated to accept the routine of most factory work, while being still a long way away from the education of the artist or intellectual who can in some measure create his own work with a minimum of outside structuring.

Such considerations concerning the limits of leisure suggest that it might be easier to make leisure more meaningful if one at the same time could make work more demanding. When work itself is infiltrated with leisure (as it is today in many jobs where the time-study man has been stymied), leisure may lose its savor, often becoming not much more than a continuation outside the plant of the sociability and inanity that go on within the plant. It might be slightly less difficult to reorganize work routines so that they became less routine, more challenging, and hence more instructive, than to cope all at once with the burdens placed on leisure by the evaporation of the meaning of work. This evaporation has occurred as a result of the same commercial and industrial developments that have turned leisure from a communal affair, celebrated by festivals or other shared activities, into an individualized pursuit, hence a "problem." Thus, we have lost not only, as already indicated, the folk traditions that have in many cultures integrated work and leisure, but also those that have integrated leisure with the community's framework (in Fromm's terms) or orientation and devotion. In this situation, I believe that we cannot take advantage of what remains of our pre-industrial heritage to make leisure more creative, individually and socially, if work is not creative, too. And not only have we lost the folk and peasant traditions: we are rapidly losing those which have developed under industrialism itself—whether of the John Henry variety or of the free-swearing, free-swinging construction engineer who gets roads and dams built: such legends hold little allure in an opulent society, even when building continues at a rapid pace. It is from the Soviet Union that the story comes of a mill foreman who, though complaining of his pay, says he "must be content with the 'thrill of producing something anyway.'" Though he may have been speaking in part for the record, there is no doubt that production remains exciting for many where industrialism is the unfinished business of a rising power. Americans, however, cannot artificially recreate that atmosphere; we cannot make factory or other industrial and commercial work over on the model of army basic training or campcraft just to make it hard (though in fact many workers do enjoy making a game of output, for instance, working up the line on an assembly-line, in order to establish control and dramatize their activity). One alternative is to redesign our factories with an eye to the educational or challenging quality of each job, following the example set by some industrial units which have eliminated assembly lines and are giving workers larger units to assemble, or what is sometimes termed "job enlargement." The march of specialization which had originally been based on steam production but has in our day become an end in itself with its own dynamic and momentum could thereby be reversed. Undoubtedly, work flows could be redesigned to maximize the demands on the worker's intelligence, while retaining present advances in making work quiet, free of dirt, and relatively unstrenuous.

Leisure—Society's Blotting Paper

It has become clear that post-industrial society no longer requires arduous and routinized work on the one hand, or, on the other hand, that kind of seemingly varied work, such as that of the salesman, in which the worker is compelled to exploit his own personality. Nevertheless, I have been arguing that Americans remain too unequivocally the children of industry, even when automation threatens to disinherit us, for us to be able to resort to leisure as a counterbalance for the deficiencies of work. Even so, leisure is coming to occupy for adults something of the position the school already occupies for youngsters, of being the institution which seems "available" to bear the brunt of all society's derelictions in other spheres. Thus, just as schools are asked to become quasi-parental, quasi-custodial, quasi-psychiatric, and quasi-everything else, filling in for tasks other institutions leave undone or badly done, with the result that the schools often cannot do their job of education adequately; so leisure is now being required to take up the energies left untapped everywhere else in our social order, with the result that it often fails in its original task of recreation for most of us most of the time and of creativity for some of us some of the time. The hopes I had put on leisure (in *The Lonely Crowd*) reflect, I suppose, my despair about the possibility of making work in modern society more meaningful and more demanding for the mass of men—a need which has come upon us so rapidly that the taste of abundance we have had in the past now threatens to turn into a glut.

My despair on this score, I must add, was not greatly alleviated by the feeling in the group of union leaders mentioned above that it was impossible either to get unions or management in the least interested in making work more humanly satisfying. I hoped the union leaders might cooperate with management in, so to speak, turning the engineers around, and forcing them to design men back into their machines rather than out of them. In this connection, I recall talking with aircraft engineers who were irritated with the "human factor," and eager to put a machine wherever a man might go wrong, rather than to design equipment that maximized the still enormous resourcefulness of the human mind. I recall the highway engineers who designed thruways that would look good to other engineers or to engineering-minded Americans—until the death toll made them realize that boredom could be a greater danger to man than speed and obstacles. And I thought of the subdividers who bulldozed down all trees to make it easier to build a road or a suburb, with no authorities around to forbid such wanton simplification of their own task along with such destruction of history and life. As the discussion with the union officials continued, it became clearer to me that the workers themselves were too much of this same school of engineering thought really to believe in the reorganization of industry. The kind of utopia of meaningful work pictured in Percival and Paul Goodman's book *Communitas* made no sense to them.

In this perspective, the rebellion of workers against modern industry is usually mere rebellion, mere goofing off. Many are quite prepared to go on wildcat strikes (Daniel Bell notes that in 1954–55 there were forty such in just one Westinghouse plant in East Pittsburgh); they are quite prepared to deceive the time-study man and to catch forty winks on the night shift, and otherwise to sabotage full production while still "making out" in terms of the group's norms—being in this like students who might cheat on exams or cut classes but could not conceive of reorganization of the curriculum or of asking for heavier assignments. The great victory of modern industry is that even its victims, the bored workers, cannot imagine any other way of organizing work, now that the tradition of the early nineteenth century Luddites, who smashed machines, has disappeared with the general acceptance of progress. We must thus think of restriction of output and other sabotage of production as mere symptoms.

Furthermore, the resentment which manifests itself in these symptoms helps engender a vicious circle, since it confirms the opinion of management that workers must be disciplined by bringing them together in great factories and subjecting them to the relentless pressure of assembly lines—as against the possibility, for instance, that work could be decentralized so that workers would not have to commute long distances and could proceed more at their own pace and place. In the high-wage industries given over to "conspicuous production," management has the resources to be concerned with the amenities of work—the group harmony, the decor, the cafeteria and other ancillary services—and to make provision for the worker's leisure, such as bowling teams, golf courses, and adult education courses too; in fact, a whole range of extracurricular pleasures and benefits. Sometimes these benefits include profit-sharing, but they are much less likely to include decision-sharing, for of course managers object less to giving away money, especially money that would otherwise go to stockholders or to the government in taxes, than to giving away power and prestige and freedom of action to workers whose unionized demands reflect merely their discontent and scarcely at all their desires for reconstruction.

It is obvious in addition that managers are not free to reorganize their plants in order to provide their workers with a more satisfying work environment, if this might risk higher costs, unless their competitors are prepared to go along. Yet competition is not the whole story, for the situation is hardly better and is often worse in nationalized industries in Great Britain and Western Europe generally, while the situation of industrial workers in the Soviet Union today reminds one of the worst excesses of the Victorian era and the earlier days of the Industrial Revolution in the West. Managers of whatever ideological stripe seek to measure themselves against a single, uni-dimensional standard by which they can judge performance and thus are drawn to simplified work routines and an unremitting drive for maximum output. To open the possible consideration of factories as making not only things but also men, and as providing not only comfort and pay but also challenge and education, this would itself be a challenge to the way we have assimilated technology for the last three hundred years; and it would compel us to search for more Gestaltist and amorphous standards, in which we were no longer so clear as to what is process and what is product. There have, to be sure, been paternalistic employers (such as the Lowell mills in the 1840s or the Pullman plant a half-century ago) concerned with the education and uplift of their operatives—often to the eventual resentment and unionization of the latter (who felt it was enough to have to work for the bosses without imitating their preferred inhibitions). But these were efforts to compensate outside the plant for the dehumanization regarded as inevitable within. What I am asking for now is hardly less than reorganizing work itself so that man can live humanely on as well as off the job.

Strenuous Work

The work of the managers themselves, of course, striving to get out production in the face of technical and human obstacles, is seldom boring, although if the product itself is socially valueless, a point may be reached where work upon it, despite technical challenges, is felt as stultifying. Indeed, one could argue that the great disparities of privilege today are in the realm of the nature of work rather than in the nature of compensation: it has proved easier partially to equalize the latter through high-wage and tax policies than to begin at all on the former, which would require still greater readjustments. In that brilliant precursor of much contemporary science-fiction, Aldous Huxley's *Brave New World,* the lower cadres are given over to fairly undiluted hedonism while serious work and thought are reserved for the ruling "Alphas." Likewise, a recent science-fiction story once more illuminates the issue (it is my impression that science-fiction is almost the only genuinely subversive new literature in wide circulation today): this is a story by Frederick Pohl called "The Midas Plague" which pictures a society in which the upper classes are privileged by being allowed to spend less time and zeal in enforced consumption; they are permitted to live in smaller houses and to keep busy fewer robots in performing services for them. Their ration points— rations to extend rather than to limit consumption—are fewer; their cars are smaller; the things and gadgets that surround them are less oppressive. Best of all, they are allowed to work at work rather than having to spend four or five days a week simply as voracious consumers. That is, as one rises in the status system by excelling at consumership, one is allowed a larger and larger scope for what Veblen called the instinct of workmanship.

As already indicated, the world presented in "The Midas Plague," as in so much science-fiction, is all too little a fiction. For, if we except a number of farmers and skilled workers, such as tool and die makers, it is the professional and executive groups who at present have the most demanding and interesting work and for whom, at least until retirement, leisure is least a time to kill. The study by Nancy Morse and Robert Weiss referred to earlier indicates that on the whole these groups find most satisfaction in their work. A survey by *Fortune* last year showed that top executives, despite giving the appearance of being relaxed and taking it easy as our mores demand, work an average of sixty hours a week or more. In many other fields, the leisure revolution has increased the demands on those who service the leisure of others or who have charge of keeping the economy and the society, or considerable segments of it, from falling apart. High civil servants and diplomats probably work as hard or harder than ever—indeed it is not easy today to imagine writers like Hawthorne or Trollope holding civil service sinecures as a way of supporting themselves as novelists. Many priests and ministers, with expanding parishes and congregations, and with more expected of them in the way of ancillary services, find themselves as busy as any top executive. The same is true of a good many teachers and professors who are presumably training others to spend their leisure wisely! Physicians are notorious for their coronaries and their lack of care for their own health and comfort: as the public has more and more time to spend with doctors (often a kind of window shopping on themselves) and as there are fewer doctors in proportion to wealth and population, the medical men are forced to work seventy hours a week to pay for their monopoly position, their glamor, their high incomes, and their prestige. (The doctors at least have aides and antibiotics to help them out, but teachers and other ill-paid service workers have no similar labor-saving devices.) All in all, as I have suggested, those who are privileged in being able to choose their own work are becoming increasingly underprivileged with respect to leisure and perhaps also with respect to the pace at which, in the face of the waiting customers, they must respond to the demands upon them. A polarization is occurring between the toiling classes and the leisure masses.

In our egalitarian society, however, it would be surprising if the attitude of the masses did not influence the classes (there are of course also influences running the other way). As I remarked at the outset, I have the impression that a general decline is occurring in the zest for work, a decline which is affecting even those professional and intellectual groups whose complaint to their wives that they are over-worked has often in the past been a way of concealing the fact that their work interested them rather more than did their wives. To return to the case of the doctors, for example, there is some slight evidence that application lists to medical school are no longer so full, a decline which is attributed to the belief among young people that medical education is too arduous and takes too long before one is stabilized on a plateau of suburban life and domesticity. Similar tendencies would appear to be affecting those already in medical school. Howard S. Becker and Blanche Geer report (from the study of medical education at the University of Kansas being carried out under the direction of Professor Everett C. Hughes) that the teaching faculty complains that the students are no longer as interested in the more theoretical or scientific aspects of medicine: three-quarters of them are married and, instead of sitting around waiting for night duty or talking about their work, they are eager to go home, help the wife get dinner, and relax with television.

Likewise, there is evidence that young men in the big law firms, although they still work harder than most of their clients, do not glory in putting in night work and weekend hours as they once did. And several architects have told me that similar changes are showing up even in this field, which is famous for the enthusiasm of its devotees and the zest for work built up during *charettes* at architectural school. (Possibly, this may reflect in part the loss of the enthusiasm of the crusade on behalf of "modern" and the routinization of what had once been an esoteric creed.)

If such tendencies are showing up in the professions to which, in the past, men have been most devoted, it is not surprising that they should also be appearing in large-scale business enterprise. Though top executives may work as hard as ever—in part perhaps because, being trained in an earlier day, they can hardly help doing so—their subordinates are somewhat less work-minded. The recruiters who visit college campuses in order to sign up promising seniors or graduate students for large corporations have frequently noted that the students appear at least as interested in the fringe benefits as in the nature of the work itself; I would myself interpret this to signify that they have given up the notion that the work itself can be exciting and have an outlook which is not so very different from that of the typical labor union member: they want and expect more but not so very much more than the latter. Certainly, if fiction is any clue (of course, it is at best an unreliable clue) to prevailing attitudes, the current crop of business novels is revealing, for it indicates a marked change from an earlier era of energetic if ruthless tycoons. In *The Man in the Grey Flannel Suit,* for instance, the hero, Tom Rath, chooses the quiet suburban life and domesticity over the chance for large stakes and large decisions, but possible ulcers, in a big broadcasting company. He does so after discovering that his boss, powerful and dynamic, is estranged from everything in life that matters: from his wife, his daughter, and himself— his work is only an escape. Likewise, in *Executive Suite,* there is an analogous picture of the old tycoon who is wedded to his work and isolated by it, contrasted with the young hero whose work is at once not so strenuous and more playful and "creative."

The movement to the suburbs is of course a factor in these developments, especially now that young men move to the suburbs not only for the sake of their wives and young children and the latter's schooling but also for their own sake. It is hard, for example, for a scientific laboratory to maintain a night-time climate of intense intellectual enthusiasm when its professional cadres are scattered over many suburbs and when the five-day week has become increasingly standard throughout American life (outside of a few universities which cling to the older five and a half day pattern). The sport-shirted relaxed suburban culture presents a standing "reproach" to the professional man who works at night and Saturdays instead of mowing the lawn, helping the Little League baseball team, and joining in neighborly low-pressure sociability. The suburbs continue the pattern of the fraternity house in making it hard for an individual to be a ratebuster or an isolate.

It is difficult to form a just estimate of the extent and scope of these changes. It is not new for the older generation to bewail the indolence of the young, and there is a tendency for the latter to maintain much of the older ethic screened by a new semantics and an altered ideology. Moreover, Americans in earlier periods were not uniformly work-minded. In Horace Greeley's account of his famous trip West in 1859 (which ended in his interviewing Brigham Young), he commented with disgust on the many squatters on Kansas homesteads who, in contrast to the industrious Mormons, sat around improvidently, building decent shelter neither for themselves nor for their stock (they sound a bit like Erskine Caldwell types). Similarly, the correspondence of railroad managers in the last century (and railroad managers were perhaps the most professional managerial groups as they were in charge of the largest enterprises) is full of complaints about the lack of labor discipline; this is one reason that the Chinese were brought in to work on the transcontinental roads. There were, it is evident, many backsliders in the earlier era from the all-pervading gospel of work, and the frontier, like many city slums, harbored a number of drifters. Today, in contrast, the gospel of work is far less tenacious and overbearing, but at the same time the labor force as a whole is post-industrial in the sense of having lost much of its pre-industrial resistance to the clock and to factory discipline generally.

Strenuous Leisure

So far, I have largely been discussing the uneven distribution of leisure in terms of differential attitudes towards work in different occupational groups. In comparison with the achievements of our occupational sociology, however, we have little comparable information concerning the sociology of leisure. For instance, we have very few inventories of how leisure is actually spent (apart from fairly complete information concerning exposure to the mass media). Pitirim Sorokin before World War II and more recently Albert J. Reiss, Jr. have tried to get people to keep diaries which would include accounts of their day-by-day use of leisure time; but these suffer from faulty memory and stereotyping (people often say, "one day is just like another," and report accordingly) as well as from omissions of fights and other improper activities. A more systematic study than most, by Alfred Clarke, found that radio and TV listening were the top two activities for both upper and lower prestige groups, followed by studying in the upper group and do-it-yourself activities in the lower. The latter spend much more time just driving around, as well as polishing the car; they also spend much more time in taverns. Only in the upper group do people go out to parties, as against simply dropping in on a neighbor to look at TV or chat in the kitchen; and going to meetings is also largely confined to the upper group. In both groups, commercial recreation outside the home, such as going to the movies, plays little part. This and other, more impressionistic studies point to the conclusion that the busier people, the professional and executives and better-educated groups generally, also lead a more active life in their time away from work; as the saying goes, they work hard and play hard. In Reiss's study, for example, there turned up a surgeon at a leading hospital who went to mass every morning, then to the hospital, then to attend to his private practice; he belonged to about every community organization, and he and his wife entertained three or four nights a week. Contrastingly, at the other end of the social scale, the unemployed as we know from several studies have in a psychological sense no leisure time at all; they, and the underprivileged generally, do not belong to voluntary associations (churches and unions are an occasional exception); they live what is often a shorter life on a slower timetable.

At the same time, as I have indicated above, it is among the less privileged groups relatively new to leisure and consumption that the zest for possessions retains something of its pristine energy. Consumership which is complex if not jaded among the better-educated strata seems to be relatively unequivocal among those recently released from poverty and constriction of choice. . . . With very little hope of making work more meaningful, these people look to their leisure time and consumership for the satisfactions and pride previously denied them by the social order.

I am suggesting here that millions of Americans, coming suddenly upon the inheritance of abundance, are able like other nouveau riche people in the past to coast upon the goals set out for them by their social and economic pace-setters. "Coast" is perhaps not the right word for so energetic a movement, one which continues to power the economy, as millions are moved out of dire poverty and subsistence into the strata which have some discretionary spending power; while in better educated strata the absence of goals for leisure and consumption is beginning, or so I would contend, to make itself felt. In these latter groups, it is no longer so easy to regard progress simply in terms of "more": more money, more free time, more things. There is a search for something more real as the basis for life, a search reflected in the vogue of psychoanalysis, of self-help books (and, in a few circles, of theology), of the growth of adult education courses which are non-vocational, and in the more serious non-fiction reading which is reflected in many of the new series of paperbound books. Such Americans are not satisfied simply to attain material comfort far beyond what their parents possessed or beyond what is obtained in most parts of the globe. In fact, the younger generation of reasonably well-off and well-educated Americans do not seem to me drivingly or basically materialistic; they have little ferocious desire for things for their own sake, let alone money or land for its own sake. At most it could be said that such Americans resent being deprived of those things they are supposed to have; consequently, they remain susceptible to advertising which tempts them with the halo of experience or associations surrounding goods—

although not with the goods themselves as sheer objects. Hence in these strata there is a tendency for people, once accustomed to upper-middle-class norms, to lose eagerness for bounteous spending on consumer goods. Moreover, such Americans tend more and more to secure their children's future, not by large capital acquisitions and inheritances, but by giving them a good education and the motives for achievement that go with it; they will try to pass on their values as an insurance of continuing middle-class position, rather than their possessions and their specific place in the occupational scheme. It is in such relatively sophisticated Americans that we can see foreshadowed a decline of interest in material goods that may be a long time appearing in the working class and lower white-collar groups.

Indeed, the amenities which such educated people desire, once their own families are well provided for, are not those which can be bought by individuals acting in isolation from each other. They are rather such social goods as pleasant cities and sprawl-free countrysides; adequate public services, including transport; educational and cultural facilities which stimulate all ages and stages; freedom from crowding in the sites of leisure; and in general, wise and magnanimous use of the surplus which individuals at this level no longer need. But it is just at this point that the paucity of our individual goals, when amplified at the general social level, creates the most terrifying problems.

Abundance for What?

Even the most confident economists cannot adequately picture a society which could readily stow away the goods likely to descend upon us in the next fifteen years (assuming only a modest rise in annual productivity), with any really sizable drop in defense expenditures. People who are forced by the recession or by fear of their neighbors' envy or by their own misgivings to postpone for a year the purchase of a new car may discover that a new car every three years instead of every two is quite satisfactory. And once they have two cars, a swimming pool and a boat, and summer and winter vacations, what then?

Increasingly, as we all know, the motivation researchers are being pressed to answer these questions, and to discover what the public does not yet know that it "wants." Just as we are lowering our water table by ever-deeper artesian wells and in general digging ever deeper for other treasures of the earth, so we are sinking deeper and deeper wells into people in the hope of coming upon "motives" which can power the economy or some particular sector of it. I am suggesting that such digging, such forcing emotions to externalize themselves, cannot continue much longer without man running dry.

Even now, some of the surplus whose existence presents us with such questions is being absorbed in the very process of its creation but by what I have termed the "conspicuous production" of our big corporations, acting as junior partners of the welfare state and absorbing all sorts of ancillary services for their own members and their own communities.

Defense expenditures loom so large in our political as well as economic horizon because they do offer an easy and seemingly feasible way out by creating goods which do not themselves create other goods. (They are "multipliers" only in a Keynesian sense.) But of course the international consequences as well as the long-range domestic ones point the way only to lunacy and the alternatives of destruction or the garrison state. Indeed in a recent article, "Economic Implications of Disarmament," Gerard Colm argues that it would be difficult to deploy for public services our rising productivity even without reducing defense expenditures. He sees education as potentially absorbing much the largest part of the surplus (education must be seen even now as the greatest leisure time-killer we have, keeping out of the labor force an increasingly large portion of the young). And Colm presents figures for highway and other transport, along with other public works, hospitals, and water conservation—yet these altogether hardly make up in ten years what we spend in one year for our armed forces. I would contend that expenditures which serve no real social imperative, other than propping up the economy or subduing the sibling rivalry of the armed services, will eventually produce wasteful byproducts to slow that economy down in a tangle of vested inefficiencies, excessively conspicuous production, lowered work morale, and lack of purpose and genuine inventiveness. The word "to soldier" means "to loaf" and conscription gives training in soldiering to a large proportion of the future work-force (despite islands of ascetism in the Strategic Air Command or the air-borne "brushfire" infantry). For a time, men will go on producing because they have got the habit, but the habit is not contagious. Men will scarcely go on producing as mere items in a multiplier effect or conscripts in an endless Cold War, nor will they greatly extend themselves to earn more money which they are increasingly bored with spending. To be sure, many workers have little objection to getting paid without "earning" it by traditional standards of effortfulness. And while those standards are usually irrelevant in a society of advanced technology and high expenditures on research and development, there are certainly many parts of the economy, notably in the service trades, whose gross inefficiency we only conceal from ourselves by contrasting America with pre-industrial societies or with those possessing far less adequate resources of men and machines—if we compare ourselves with the West Germans, for instance, or with the Canadians, the advance in our economy since 1946, great as it is in absolute terms, is unimpressive. The pockets of efficiency in our society are visible and made more so by the myth that we are efficient; hence, the evidence of disintegration and incompetence that is all around us strikes us as temporary or aberrant.

The Dislocation of Desire

Correspondingly, some of our desires have been made highly visible by advertising and market research and lead to equally visible results such as good cars and, intermittently, good roads to drive them over. But other desires, which require cooperation to be effective, are often lamely organized and all but invisible. Thus, while some of us have a missionary zeal for learning, which we regard as the basis of later leisure as well as later employment, we have not been helped even by the push of sputnik to get a bill for school construction past the same Congress which eagerly voted Federal money for highways (in part, no doubt, because the annual maintenance of schools falls upon a local tax base which grows constantly more inadequate while the maintenance of highways can be more easily financed from gasoline and registration taxes). Other services, not so clearly "a good thing" as secondary and university education, are even more lacking in organized institutional forms which would permit the channeling of our surplus in ways which would improve the quality and texture of daily life. For example, even the great demand for scenic beauty (anemically reflected in the new highways) cannot make itself politically felt in preserving the countryside against roadside slums and metropolitan expansion, while men of wealth are missing who could buy up whole counties and give them to the nation as a national park. We see one consequence on summer weekends when millions pour onto the roads and breathe each other's fumes and crowd each other's resorts. And we see too that leisure is cut down by the time taken to get to and from work— commuting time increased by the desire to live in the suburbs in order to enjoy leisure! As our resources dwindle in comparison with population and as individual abundance creates social blight, we will increasingly find little solace in leisure without privacy. It is extraordinary how little we have anticipated the problems of the bountiful future, other than to fall back on remedies which did not work in the less bountiful past, such as individualism, thrift, hard work, and enterprise on the one side, or harmony, togetherness, and friendliness on the other. Meanwhile, we stave off the fear of satiation in part by scanning the technological horizon for new goods which we will all learn to want, in part by the delaying tactic of a semi-planned recession, and, as already indicated, in part by the endless race of armaments.

That race has its cultural as well as Keynesian dynamic: as poll data show, a majority or large plurality of Americans expect war, though perhaps in a rather abstract way—war is one of those extrapolations from the past; like technological progress, we find it hard to resist. And, on the one hand, the threat of war is one factor in discouraging long-term plans, while, on the other hand, the continuation of the Cold War provides a sort of alternative to planning. Thus, there tends to be a state of suspended animation in the discussion concerning the quality of life a rich society should strive for; social inventiveness tends to be channeled into the defense of past gains rather than into ideas for a better proportionality between leisure and work. Like soldiers off duty, "as you were," we subsist in default of more humane hopes.

But I should add that no society has ever been in the same position as ours, of coming close to fulfilling the age-old dream of freedom from want, the dream of plenty. And I want to repeat that millions of Americans, perhaps still the great majority, find sufficient vitality in pursuit of that dream: the trip to the end of the consumer rainbow retains its magic for the previously deprived. It is only the minority where, looking further ahead, we can see already the signs of a generation, prepared for Paradise Lost, which does not know what to do with Paradise Found. Regrettably, it will not be given a long time to come to a decision. For, by concentrating all energies on preserving freedom from want and pressing for consumer satiation at ever more opulent levels, we jeopardize this achievement in a world where there are many more poor nations than rich ones and in which there are many more desires, even among ourselves, for things other than abundance.

Part Three
The New
Technology and
Emerging Issues

Three future problem areas in which science and technology are deeply involved are considered in this section: the outlook on population and resources, the rights of the individual in the society of the future and the future of the human race. Important human values come into conflict in all of these areas. The principal question raised is: should the advancement of science be submitted to a system of rational planning and control?

7
Population and Resources

Science in the past century has waged an increasingly successful war against disease. As a consequence, the mortality rate began to decline in Western Europe and America during the latter half of the nineteenth century. Because relatively inexpensive and effective means of reducing disease and mortality have become available, countries all over the world in the twentieth century have experienced declines in the death rate. The rapid expansion in the population of the world results from the fact that mortality has fallen and fertility has not yet been checked. How critical is the problem of overpopulation? What are the dangers accompanying a rapid population growth? What future does a crowded planet have in store for man? What is being done and what *can* be done to reduce human fertility? Will our natural resources be sufficient to provide for the huge population which has been projected for the future? Can science and technology alleviate the problem caused by their success? Can a stable world population be achieved? The selections in this chapter shed some light on these questions.

Aldous Huxley views the situation with a great deal of pessimism.

211

He sees the rapidly increasing population in underdeveloped societies as one of the main threats to democracy. With more mouths to feed, the economic level of the people in these societies cannot be raised. Hence, discontent and violence will be rampant, and either the Communists or the military will seize control of the governments. The highly industrialized societies, Huxley believes, must cease thinking in terms of national interest and prestige, must widen their horizons, and must consider world ecology. We should think less about placing men on the moon and more about the problems of population and resources in the twenty-first century. Only with a global picture and a commitment of monetary resources at the present time, can we begin to solve the problems of overpopulation.

Joseph Wood Krutch pinpoints other facets of overpopulation. Even in Western societies, where it is known that fertility can be controlled by contraceptive methods, populations are increasing. This indicates that man has an instinct to reproduce. Krutch asks whether it is possible to conquer this instinct. Like Huxley, he is pessimistic about the future, but for different reasons. Man must have room to move about. Man should be close to nature. Living in the crowded cities of the future, man will change—and the change will not be for the better.

Joseph Fisher is much more optimistic than Huxley or Krutch. Recent trends in family planning, he states, have not been disappointing. We still have plenty of room, and he does not foresee that the world's resources will be outstripped by its population for the next thirty years or so. He does insist that vast technological innovation and social and political adaptation will be absolutely necessary if population continues to increase after the year 2000. But he is optimistic, as is revealed in his closing statement, that we should not overlook the extraordinary capacity of man to adapt to changing situations.

A report of the National Academy of Sciences highlights the major factors that militate against fertility control and family limitations in various countries of the world. Attitudes, personal and familial factors, communications, economics, and organizational difficulties—all play a part. It is primarily the tremendous force of tradition which constitutes the barrier to programs of voluntary fertility control. But the report lists several favorable factors that are beginning to produce results. Governments and institutions are lending support to programs of fertility control, and social changes in underdeveloped countries are bound to help.

P. B. Medawar discusses the statistical methods employed in predicting population growth. Though he agrees that there will continue to be a population increase, he warns against the fallacies in prediction. It is misleading, he states, to assess the future size of population from the fertility that prevails in any one year or group of years. Fertility depends upon many factors; we do not completely understand how these factors interact; fertility varies sharply from year to year. For this reason, he does not believe that there is a possibility of our achieving a stable human population.

Aldous Huxley
THE POLITICS OF ECOLOGY

. . . On the biological level, advancing science and technology have set going a revolutionary process that seems to be destined for the next century at least, perhaps for much longer, to exercise a decisive influence upon the destinies of all human societies and their individual members. In the course of the last fifty years extremely effective methods for lowering the prevailing rates of infant and adult mortality were developed by Western scientists. These methods were very simple and could be applied with the expenditure of very little money by very small numbers of not very highly trained technicians. For these reasons, and because everyone regards life as intrinsically good and death as intrinsically bad, they were in fact applied on a worldwide scale. The results were spectacular. In the past, high birth rates were balanced by high death rates. Thanks to science, death rates have been halved but, except in the most highly industrialized, contraceptive-using countries, birth rates remain as high as ever. An enormous and accelerating increase in human numbers has been the inevitable consequence.

At the beginning of the Christian era, so demographers assure us, our planet supported a human population of about two hundred and fifty millions. When the Pilgrim Fathers stepped ashore, the figure had risen to about five hundred millions. We see, then, that in the relatively recent past it took sixteen hundred years for the human species to double its numbers. Today world population stands at three thousand millions. By the year 2000, unless something appallingly bad or miraculously good should happen in the interval, six thousand millions of us will be sitting down to

Aldous Huxley, *The Politics of Ecology: The Question of Survival* (Santa Barbara, Calif.: Center for the Study of Democratic Institutions, 1964). Reprinted by permission of the Fund for the Republic, Inc., Center for the Study of Democratic Institutions. Aldous Huxley was a noted author of many novels, essays, and short stories. Perhaps his most widely known work was *Brave New World*.

breakfast every morning. In a word, twelve times as many people are destined to double their numbers in one-fortieth of the time.

This is not the whole story. In many areas of the world human numbers are increasing at a rate much higher than the average for the whole species. In India, for example, the rate of increase is now 2.3 percent per annum. By 1990 its four hundred and fifty million inhabitants will have become nine hundred million inhabitants. A comparable rate of increase will raise the population of China to the billion mark by 1980. In Ceylon, in Egypt, in many of the countries of South and Central America, human numbers are increasing at an annual rate of 3 percent. The result will be a doubling of their present populations in approximately twenty-three years.

On the social, political, and economic levels, what is likely to happen in an underdeveloped country whose people double themselves in a single generation, or even less? An underdeveloped society is a society without adequate capital resources (for capital is what is left over after primary needs have been satisfied, and in underdeveloped countries most people never satisfy their primary needs); a society without a sufficient force of trained teachers, administrators, and technicians; a society with few or no industries and few or no developed sources of industrial power; a society, finally, with enormous arrears to be made good in food production, education, road building, housing, and sanitation. A quarter of a century from now, when there will be twice as many of them as there are today, what is the likelihood that the members of such a society will be better fed, housed, clothed, and schooled than at present? And what are the chances in such a society for the maintenance, if they already exist, or the creation, if they do not exist, of democratic institutions?

Not long ago Mr. Eugene Black, the former president of the World Bank, expressed the opinion that it would be extremely difficult, perhaps even impossible, for an underdeveloped country with a very rapid rate of population increase to achieve full industrialization. All its resources, he pointed out, would be absorbed year by year in the task of supplying, or not quite supplying, the primary needs of its new members. Merely to stand still, to maintain its current subhumanly inadequate standard of living, will require hard work and the expenditure of all the nation's available capital. Available capital may be increased by loans and gifts from abroad; but in a world where the industrialized nations are involved in power politics and an increasingly expensive armament race, there will never be enough foreign aid to make much difference. And even if the loans and gifts to underdeveloped countries were to be substantially increased, any resulting gains would be largely nullified by the uncontrolled population explosion.

The situation of these nations with such rapidly increasing populations reminds one of Lewis Carroll's parable in *Through the Looking Glass*, where Alice and the Red Queen start running at full speed and run for a long time until Alice is completely out of breath. When they stop, Alice is amazed to see that they are still at their starting point. In the looking glass world, if you wish to retain your present position, you must run as fast as you can. If you wish to get ahead, you must run at least twice as fast as you can.

If Mr. Black is correct (and there are plenty of economists and demographers who share his opinion), the outlook for most of the world's newly independent and economically non-viable nations is gloomy indeed. To those that have shall be given. Within the next ten or twenty years, if war can be avoided, poverty will almost have disappeared from the highly industrialized and contraceptive-using societies of the West. Meanwhile, in the underdeveloped and uncontrolledly breeding societies of Asia, Africa, and Latin America the condition of the masses (twice as numerous, a generation from now, as they are today) will have become no better and may even be decidedly worse than it is at present. Such a decline is foreshadowed by current statistics of the Food and Agriculture Organization of the United Nations. In some underdeveloped regions of the world, we are told, people are somewhat less adequately fed, clothed, and housed than were their parents and grandparents thirty and forty years ago. And what of elementary education? UNESCO recently provided an answer. Since the end of World War II heroic efforts have been made to teach the whole world how to read. The population explosion has largely stultified these efforts. The absolute number of illiterates is greater now than at any time.

The contraceptive revolution which, thanks to advancing science and technology, has made it possible for the highly developed societies of the West to offset the consequences of death control by a planned control of births, has had as yet no effect upon the family life of people in underdeveloped countries. This is not surprising. Death control, as I have already remarked, is easy, cheap, and can be carried out by a small force of technicians. Birth control, on the other hand, is rather expensive, involves the whole adult population, and demands of those who practice it a good deal of forethought and directed willpower. To persuade hundreds of millions of men and women to abandon their tradition-hallowed views of sexual morality, then to distribute and teach them to make use of contraceptive devices or fertility-controlling drugs—this is a huge and difficult task, so huge and so difficult that it seems very unlikely that it can be successfully carried out, within a sufficiently short space of time, in any of the countries where control of the birth rate is most urgently needed.

Extreme poverty, when combined with ignorance, breeds that

lack of desire for better things which has been called "wantlessness"—the resigned acceptance of a subhuman lot. But extreme poverty, when it is combined with the knowledge that some societies are affluent, breeds envious desires and the expectation that these desires must of necessity, and very soon, be satisfied. By means of the mass media (those easily exportable products of advancing science and technology) some knowledge of what life is like in affluent societies has been widely disseminated throughout the world's underdeveloped regions. But, alas, the science and technology which have given the industrial West its cars, refrigerators, and contraceptives have given the people of Asia, Africa, and Latin America only movies and radio broadcasts, which they are too simple-minded to be able to criticize, together with a population explosion, which they are still too poor and too tradition-bound to be able to control by deliberate family planning.

In the context of a 3, or even of a mere 2 percent annual increase in numbers, high expectations are foredoomed to disappointment. From disappointment, through resentful frustration, to widespread social unrest the road is short. Shorter still is the road from social unrest, through chaos, to dictatorship, possibly of the Communist party, more probably of generals and colonels. It would seem, then, that for two-thirds of the human race now suffering from the consequences of uncontrolled breeding in a context of industrial backwardness, poverty, and illiteracy, the prospects for democracy, during the next ten or twenty years, are very poor.

A rapid and accelerating population increase that will nullify the best efforts of underdeveloped societies to better their lot and will keep two-thirds of the human race in a condition of misery in anarchy or of misery under dictatorship, and the intensive preparations for a new kind of war that, if it breaks out, may bring irretrievable ruin to the one-third of the human race now living prosperously in highly industrialized societies—these are the two main threats to democracy now confronting us. Can these threats be eliminated? Or, if not eliminated, at least reduced?

My own view is that only by shifting our collective attention from the merely political to the basic biological aspects of the human situation can we hope to mitigate and shorten the time of troubles into which, it would seem, we are now moving. We cannot do without politics; but we can no longer afford to indulge in bad, unrealistic politics. To work for the survival of the species as a whole and for the actualization in the greatest possible number of individual men and women of their potentialities for good will, intelligence, and creativity—this, in the world of today, is good, realistic politics. To cultivate the religion of idolatrous nationalism, to subordinate the interests of the species and its individual members to the interests of a single national state and its ruling minority—in the context of the population explosion, missiles, and atomic warheads, this is bad and thoroughly unrealistic politics. Unfortunately, it is to bad and unrealistic politics that our rulers are now committed.

Ecology is the science of the mutual relations of organisms with their environment and with one another. Only when we get it into our collective head that the basic problem confronting twentieth-century man is an ecological problem will our politics improve and become realistic. How does the human race propose to survive and, if possible, improve the lot and the intrinsic quality of its individual members? Do we propose to live on this planet in symbiotic harmony with our environment? Or, preferring to be wantonly stupid, shall we choose to live like murderous and suicidal parasites that kill their host and so destroy themselves?

Committing that sin of overweening bumptiousness, which the Greeks called *hubris*, we behave as though we were not members of earth's ecological community, as though we were privileged and, in some sort, supernatural beings and could throw our weight around like gods. But in fact we are, among other things, animals—emergent parts of the natural order. If our politicians were realists, they would think rather less about missiles and the problem of landing a couple of astronauts on the moon, rather more about hunger and moral squalor and the problem of enabling three billion men, women, and children, who will soon be six billions, to lead a tolerably human existence without, in the process, ruining and befouling their planetary environment.

Animals have no souls; therefore, according to the most authoritative Christian theologians, they may be treated as though they were things. The truth, as we are now beginning to realize, is that even things ought not to be treated as *mere* things. They should be treated as though they were parts of a vast living organism. "Do as you would be done by." The Golden Rule applies to our dealings with nature no less than to our dealings with our fellow-men. If we hope to be well treated by nature, we must stop talking about "mere things" and start treating our planet with intelligence and consideration.

Power politics in the context of nationalism raises problems that, except by war, are practically insoluble. The problems of ecology, on the other hand, admit of a rational solution and can be tackled without the arousal of those violent passions always associated with dogmatic ideology and nationalistic idolatry. There may be arguments about the best way of raising wheat in a cold climate or of re-afforesting a denuded mountain. But such arguments never lead to organized slaughter. Organized slaughter is the result of arguments about such questions as the following: Which is the best nation? The best religion? The best political theory? The best form of government? Why are other people so stupid and wicked? Why can't they see how good and intelligent *we* are? Why do they resist our beneficent efforts to bring them under our control and make them like ourselves?

To questions of this kind the final answer has always been war. "War," said Clausewitz, "is not merely a political act, but also a political instrument, a continuation of political relationships, a carrying out of the same by other means." This was true enough in the eighteen thirties, when Clausewitz published his famous treatise; and it continued to be true until 1945. Now, pretty obviously, nuclear weapons, long-range rockets, nerve gases, bacterial aerosols, and the "Laser" (that highly promising, latest addition to the world's military arsenals) have given the lie to Clausewitz. All-out war with modern weapons is no longer a continuation of previous policy; it is a complete and irreversible break with previous policy.

Power politics, nationalism, and dogmatic ideology are luxuries that the human race can no longer afford. Nor, as a species, can we afford the luxury of ignoring man's ecological situation. By shifting our attention from the now completely irrelevant and anachronistic politics of nationalism and military power to the problems of the human species and the still inchoate politics of human ecology we shall be killing two birds with one stone—reducing the threat of sudden destruction by scientific war and at the same time reducing the threat of more gradual biological disaster.

The beginnings of ecological politics are to be found in the special services of the United Nations Organization. UNESCO, the Food and Agriculture Organization, the World Health Organization, the various Technical Aid Services—all these are, partially or completely, concerned with the ecological problems of the human species. In a world where political problems are thought of and worked upon within a frame of reference whose coordinates are nationalism and military power, these ecology-oriented organizations are regarded as peripheral. If the problems of humanity could be thought about and acted upon within a frame of reference that has survival for the species, the well-being of individuals, and the actualization of man's desirable potentialities as its coordinates, these peripheral organizations would become central. The subordinate politics of survival, happiness, and personal fulfillment would take the place now occupied by the politics of power, ideology, nationalistic idolatry, and unrelieved misery.

In the process of reaching this kind of politics we shall find, no doubt, that we have done something, in President Wilson's prematurely optimistic words, "to make the world safe for democracy."

Joseph Wood Krutch
A NATURALIST LOOKS AT OVERPOPULATION

One of the many indications that the population explosion poses the most desperate problem of our day is the fact that it inevitably arises in connection with every approach to the analysis of our civilization and its prospects. To the critic of culture it is a part of our emphasis on quantity rather than quality. To the economist it raises the question of economic stability. To the political scientist it evokes the specter of wars for Lebensraum; to the conservationist the equally terrifying specter of universal starvation.

To the specialists in their various fields I leave the discussions appropriate to them and say only something about the situation as it appears to a naturalist; to one who is, of course, aware of its other aspects but tends to think first of man's place in nature and the consequences of modern man's refusal to accept the fact that he is indeed part of a scheme which he can to some extent modify but which he cannot supersede by a scheme of his own making.

It is true, of course, that man became man rather than simply a member of the animal kingdom when he ceased merely to accept and submit to the conditions of the natural world. But it is also true that for many thousands of years his resistance to the laws of animal nature and his modifications of his environment were so minor that they did not seriously interfere with natural law and required no such elaborate management of compensating adjustments as became necessary as soon as his intentions, desires, and will became effective enough to interfere with the scheme of nature.

It was not until well into the nineteenth century that his interferences did become extensive enough to force a dawning realization of the fact that you cannot "control nature" at one point without taking steps to readjust at another the balance which has been upset. Improved methods of agriculture exhaust the soil unless artificial steps are taken to conserve and renew it. You cannot destroy all the vermin without risking the destruction of useful animals. You cannot, as we are just discovering, poison noxious insects without risking the extinction of birds who are an even more effective control. It is not that we should not interfere with nature, but that we must face the consequences of this interference and counteract or ameliorate them by other interferences. You dare not, to put it as simply as possible, attempt to manage at one point and to let nature take her course at another.

Considered in connection with this fact the population explosion becomes merely a special (and especially ominous) example of a phenomenon characteristic of civilized man's peculiar place in nature where he is the only creature capable of effectively interfering with her operations while he remains at the same time not wise enough always to foresee the unwanted consequences of his interference. To reduce it again to the simplest possible terms, he has interfered with nature by preserving individual lives far more successfully than nature had ever been able to preserve them; at the same time he has allowed nature to take her course so far as propagation is concerned. As a consequence either one of two things must happen. Either he must control birth as well as death or nature will step in and by her own rough but effective methods—starvation, disease, or the brutal death struggle for food and living room—eliminate the excess which failure to manage the consequences of his management has produced. No matter what fantastic increases technology may bring in the number of men the earth is able to support, the limit must be reached sooner or later.

Every ecologist knows that nature left to herself works out a balance of populations adjusted to the available space and food supply, and that this balance, which involves the various aspects of competition including the predator and his prey, is often remarkably stable over long periods of time. But every ecologist knows also that it may be disturbed and then destroyed by what might appear to be the very slight intervention of man. Introduce and then forget a few goats into the biota of an isolated island, and in a few years nothing but goats—many of them starving—will remain. Nature is efficient but slow. It takes centuries for her to work out a balance. Man can in a few decades make a desert which nature cannot reclaim in centuries. So it is also with instinct, which is geared to millennia, while consciously directed purpose is effective within a few years. The instinct which tells us that the more children we can produce the better, developed in us when man was dominated by nature. It persists fatally in a world he has come to manage and mismanage.

Early proponents of planned parenthood assumed that once easy and reliable methods of birth control were available, convenient, and legal the only remaining impediment to a rational solution of the problem would be that of religious or moral resistance. But in my opinion the existence of the ancient instinct deep in the biological organism is a more formidable enemy than religious dogma. In the United States at least the population has been increasing at an accelerated rate at the same time that methods of birth control have become better known and more readily accessible. The only possible explanation is simply that people continue to *want* more children than is desirable now that the mortality rate has been so greatly reduced. Many who are intellectually convinced that population growth should be reduced nevertheless rejoice in at least their own large families because the impulse to increase and multiply was an instinct long before it was a biblical injunction. Man the thinker lags behind man the technician. No less important is the fact that his instincts lag, not years but millennia, behind even his thinking. The most crucial question is not can he be made to *believe* that too many children are undesirable, but can he conquer his instincts sufficiently to make him *feel* what his intellect has convinced him of?

So much for the special ways in which the naturalist sees the problem. He tends also to be more acutely aware than others of a particular aspect of the undesirable consequences of overpopulation. Many sociologists and political scientists recognize the fact that the question is not simply how many people the earth could possibly support, but what is the optimum number from the standpoint of the possibility of a good life. Just as it is foolish to ask what is the largest number of children a family could possibly consist of rather than how many constitute an ideal family unit, so it is foolish to ask how many could be crowded onto our globe rather than what number can live happily there. Men need not only food and a place to sleep but also room to move about in. It is at least possible to believe that cities are already too big and that life would become almost intolerable if they were both more densely crowded and so merged one with another that there was no escaping from them.

Of this the naturalist is often more acutely aware than either the sociologist or the political scientist because he is more completely convinced than they sometimes are that the best life for the human being is one which is led, partly at least, in the context of nature rather than in a context which consists exclusively of the man-made environment. For a large part of the existing human race in the centers of civilization, contact with the natural world is tending to diminish almost to the vanishing point while he has little experience with anything except bricks, steel and concrete on the one hand and mechanical contrivances on the other. As the cities spread and the country shrinks he is more and more imprisoned with his fellows in a world that has ceased to be even aware of many of the things of which he was once an intimate part. Already he has pushed into extinction many of the creatures with which he once shared the earth.

Those who feel that he has already begun to suffer from this fact, talk about recreational areas, about nature education, about national parks and even about wilderness areas. To some extent they can still meet the objections of those who say that we cannot afford to forego the use of any of our forests, or mountains, or deserts. But if our population continues to grow at its present rate, it will soon become evident that we do indeed need every available acre of possibly usable land either for agriculture or for building lots. Much of what is called conservation today is no more than a useful delaying action. The time may soon come when it will no longer be possible to protest against the despoliation of this or that park, or forest, or river. Hence the conservationist also must face the fact that behind almost every problem of today lies the problem of population. Unless that problem is solved, none of the others can be.

Let us suppose for a moment that those are in the right who say that the context of nature has ceased to be the most desirable context for civilized life, that man can live in a wholly man-made world and that he will in time forget all that he once drew from his contemplation of that world of which he has ceased to be a part. Let us suppose further that his increase in numbers stopped before space itself gave out, and that he has reached what some seem to think of as the ideal state, i.e., living in cities which are almost coextensive with the surface of the earth, nourishing himself on products of laboratories rather than farms, and dealing only with either other men or the machines they have created.

What will he then have become? Will he not have become a creature whose whole being has ceased to resemble Homo sapiens as we in our history have known him? He will have ceased to be consciously a part of that nature from which he sprang. He will no longer have, as he now does, the companionship of other creatures who share with him the mysterious privilege of being alive. The emotions which have inspired a large part of all our literature, music, and art will no longer be meaningful to him. No flower will suggest thoughts too deep for tears. No bird song will remind him of the kind of joy he no longer knows. Will the human race have then become men-like-gods, or only men-like-ants?

To this question the naturalist has his own answer just as he has his own answer to the question why population continues to grow so rapidly in a world already at least beginning to be aware that this growth is a threat. His approach may seem to others somewhat oblique, even distorted by his special interests. But at least his conclusions are the same as those to which many other approaches no less inevitably lead.

Joseph L. Fisher
PERSPECTIVES ON POPULATION AND RESOURCES

If the population of the world were to go on increasing at the present rate of nearly 2 percent a year, today's three billion persons would double by the year 2000 and would double again every thirty-seven years thereafter. By 2500 A.D. the globe would be one vast anthill with an average density over all the land areas equal to that now to be found on Manhattan Island below Central Park during the daytime. If population were to increase at one percent a year, the same result would inevitably follow; it would just take longer.

On the other hand, if the three billion men, women, and children now living on earth were packed into a box the shape of a cube, allowing a space 6 feet by 2 feet by 1 foot for each one, the box would be about five-eighths of a mile on an edge. If this box were pushed off the edge of the Grand Canyon of the Colorado and tumbled to the bottom, it would appear to be about the size of a child's play block to an observer looking down from the rim. On this basis of "standing room only," the anthill of people that would exist if all the world were as crowded as Manhattan could fit in the Grand Canyon and hardly be noticed.

But who wants to be wedged into a box? Such examples are good for amusing or frightening readers of the Sunday supplements and pseudo-science fiction, but for little else. They do, perhaps, point to the importance of the way one looks at population and resources: one's perspective at the corner of Fifth Avenue and 42nd Street at noon is quite different from that on the Grand Canyon's rim. Otherwise they are fantasies, statistically impeccable though they may be. They are of no help to persons seeking to understand and mitigate the many large problems that grow out of the resources-population relationship.

Despite the pace of change of the modern world and the chance

Joseph L. Fisher, "Perspectives on Population and Resources," from the *1963 Annual Report of Resources for the Future, Inc.,* (Washington, D.C., 1963). Reprinted by permission. Dr. Fisher, an economist, is president of Resources for the Future, Inc., Washington, D.C.

of unforeseen events, history remains our most reliable guide to the unfolding future. Few of the great innovations fail to cast some shadow before them. The remarkable advances in atomic energy—some of which, like the use of radio-active isotopes, have already found widespread application, and others of which, like the production of electric power, are now on the verge of widespread development—were foretold at least several decades ago in the findings of the scientists. As long ago as 1905, Einstein put forth his hypothesis that energy varied directly with mass times the velocity of light squared. Not long afterward Goddard began experimenting with rockets, building upon scientific discoveries going back at least as far as Newton and designs hinted at by Leonardo da Vinci.

In speculating about the future of population and resources we are influenced not only by the dismal analyses of Malthus and Ricardo a hundred and fifty years ago and by the subsequent more optimistic speculations of scientists and engineers, but we may also be guided by an examination of ever-improving statistical knowledge about population and resources.

Central to our recent book, *Resources in America's Future*, were a number of studies in which, based largely on past and current trends, we undertook to look ahead as far as 1980 and 2000 in terms of systematic and disciplined projections of population, demand for natural resources, and resource supply problems. These studies have elaborated for the United States a picture in which anticipated population growth can be accommodated so far as supplies of food products, most construction materials, energy sources, water, and other raw materials are concerned—but not without numerous problems such as having enough good-quality fresh water in a particular place, or enough high-grade sawtimber at a particular time, or enough open space and recreation land near large cities. But the over-all view is one of adequacy to support many more people at rising levels of living.

The analyses accompanying these projections specify clearly that the favorable trends will not continue unless technologic advances and economic adaptations of them continue, unless foreign sources of raw materials remain open, and unless government resource policies and private management of resource enterprises improve in farsightedness, flexibility, and consistency. But each of these provisos is judged to present difficulties and opportunities well within the capacity of research, policy, and action to deal with successfully.

These rather comforting conclusions are developed for the United States; the findings should not be transferred to other parts of the world, certainly the more densely populated and less developed areas, without looking carefully into demographic, resource, and other trends in these places. In a monograph nearing completion Neal Potter and I have made a preliminary attempt to examine these trends for other world areas on the basis of rather sketchy and unreliable statistical trends. For what they are worth, the trends indicate that the very rapid population increase in most of the less developed countries will continue to be accompanied by even more rapid increases in demand for food products, energy supplies, fresh water, and metal products. There will be a combination, that is, of more people with larger requirements per person. In the last few decades most of these countries have been able to meet increases in such demands and to register small but encouraging gains in levels of living. To continue these gains and boost them to higher levels is by no means impossible, but it will require the strenuous effort of the labor force plus vigorous enterprise in both government and private sectors of the countries' economies. Further assistance from more advanced countries undoubtedly will be of critical importance, as will the maintenance and improvement of a general world system in which all countries may pursue their objectives in peace and in co-operation with one another.

We venture the very tentative view that for the world as a whole effective demand for resources by the year 2000 might require increases in supply of the following magnitudes:

1. A tripling of aggregate food output just to provide adequate calories, and considerably more to provide adequate proteins and vitamins.
2. A fivefold increase in energy output.
3. Perhaps a fivefold increase in output of iron ore and ferroalloys, and somewhat less in copper, but a much larger increase in bauxite-aluminum.
4. A possible tripling or more of lumber output.

These estimates were reached after considering population and economic trends in various areas of the world during the past decade or more, and after considering per capita resource demands that might arise if less developed areas reached levels now found in the more developed places. The population projections used—nearly 7 billion by 2000—were those most recently published by the United Nations as "high" figures. Recent evidence indicates that the high estimates may prove to be nearer the mark than lower estimates; furthermore, high estimates have the advantage of testing more severely the adequacy of resource supplies. If a country can meet a high demand, it should have less trouble meeting any lower level.

No uniform picture of resource adequacy is presented by the various major world regions. The outlook can be optimistic, at least to the end of this century, for the United States, Canada, Western Europe, the Soviet Union, Eastern Europe, Australia, New Zealand, and a few other places. In the densely populated, less developed areas the outlook is precarious, especially for food supplies. The prospects for fairly rapidly increasing per capita energy consumption appear much more favorable. Fortunately, more abundant and reasonably cheap energy, plus related capital investments and knowledge, can lift food output through the production of more fertilizers, the pumping of irrigation water, greater use of mechanized farm equipment, and through rural electrification. But the problem of sufficient food, in quantity and quality, will remain a severe one.

Such an effort to look ahead at the world population-resource picture serves to highlight the kind of information we need to answer more definitely the question: Are resources becoming more or less scarce in various parts of the world? Only after reliable information becomes available on trends of resource production, consumption, price, sources, and the like, shall we be able to make projections that are meaningful and examine in specific terms the position of the less developed countries in relation to sustained increases in their levels of living. For the time being, the matter will have to remain largely speculative with the answer hinging on many *if's* regarding technological innovation, efforts to reduce the birth rate, the transfer of investment funds and technical aid from more developed countries, and so on.

The question inevitably arises: Would the world, or the heavily populated poorer countries, be better off with fewer people or with slower rates of population increase? The search for the optimum population or optimum rate of population increase is a difficult one, whatever the term "optimum" may mean. Economists usually mean by "optimum population increase" (or decrease) that rate which maximizes per capita income over time. The optimum population, therefore, depends not only on the rate of population increase, the discovery and availability of raw materials, and the rate of technological development, but also on the capacity of social organizations and institutions to embrace change. Much depends also on how hard and long people want to work; the trade-off point between more leisure time and more work is significant. People and cultures take different views on this question.

It is quite likely that the material level of living in the less developed countries would increase more rapidly if there were fewer people and if population increase were less, although simply to assert this does not prove it. Babies eventually grow up and become producers as well as consumers. By stimulating demand, a growing population casts a favorable influence over the amount of investment that developers are willing to make. On the other hand, a very large population can make it difficult for a country to produce a margin over and above what is needed simply to keep the population alive. New capital formation is hard to come by, children have to go to work before they are sufficiently educated and trained for more productive jobs, health standards will be low with insufficient amounts and qualities of food, and horizons of ambitions will tend to be limited to scraping enough together to meet immediate needs.

The upshot of our preliminary world studies and projections seems to be that in the perspective of three or four decades ahead the population-resources outlook is not without elements of hope. The trend in living levels in most places has been upward, though in many instances painfully slow. It is an open question whether material aspirations will run so far in advance of what can be achieved that mass frustration will set in. This in turn would be destructive of peaceful and reasonably democratic social orders. Modest material gains may not be enough. All the resource economist can say is that foreseeable population increases over the next thirty or so years will not inevitably outstrip resource supplies. The opposite seems more likely: that improved technology applied more widely, harder work, and better management will make possible continued gains in levels of living. Furthermore, a number of less developed countries appear to be on the threshold of take-off into rapid economic development following the recent path of such countries as Japan and the Soviet Union and the earlier path of the countries of Western Europe and Northern America.

In certain of the less material aspects of life, many observers foresee dire consequences in continued rapid population increase. Open spaces will diminish; natural areas will be spoiled; soil, air, and water will be increasingly polluted; and traditional ways of life will fall victims of the increased density of people and economic activity. These conclusions follow from a particular view of the world and its future, to which demonstrations of material adequacy are beside the point. Inevitably, for such persons, the answer in large measure lies in reducing the rate of increase in population; for some it means reducing the actual number of people. This point of view, especially in its extreme form, fails to recognize current trends: almost certainly there are going to be more people for some years ahead regardless of the problems they may cause or what efforts may be undertaken to slow the rate of growth. A more moderate approach would entail efforts to check population increase combined with more emphasis on careful planning to retain numerous natural areas and to abate environmental pollution.

In this regard recent trends are not entirely disappointing. In the United States, for example, a century ago we had no system of national forests and national parks, whereas now more than 200 million acres are in these categories. A number of wilderness areas have already been designated and Congress for several years has seemed to be on the verge of giving official status as protected areas to large additional areas. Stream pollution has become a more vexing problem in many respects as cities have grown and industries have spread; on the other hand, the more extreme consequences of pollution, such as epidemics of typhoid, seem to be a thing of the past. Furthermore, water pollution abatement techniques are improving; public bodies and private corporations seem to be willing to devote more money to these activities, and we are beginning to undertake water quality control for whole river basins on the basis of systematic analysis of interrelated hydrologic, biochemical, economic, and other data that bear on the problem.

So far as the bulk of the world's population in Asia, Africa, and Latin America is concerned, demographic, technologic, and economic evidence is not conclusive on the question of population versus resources. The coin could come down on either side. History permits a cautious optimism, as do the most disciplined projections that we have been able to muster.

Where does this leave us with regard to programs for the conservation of natural resources? Will these programs be necessary to survival, to rising levels of living? Or will they prove to be more or less useless, victims of the onrush of science and technology and the cleverness of social adaptation?

Several reasons for vigorous efforts toward conservation will remain important, but fear of running out of things is not one of the better ones. Conservation, or wise and careful use with an eye to the future as well as the present, will be desirable as a matter of prudence. "Waste not, want not" is still a serviceable maxim. It can, in fact, be said that conservation is society's insurance policy against the risk that the rate of technological development will slow down, or that the rate of population increase will not slow down, or that projections of resource demands and supplies will be far off the mark, as they have been frequently in the past. A large share of conservation activity makes good sense by economic calculations, but society would be well advised to carry out even more. The general welfare for future years can justify fairly large premiums in the form of programs for soil and water conservation and for the preservation of scenery and wildlife, although, here too, it is important to do things as economically as possible.

Much of the enthusiasm and dedication of the conservation movement can usefully be directed toward combatting tendencies toward resource deterioration. Efforts in planning, investment, and education will be necessary if quality standards are to be maintained and improved.

Pollution of water, soil, and air, and disfigurement of the general environment are formidable antagonists today. In many ways the resource and environmental quality has improved during past decades. Typhoid and malaria have been all but eliminated in this country and are being brought rapidly under control in many less developed regions of the world. More and more houses are being constructed to meet acceptable standards. Soil conservation and rural electrification are spreading in most countries. But in terms of technical, economic, and aesthetic possibilities, quality performance in handling resources is far below what it could be.

Looking beyond the year 2000, continued rapid population increase unmatched by continued technological innovation and social and policy adaptation would lead to disaster, as many have prophesied. However, the capacity of human beings to adjust their behavior and institutions to emerging problems should not be underrated. Birth control and family planning, so full of difficulties today, could undergo substantial change during several decades while population continued to increase at 2 percent a year. On this matter, research in the biological and social sciences is progressing and may well open new avenues to the solution of age-old problems. The rapid spread of urbanization in virtually all parts of the world, including the less developed countries, will also be a factor working in the direction of smaller families, as will gains in family income, if the experience of the more developed countries is any criterion. To the extent that the technical aid programs of the advanced countries can include research, information, and education about family planning for voluntary use in the less developed, high-birth-rate countries, the more opportunities there will be for bringing population increase within the ambit of individual choice and action. Limitation of population may be desirable not so much because of the possible effect of smaller numbers on living levels, but as a way of asserting some degree of rational influence over one more factor in man's relationship with his environment.

In view of the uncertainties that lie in the more distant future—technological developments impossible to foresee, resource discoveries not now dreamed of, and unthought-of measures of individual and social control in response to obvious needs—it seems unwise to try to look in any systematic and disciplined way much beyond the end of the century. Prophets of course will want to look much farther into the future, but social scientists and technical people had better not try to look farther ahead than they can see, at least dimly. And even the prophets should consider the possibilities of discovery and technological advance as well as the trends of birth and death. More significant but more difficult, they should not overlook the extraordinary capacity of human beings and institutions to react to emerging problems in new and constructive ways.

In any case the significant trends and forces bearing on population and resources should be monitored carefully and frequently so that changes in direction may be seen promptly and opportunities for helpful action may be seized.

SOCIAL FACTORS OF FERTILITY REGULATION

Birth rates can be lowered by any one of a variety of practices: by late marriage and not marrying, as in Ireland; by induced abortion, as in Japan and the eastern European countries; or by contraception, as in all the western countries. An increase of five years in age of marriage in India would result in a decline of about 20 percent in the birth rate; a decrease of 15 percent in the proportion of people married would result in a corresponding decrease in the birth rate. But the marriage practices of a society are closely bound up with its social and cultural institutions and hence are not easily or quickly changed. Such shifts probably have to come as part of those long-term and basic changes in the very fabric of a society that accompany the transition from traditional to modern status.

Induced abortion is widely and legally practiced in some countries, and it is quite widely but illegally, and badly, practiced in many others. It is, however, unacceptable to most societies on religious or moral grounds. Indeed, the very fact of widespread abortion is itself an important argument for voluntary fertility regulation. (It is estimated that there are over six million induced abortions a year in the world, and quite possibly double that number.)

The most accessible means of fertility regulation, then, appears to be contraception. . . . Here we are concerned only with the social aspects of the acceptance and use (of currently available methods of contraception) with attitudes about family size and family limitation and the bases thereof, spread of information about reproduction and contraceptive methods, and the practice of family planning.

. . . We must inquire into the social factors, broadly defined, that are involved in population growth and its control. Here we deal with

From *Growth of World Population,* National Academy of Sciences (Washington, D.C., 1963), pp. 20–27. Reprinted by permission.

many of the basic elements affecting human behavior: cultural institutions, religious beliefs, economic arrangements, family organization, sexual practices. All these and more are involved in the determination of attitudes and practices related to human fertility and in an effort to change such attitudes and practices.

It is encouraging to note that the norm of the small family and the practice of family limitation have been established across a wide range of societies: across religious affiliations (Catholic Southern Europe and Protestant Northern Europe); political ideologies (the United States and the Soviet bloc); industrial and agricultural economies, rich and poor nations, better-educated and poorer-educated societies (all European); the West and the East (as in Japan); and, just beginning, the tropical countries as well as the temperate ones.

Almost every survey on attitudes toward family planning, from urban areas in the United States to villages in India, shows that a large proportion of people say they are favorable to the idea of limiting family size, and especially after the third or fourth child—roughly 60 to 80 percent over all, both men and women. The figures vary somewhat from one locality to another and, of course, the interview questions are varied, but there is an impressive body of favorable interview responses from Mysore and Singur in India; from low-income women in Pakistan; from Mexican factory workers; from Ceylon and Japan; from Jamaica and Puerto Rico; from the United States and Great Britain. Many persons of the world are now persuaded, at least in principle, of the desirability of limiting family size—limiting the birth of children to the number wanted, when they are wanted. The major single reason for this attitude toward family planning, in all areas where it exists, is concern for the economic welfare of the family—a better standard of living and a better chance in life for all children.

Information about family planning is unevenly disseminated in all countries, especially in the less-developed areas; it is usually sparse and rudimentary among the large, poorer, rural masses. Studies in certain districts of India have shown, for example, that even elementary knowledge about contraceptive methods is limited to approximately 20 to 25 percent of the married population, and is even more limited among the illiterate in rural areas. Among such populations, most people do not know of the possibility of birth control except by abstinence; such knowledge of contraceptive methods as there is is poor; folk superstitions are abundant.

The *use* of contraception is also uneven throughout the world. In the United States, 70 to 80 percent of all married couples have used contraceptive devices. In Puerto Rico, the figure is approximately 40 percent; in the Far East, except for Japan, perhaps not over 10 percent. Given the prevailing conditions of life in the less-developed areas, only the simplest methods can be employed.

In every population, the urban, the better-educated, and the more modernized groups accept and use contraception earliest, most often, and most effectively. Such people are a small minority among the populations in less-developed areas, of course; even a large decrease in their birth rates would have little effect upon the total national figures.

This quick review begins to suggest some of the social factors that in different areas stand in the way of family limitation in emerging nations.

Familial Factors

High marriage rates: Almost all mature women are married.

Early marriage: Virtually the whole range of reproductive years is available for childbearing.

Status of women: Few alternatives to the domestic role are available; the customary male dominance confines women to care of home and children.

Desire for children, especially sons: This may be for familial reasons (care of parents in their old age), economic reasons (workers in an agricultural economy), or status reasons (many sons implying a manly father). A wide range of social values has traditionally supported the appropriateness of the large family, especially when coupled with traditionally high mortality rates.

Little differential fertility: The model of the small family is not apparent within the society.

Personal Factors

Housing facilities: There is little or no privacy for parents, and there are few facilities for sanitation, storage of contraceptive supplies, and other personal requirements.

Social support: In some societies there may be little conversation about the subject because of its personal nature, and hence little opportunity for the development of necessary social rapport and support; the occasional practitioner of family planning may therefore feel that he is an alien in his own community.

Absence of social rewards: As a consequence of the above, the innovator in family planning does not receive the social rewards needed to encourage his innovating behavior (as he might, for example, in connection with innovation directed toward improving agricultural practices), and the reward of not having unwanted children is both remote and, with many traditional methods of contraception, problematic.

Attitudinal Factors

Religious, moral, political, or ideological objections to fertility control: These often apply to particular contraceptive methods, and sometimes to any method whatever.

Peasant inertia, apathy, resistance to change: These tend to color the whole of life in many societies, and thus to make innovation of any kind difficult.

Strength of motivation: The highest motivation for fertility control may be felt when nothing needs to be done, i.e., during pregnancy or soon after delivery. With some contraceptive methods, it may even be that motivation declines with successful practice, through carelessness and false confidence.

Communication Factors

Ignorance of purposes, means, and consequences of family planning: The concept of voluntary fertility control is often accepted when presented, but communication is sometimes difficult.

Low literacy: Especially when women are illiterate, informational programs are handicapped from the outset.

Perception of lowered mortality: Decline in the death rate is not always quickly apparent, so considerable time is required to establish the recognition that it is no longer necessary to bear several children in order for some to survive; in some cases, a decline in infant mortality within the community is viewed as an increase in births, with no appreciation of the fact that the death rate has been reduced.

Lack of communication between husband and wife: The necessary joint decision may be difficult when sex and reproduction are not considered appropriate topics of conversation between husband and wife.

Organizational Factors

Dispersal: Populations are typically divided into many small villages, complicating the problems of communication and supply.

Lack of trained personnel: The necessary administrative leadership and technical competence to support a mass program are often lacking.

Economic Factors

Lack of distribution facilities: Economic arrangements are typically inadequate to cope with problems of distribution, partly because of
the dispersal of populations noted above and partly because of the
rudimentary character of economic systems.

Costs: These may be too high for the individual or the society.

In short, a program for voluntary fertility control often faces an
apparently insurmountable barrier of traditional behavior in traditional
societies, reinforced by social customs and cultural arrangements of long
standing. These are formidable obstacles to the success of any effort to
promote voluntary fertility control in the type of society that needs it
most. The difficulties are altogether real and discouragingly numerous.
Only the importance of the task would appear to justify the necessary
effort.

But there are also some favorable factors in the situation that
should not be overlooked or underestimated. The first is the growing
recognition of the problem by major social institutions, including governments, and their consequent support of study and action programs on
population control. Among the governments most involved, India, Pakistan, and Korea have taken steps toward a solution. During the long
decline of the birth rate in the West, there was active resistance by major
legal, governmental, medical, and religious institutions, but family planning was nevertheless undertaken by individual couples without institutional support. In many of the less-developed areas, there is now active
institutional support, and governments are in the forefront of the movement rather than lagging behind.

Another favorable factor is large-scale social change. The pace of
the modern world is being felt even in the most backward areas, and there
are accelerating trends toward industrialization, rationalization of agriculture, better health and sanitation, greater literacy and education, the
freeing of women—in short, toward modernization of societies in general.
Fertility regulation is part of this movement and hence benefits from
whatever advances are made. Unfortunately, such progress is slow.

In the past decade or so, there have been several systematic
attempts to study the impact of efforts to spread the practice of family
planning. (By "systematic" we mean more or less controlled experiments
in natural settings with reasonably careful measurement of the consequences beyond clinical activity.) Eight to ten such efforts are now going
on, some of them continuations of earlier efforts. Such studies have been

or are being made in India, Pakistan, Ceylon, Taiwan, Japan, Puerto Rico, Jamaica, and the United States. In spite of the critical importance of the problem, however, only about fifteen of these limited efforts have been made to find out whether and how voluntary regulation of fertility can— with presently available techniques—be implemented among populations that need it most.

We can draw some tentative conclusions from these studies:

1. There is a wide range of motivation for family planning in all societies investigated. Substantial numbers of people at the lower end of the economic and literacy range perhaps cannot be interested, at least within a period of five years or so, but a significant number at the other end (especially those with large families), representing at least a fourth to a third of the community, appears to be ready now. Voluntary fertility regulation in such countries, at least with traditional methods, is thus much more a matter of stopping childbearing than of spacing it. In all probability, the best way to motivate new users is to satisfy those that are already motivated.

2. Clinical programs alone do not appear to be sufficient for the task.

3. Continued promotion in the field is necessary for continued effect; the point of self-maintaining activity is hard to reach. At the same time, it seems clear that it is not necessary to reach an entire population in order to achieve substantial effect. In some areas the people themselves help to spread information through informal and often highly effective channels.

4. Personal communication between field workers or local leaders and the people is apparently the best single influence for the adoption of voluntary fertility control in many areas, though mass communication may become increasingly important.

5. Experimental efforts to promote family planning with traditional contraceptives that require sustained motivation and preparatory action often fail. The number of people willing to accept the idea is not large and the number of continuing users is even smaller.

6. Results of the few successful efforts so far suggest that the use of traditional contraceptives can be expected to produce an average reduction of five to seven points in the birth rate in less-developed areas in a period of five years (for example, from 42 births per thousand population to 35–37 per thousand). Because of the backlog of interest among large families, the reduction is often greater in the first year than in subsequent years.

7. Despite all the difficulties, successful results can be obtained. In a set of Indian villages, continuous personal contact by field workers providing information, support, and supplies led to a five-point reduction

in the birth rate in a period of four years. In some villages in Ceylon a similar program has apparently produced a seven-point decrease within three years. In a county of Taiwan, personal contact through a health service resulted in a birth rate for the users of contraception ten points below that of a matched group. In some Japanese villages a similar program was successful in turning a substantial proportion of couples from abortion to contraception. In Puerto Rico, an informational program increased the use of contraceptive methods by 10 to 20 percent, and the distribution of free supplies through volunteer leaders attracted new users among those with many children. A similar informational program in Jamaica doubled the proportion of users in urban but not in rural areas. As a result of a current effort in the United States among deprived groups with birth rates as high as India's about 20 percent of the subjects with two or more children have so far undertaken family planning.

But there have been failures as well as successes. As yet, we have an extremely small and tentative body of knowledge on social factors with which to attack an extremely large and complex problem. In contrast to hundreds of demographic and bio-medical studies, there are only a few social studies.

The above listing indicates a great disparity between what we know and what we need to know in order to deal effectively with the problem. Further study is certainly needed. More specifically, experimental efforts in natural settings, conducted with resources available locally on a mass basis, must be multiplied many times in order to learn how family planning can be implemented in all societies that recognize the need for it. Such efforts, across a range of countries and with a range of methods, should produce knowledge and techniques on which general programs can be based.

Such efforts must be closely tied to the local administrative machinery by which such programs must ultimately be managed in particular countries and districts. That machinery is typically based on or in the health services. A new type of professional practitioner, the family-planning administrator, is needed to develop programs; training institutions and programs for such administrators in both health and the social sciences should be high on the list of priorities.

Effective programs also require the services of specialists in information and education from such fields as agricultural extension, audio-visual methods, marketing, and advertising, to disseminate information effectively and provide motivation for broader use.

In no other social problem is the interconnection between human and technical factors so critically important as in fertility regulation. The better the contraceptive—better in ease of use and in effectiveness—the less the social resistance to the acceptance of family planning and the greater the efficiency of implementing voluntary fertility regulation where it is needed. Thus the two sets of factors, the social and the bio-medical, are closely interwoven, and the social acceptability of family planning depends heavily on the development of applied knowledge in the bio-medical field. . . .

P. B. Medawar
THE FALLIBILITY OF PREDICTION

. . . I should now like to turn to the deeply important problem of trying to predict and to regulate the size of a human population. . . . It is an instructive paradox that we are usually oppressed either by the fact that the birth-rate is unduly high or by the fact that it is unduly low; and the world today is such that we can worry about both at once. For reasons I shall now try to explain, there is not much likelihood that we shall ever cease to be worried by the one problem or the other, though we can hope for long periods of respite in which we need not worry very much. Populations are potentially capable of growing at compound interest, but cannot in fact grow for any great length of time at any net rate of compound interest which is persistently above or below zero. If the rate remains persistently below zero the population will die out (for that is what a negative rate implies); and if the rate stays persistently above zero the population will grow without limit and must eventually starve. No one contests these simple truths; people hold different opinions about the problem of overpopulation, but the differences are about its immediate urgency and about the tactics that should be adopted at this present time. But as my chief concern is with method, with the process of foretelling, I propose to discuss the problems of prediction and analysis that concern Great Britain and, to a greater or lesser degree, the rest of the Western world.

Before the war a number of highly skilled demographers said that if the prevailing patterns of birth-rates and death-rates were to continue then the population of most advanced industrial countries would go down steeply, in a matter of tens of years. They pointed out—what seems

From P. B. Medawar, *The Future of Man* (London: Methuen & Co., Ltd., New York: Basic Books, Inc., 1959), pp. 16–26. Reprinted by permission. Dr. Medawar is a Nobel laureate.

obvious now, though it was far from obvious then, even to some biologists
—that no comfort was to be got from the fact that the populations of most
of these countries were still increasing, because the increase was mainly
due to the success of ingenious modern ways of postponing the death of
people beyond child-bearing age. As a separate consideration, various
forecasts were made of the size of our own population at various intervals
up to the year 2000. It is already possible to see that these predictions
were systematically mistaken: they were all too low. One of them, putting
the population of England and Wales below 30,000,000 in the year 2000,
falls short by 20,000,000 of what the Registrar General now thinks of as a
likely figure.

Before I discuss the shortcomings of these pre-war forecasts I do
want to make it clear that they were expressly carried out as statistical
exercises on the basis of a number of perfectly understandable assumptions, and that it would be a disaster if experts stopped making predictions of this degree of importance merely for fear of being wrong.
Moreover, they were a big improvement, in point of method, on some of
the forecasts or diagnoses made even a few years before. As late as 1930 an
eminent foreign biologist declared that nothing could provide a more
sensitive measure of the biological health of a population than the ratio of
the annual numbers of births and deaths. When he turned the searchlight
of this conception upon Great Britain he found no cause whatsoever for
alarm. What makes his judgment so infuriating is that it happened to be
more nearly right, in its general tendency, than estimates based upon
reasoning incomparably more exact.

I suppose there were three main sources of error in these earlier
predictions. The first was lack of information. In spite of its obvious
importance, we in Great Britain did not begin to record the ages at which
mothers bear their children until 1938, about ninety years after the need
for information of this type had been explicitly foreseen; and we still do
not record the age of the father. But, more than that, we need to know
about the size of families, and how many families there are of each
particular size, and how families are successively built up in each year
after marriage. If pre-war demographers had had the kind of information
that has since been provided by the Family Census of 1946 and the
general census of 1951 they would have approached their problems in a
different way: indeed, it was because of their insistence that the Family
Census of 1946 was carried out.

A second source of error was to place too much confidence in the
power of an index like the so-called 'net reproduction rate' to measure a
population's biological fitness, its power to replace itself from one generation to the next. Not so very long ago a socially conscious person who
heard mention of the net reproduction rate at once assumed a grave

expression, which showed that he understood its import, and may have been intended to show that he knew exactly what it meant. It is, in fact, a measure of fertility which makes allowance for mortality—which does not assume, as cruder measures do, that everyone is lucky enough to live up to and right through the period of reproduction. It is usually based on the female population only, and only on female births, and it is arrived at by an arithmetic exercise which there is no need to describe. Conceived in just those terms—as a well-defined computation which takes into account both gain by birth and loss by death—it is a good way of summarizing in one figure some of the more important information about the mortality and fertility that happens at that time to be in force. It was perfectly well understood that the computation itself gave one no authority to assume that fertility and mortality would not alter; but, when it is used as a measure of replacement, the net reproduction rate can only be as valid as our reasons are for thinking that fertility and mortality will in fact remain constant.

In real life the net reproduction rate fluctuates far more from year to year than one would expect of any index that professes to be a fundamental measurement of reproductive health.Between 1930 and 1940 the net reproduction rate in America, as in many European countries, was below unity, that is, below the level of exact replacement, one for one. In 1952 it reached the fantastic figure of 1.56, corresponding to growth by compound interest at the rate of 56 percent per generation; but not even an American population could change in a few years from one whose future was looked at pensively to one which looked as if it would get completely out of hand. The net reproduction rate is extremely sensitive to changes in, for example, the ages at which women bear their children—to changes which need not be of great importance when thought of in terms of the span of a human reproductive life. But there is a more fundamental objection to using the net reproduction rate, or any other index like it, to predict what will happen in years ahead; to make it clear I must explain what is meant by a 'stable' population.

A population has not merely a size; it has also a structure; and to describe a population at any moment one must know not only its total number but how that total is built up of people of every different age. A 'stable' population is so called because it has a constant or steady age-structure or age-distribution, one which will not change so long as the rates of fertility and mortality remain constant. Unlike any real population I am aware of, it can reproduce its structure from one generation to the next, and even regenerate or restore itself if some upheaval like a war or depression should temporarily change its shape. A stable population grows at a constant net rate of compound interest which may, of course, be zero, so that births and deaths cancel each other, and the population stays constant in size as well as shape. Stability can be achieved only if the same age-specific rates of mortality and fertility have been in force for something like 100 years. No large population has ever achieved such a stability, and it is not at all likely that it ever will. This is why students of populations wear censorious frowns when people talk, as they so often do, of 'stabilizing' the population of the world or of one country or another at any particular figure they may have in mind; for, short of tyranny, it is not at all clear how any such stability could be achieved.

When it is used for predictive purposes, the net reproduction rate can be thought of as a preview of what the population's rate of increase would eventually come to be if fertility and mortality remained constant long enough for a state of stability to be achieved. But if the population is not stable to begin with (in fact it will not be) then its composition by age and sex will certainly alter—not *in spite of* the fact that fertility remains the same but *because* it remains the same. The assumption that fertility will remain constant therefore implies that the population will change in structure; and these changes, in turn, make it likely—though not logically certain—that fertility itself will change. At the very least they will make us look anew at our reasons for assuming that it would remain constant. The net reproduction rate cannot be used as if we were taking the nation's temperature; as if we were assessing its state of reproductive health. It has yet to be shown that any one index of fertility can be used for such a purpose.

All this sounds very disheartening; but out of the uneasiness and dissatisfaction of demographers a rather different style of analysis has emerged. The matter of principle involved is this. The life of a nation goes on from day to day and from year to year, and the changes that happen, historical changes, are marked against a scale of calendar time. But the lives and livelihoods and reproduction of men and women are marked against years of age, and the natural unit of demographical prediction is not, therefore, a calendar year or a sub-division of a century but a life or a sub-division of a life. The rates of fertility that will prevail here in five years' time will be shaped by today's teenagers, wondering when or whether they will get married; by people in their early twenties having their first children, and by people in their thirties having their later children or their last. Every such group has different experiences behind it and different prospects before it, but the fertility index we compute in five years' time will remain indifferent to them all. Yet it cannot be assumed that those who are twenty in 1965 will have the same fertility as the forty-year-olds had when *they* were twenty; or that they will grow up to have the fertility the forty-year-olds happened to have had in 1965.

The analysis of populations in terms of the changes that occur from one calendar year or decade to another is sometimes called 'secular analysis,' and obviously it must be reinforced by analysis of a different style: one which takes all the people born in one year or married in one year and follows them through their lives. Analysis of this kind is called 'cohort analysis'—it slices time lengthways instead of cutting across it year by year. The adoption of cohort analysis is the most important advance in practical demography of the past ten years. No one pretends that its adoption is an intellectual triumph; as I said, it was mainly lack of information that prevented its coming into use before; but in any empirical sense it has been highly informative and revealing.

Cohort analysis makes it easier to resolve fertility into factors— sex ratio, marriage rates, the ages at which people marry; above all, it has shown how important it is to know the pattern in which married couples build their families. No other method could have shown so clearly that the tremendous increase in the birth-rate which began towards the end of the war was mainly due to a change in the pattern of making families: people began to have in 1942 and 1943 the children they would normally have had two or three years beforehand. The postponement of births need not imply that families are going to be smaller than they otherwise would have been, and need not therefore have very much bearing on the problem of replacement. It is during times such as these, with changes in the rates and ages of marriage and in the pattern of building families, that indices like the net reproduction rate are least informative.

The most striking single fact that has emerged from cohort analysis is the remarkably unwavering trend of the size of completed families. It has fallen smoothly from an average of just over six for couples married in the eighteen-sixties to an average of just over two for those who married in the nineteen-thirties. There is an increasing element of guess-work in estimating the number of children of later marriages because not all of them have yet been born; cohort analysis can never be completely up to date. But there is a stability about the pattern of making families which suggests that forecasts founded upon cohort analysis are going to be nearer the mark than any made before the war.

As for replacement, I do not know that any demographer, on present evidence, now fears a serious decline in the population of Great Britain. The latest estimates suggest that we are just about breaking even; demographers are perhaps temperamentally disinclined to put them higher, if only to correct the illusion that all must now be well because the birth-rate went up so rapidly after the war. There are signs, though, that the most recently married couples are going to have larger families; certainly the marriage rate has been going up and the average age at marriage going down—although this does not imply that people who marry nowadays in their early twenties are going to have families of the same size as those who married in their early twenties before the war. In so far as purely biological pressures can influence marriage rates and ages, I guess that the present upward turn may be genuine and not just temporary.

. . . The average age at which children become sexually mature is still going down. Pressures of this kind may not be strong but they are very insistent; combined with everything that goes with a system of social security they could well increase fertility or, at least, change families to a pattern in which married couples have all the children they intend to have by an earlier age than hitherto. I should not be in the least surprised if in the nineteen-seventies or nineteen-eighties we in Great Britain were to start exchanging uneasy glances about the dangers of overpopulation, and wondering where things were going to end.

I have been saying that human lives, generation by generation, have a much longer stride than the march of history by calendar years or decades, so that it can be very misleading to assess the reproductive health or future size of a population from the fertility that prevails in any one year or group of years. The advantage of cohort analysis is that it makes it easier to resolve fertility into factors which have a meaning in terms of the way in which people actually behave. Predictions founded upon cohort analysis are somewhat more exact in the sense that one can foresee a little more clearly what follows from one's assumptions; and if these predictions are wrong, as to some extent they surely will be, it will be easier in retrospect to see which assumptions were faulty and which factors changed in unforeseeable ways. This is about all that can be expected of predictions of this degree of complexity, though many biologists and demographers did at one time hope for more—to reveal in the growth of human populations the unfolding of grand historical principles with the exigency and thrust of physical laws.

Furthermore, it is a technical error to suppose that in real life one can stabilize a human population, in the sense of bringing it to a state in which it will no longer change as a result of its own internal properties. Short of tyranny, all that can be done in an administrative sense is to coax and warn and bribe a population, to try to prevent its becoming unduly small; and to change these policies, with no sense of inconsistency or grievance, if it thereupon shows signs of becoming unduly large. In other words, policies can be adopted which fall equally far short of tyranny and of *laissez-faire;* they can be energetic and reasonable and effective without claiming to hold good in perpetuity or to be governed by the workings of grand demographic laws. I have a feeling that the same may be true, and true for much the same kind of reason, of other still more complex human affairs.

8
The New Technology and the Individual

Everyone likes to think that he has a right to some degree of privacy—that he can converse in private and can withhold information that he considers privileged. One shrinks from the idea (so often present in utopian novels and science fiction) of the use of drugs to induce either euphoria or passivity or to extract information. One fears the possibility that his thoughts and, as a result, his actions may be subject to control. In several areas, science and scientifically based technology appear to be aiding the invasion of these individual rights. Although the selections in this chapter cover diverse subject matter, collectively they explore the extent to which science and technology have compromised individual rights. They raise some important questions. If certain individual rights are sacred, should limits be set on science and technology in areas where they threaten these rights? Should law-enforcement agencies be able to use all of the tools that technology can provide to detect crime? Should not science be employed to promote good behavior?

Stanley Meisler describes the startling growth in the use of lie-detection equipment. He has serious reservations about the techniques used; he questions whether the instruments themselves are accurate and whether the operators have adequate training. He relates some of the unfortunate consequences that have resulted for human beings from the use of the equipment. He concludes that the potential harm of polygraph equipment is so great that steps should be taken immediately to end the practice—by law if necessary.

Sam Dash details the various electronic devices currently available to enable eavesdroppers to record private conversations, even at considerable distances. He discusses the widespread practice of wiretapping and describes how electronic tapes can be altered to produce spurious conversations. Robert F. Kennedy, arguing for legalized wiretapping, states that the individual's right to privacy is subordinate to the greater good of society. Herman Schwartz denies this and believes that any type of electronic eavesdropping is in direct violation of the Fourth Amendment of the Constitution.

In a different area, Jonathan Cole treats the subject of the control of the mind by drugs. Drugs are used extensively in the treatment of the mentally ill; it is from this area that Cole derives much of his information. Drugs, he states, produce quite different effects in psychiatrically ill and normal persons. Moreover, they affect patients in different ways, and there is no way of predicting the reaction of a person to any particular drug. The setting in which the drug is administered, including the expectations of the person administering the drug, apparently has a definite role in the effect of the drug. Drugs, he concludes, are not useful tools for the control of the human mind, and he doubts that at this time, drugs can be developed that will have any specific predictable effects on man.

The brainwashing of Chinese intellectuals is the subject of Robert J. Lifton's article. He points out how the feelings of personal guilt and shame, confessions, the effects of group pressures, and environmental manipulation can be employed to control the thoughts of humans, resulting in a change of identity and belief. It is a valuable description of how the human being can be manipulated.

B. F. Skinner argues that Americans are now controlling behavior through education, moral discourse, and persuasion but persist in the illusion that these practices do not constitute thought control because these methods are free from coercion. Such cultural engineering, he maintains, produced our form of democracy and continues to sustain it. But, Skinner states, the behavior of man can stand a great deal of improvement, and we should grasp the opportunity that science offers in controlling man for his own benefit. Skinner admits there are some dangers in this approach, but he believes we cannot continue to rely on accident for our cultural evolution. We should use science in the interests of humanity and profit from its results. (The reader may wish to refer to the Joseph Wood Krutch selection in Chapter 2 when reading this article by Skinner.)

Stanley Meisler
LIE DETECTORS: TRIAL BY GADGET

The first lie detector, employed centuries ago, was a handful of rice dropped into the mouth of a suspect. If the rice stayed dry while he answered questions, he clearly was a liar—exposed under the questionable theory that a liar's salivary glands would dry up when gripped by fear. The lie detector used most commonly today is far more sophisticated. Developed by the psychologist and criminologist Leonard Keeler almost forty years ago, it comprises a pneumatic tube that fits across a subject's chest to measure breathing, an inflatable rubber cuff that wraps around the arm to measure blood pressure and a pair of electrodes that touch the fingers and, by the flow of current, measure the dampness of the palm. These instuments activate pens that draw wiggles and waves on a rolling sheet of paper—a process that gives the lie detector its modern name, polygraph, Greek for "many writings." In theory, an examiner can look at the chart, note any unusual wiggles and waves, and nab his man. This polygraph, obviously more complicated than a few grains of rice, is also touted as more accurate. In truth, it is not.

In America, the polygraph has become big business and a fixed part of the national consciousness. Local police officers, tired of more disagreeable and fatiguing methods of questioning, use lie detectors on the husband who glibly announces that he was upstairs snoozing when someone downstairs whacked his wife's head with a bat. Politicians deny they are scalawags and scoundrels and then offer to take a lie-detector test to prove it. Big stores use lie detectors to discover whether prospective employees are, ever have been or ever will be pilferers, perverts or pinkos.

The federal government is devoted to polygraphs. A recent

Stanley Meisler, "Lie Detectors: Trial by Gadget," *The Nation*, 199 (Sept. 28, 1964), 159–162, 176. Reprinted by permission. Mr. Meisler is a Washington newsman.

survey by the House Subcommittee on Government Operations, headed by Rep. John E. Moss (D., Calif.) revealed that nineteen federal agencies use them. Two of these—the Central Intelligence Agency and the National Security Agency—characteristically classify their use of polygraphs. The other seventeen, according to the report, gave 19,122 lie-detector tests in fiscal 1963. The federal government in that same year owned 512 lie detectors worth $428,066, and had 639 employees, paid $4.3 million a year, who were trained, in some fashion, to operate them. In addition, federal agencies employed private investigators to conduct 322 tests during the year. The government uses the polygraph for many reasons: to investigate leaks of information and other security cases; to question Vietcong guerrillas captured in Vietnam; to investigate crimes at military bases, post offices and other federal jurisdictions; and to screen applicants for federal jobs. A year ago, the Federal Aviation Agency hoped to adopt some simple device to detect bomb-carrying passengers. Under the plan, a passenger would check his baggage at the airline counter, put his hand on a lie detector, and swear he had no bomb. The FAA, however, dropped the plan when no manufacturer could meet the specifications. There have been more extreme proposals for government use of the polygraph. A Rand Corporation study several years ago suggested that they might be used to police an arms-control agreement with the Russians. The U.S. would periodically examine high Russian officials with lie detectors to make certain that they were living up to the agreement.

No thorough survey has been made on the prevalence of lie detectors in state and local government and in private business, but it must greatly exceed the use within the federal government. There are now 500 lie-detector firms, employing 1,000 to 1,500 polygraph examiners, who question subjects at a cost of about $35 a test. *Bussiness Week* says that 80 percent of their income comes from business firms that want to know if their employees or prospective employees are honest. The income of one of the major security firms, John E. Reid & Associates, increased 26 percent in 1960. Other figures give some hint of the money in lie detection: the two chief manufacturers, the Stoelting Company and Associated Research, both of Chicago, charge from $900 to $1,800 for a polygraph. At least three private schools train operators. A typical one, Cleve Backster's School of Lie Detection in New York, charges $500 for its six-week course.

The polygraph industry has developed a scientific veneer and a jargon. The operators belong to the American Academy of Polygraph Examiners, the Academy for Scientific Interrogation and the National Board of Polygraph Examiners; in a handful of states they are licensed. They talk about "peak of tension" tests and "control type" questions and "preventive security," and they boast, as George Lindberg of John E. Reid & Associates did in testimony before the Moss subcommittee, "we can make decisions in better than 90 percent of the cases tested . . . [with] an accuracy capability of less than 1 percent error. . . ."

The obsession of lie detectives with scientific language emerges in an exchange during the Moss subcommittee hearings—hearings, incidentally, that revealed more about the practice of lie detection in America than had ever been put on the public record:

> MOSS: Those questions are developed by the operator?
> CLEVE BACKSTER: By the examiner, sir.
> MOSS: The examiner. Is he different than the operator?
> BACKSTER: He certainly is.
> MOSS: Always?
> BACKSTER: Yes, in our language he is.
> MOSS: . . . In your own personal experience in the type of schooling that you provide and that you recommended here today, is there a difference?
> BACKSTER: Yes, sir; because when a person says operator it costs him 10 cents each time at our school.
> MOSS: Are we in a matter of personal pride or are we in a matter of semantics?
> BACKSTER: We are in a matter of standard phraseology used in a highly refined field.

The lie-detector experts have developed a complex system of questioning designed to exclude the possibility that the wiggles and waves on a chart could come from honest jitters instead of guilt. The examiner includes a control question designed to elicit some guilt feelings from a person who is telling the truth on the really important question. If a person's emotions produce physiological excitement on the control question but not on the hot question, he is normal and innocent. If, on the other hand, his emotions spark on the hot question but not on the control question, he must be lying. This theory was discussed at length with Backster at the subcommittee hearings:

> BACKSTER: That [the control question] would be such as "during the first 18 years of your life, do you remember ever doing something to hurt somebody who trusted you?"
> REP. HENRY S. REUSS (D., Wis.): . . . Then you get a little upward squiggle of the needle at that point, and you are thus inferring that the fellow must be leveling with you because he gets a little perturbation because, as you know, he must have done something to hurt somebody who loved him?
> BACKSTER: Sir, we expected him to respond to that particular question if he were not wrong on the relevant question. His psychological perception set if he were wrong on the target issue [*i.e., a liar*]

. . . would be aimed toward that which could hurt him most and he would go right by the [control question] . . . showing no significant response. This is a verified principle and validated.

REUSS: Where did you get this great truth from?

BACKSTER: Mr. John Reid [the Chicago polygraph expert] is the one who got the initial great truth regarding this, and I am very happy for it because it was the first breakthrough in lie detection for years.

Fred E. Inbau of the Northwestern University School of Law, co-author with Reid of the standard text in the polygraph field, defended this "great truth" and others like it by analogy. He reminded the subcommittee: "At one time it was said that the bumblebee according to the laws of aerodynamics should not be able to fly, but the bumblebee hadn't heard about this and went ahead flying anyway."

But logic like this has not impressed Congress. "I have yet to see any convincing evidence," said Representative Reuss, "that the so-called lie detector is of any legitimate use at all other than in its psychological effects on the subject, and this could be done with a box and some whirring noises and lights quite as well. . . ." Reuss examined the Inbau and Reid statistics closely and discovered that, although the two polygraph experts claimed an error of only 1 percent, they could verify only 18.9 percent of their cases.

The fact is that no experimental research has been done to prove that lie detectors work or that they don't. Dr. John I. Lacey, a psychophysiologist at Antioch College, told the subcommittee that "the field of lie detection has . . . developed outside of the confines of any of the recognized scientific disciplines." After an exhaustive study for the Department of Defense two years ago, Dr. Jesse Orlansky of the Institute for Defense Analyses wrote: "Although the polygraph enjoys wide usage, we are not able to estimate its value. It is possible that the regard in which it is held is due largely to the ability of the examiners to conduct effective interviews and only slightly to the polygraph instrument itself; or the reverse. We do not know." Ironically, the Department of Defense, one of the federal government's most prolific users of lie detectors, received the report, classified it and then ignored it. Moss subcommittee investigators later uncovered it.

Some doubt has also fallen upon the instrument itself. It may not be as technically sophisticated as some polygraph experts pretend. Dr. Lacey, for example, described it as "a fairly crude piece of instrumentation." He said the manufacturers have made "no attempt to take advantage of the many, many things we have learned in the past two decades about the recording of physiological responses . . . the nature of the examiner-examinee interaction . . . new methods of display, new methods of computation." And a recent article in the *Harvard Business Review* concluded that the polygraph can be unreliable unless the operator takes into account room temperature, humidity, time of day, air content and the recent activities of the subject.

While the polygraph industry's claims to high science have been shattered by the available psychiatric and physiological evidence, the instrument does seem to have a limited value. The scientists who testified before the subcommittee agreed that polygraphs work better than chance —perhaps with 70 percent accuracy—and, in the hands of trained and competent operators, could turn up useful clues for further investigation.

But very few polygraph operators have the competence and training. "There are a number of individuals," Dr. Joseph F. Kubis, a Fordham University psychologist, told the subcommittee, "who buy these instruments, do not take any training, set up, as it were, a shingle, and operate with this instrument. . . . There are more of them than we can see and identify." Even Professor Inbau admitted that 80 percent of the operators are insufficiently trained.

In a field so unsupervised, the Moss subcommittee had difficulty finding out just how much training a polygraph examiner required. "The more training the better, obviously," said Dr. Martin L. Orne, Harvard psychiatrist. "But there would be no point in saying that you should have only Ph.D. psychologists. They are not available." But in general the scientists who testified tended to see a need for far more training than did the representatives of the polygraph industry. Dr. Kubis thought that operators should have a minimum of six months' training in use of the machine and then a year of further experience interpreting the results. Dr. Lacey said he could discuss standards only by describing the background of those who read the physiological machines in his laboratories. Nurses, X-ray technicians and college graduates, he testified, were allowed to operate the machines in his lab after at least six months' training. But he went on, "I am not comfortable leaving them alone . . . for the complete interpretation of a set of data . . . in three years."

Within the industry, Inbau, Reid and Reid's associate, George Lindberg, prepared a paper for the Moss subcommittee setting their proposed minimum requirements as a college degree, six months' training in use of the polygraph, and then six months' personal supervision of the student as he conducts examinations. These standards, however, did not please Backster, who runs a six-week school. "I don't understand," he said, "by virtue of these standards that are so stipulated how with less than perhaps fifty people who have acquired their training by this method, the other 2,000-some examiners have managed to get along."

At the moment, Backster's standards prevail, particularly in the federal government. A former employee of the CIA, Backster set up its lie-detector program and, as he testified, "on one occasion or another I have been a consultant to most every government agency that is using the polygraph today." Almost half the federal agencies require no further background of a trainee than a high school diploma, and the extent of federal training ranges from the maximum of a seven-week course in the Army to the five- to eight-day course given by the Navy. This sorry record prompted Moss to conclude, "I have a real concern, in fact, a firm conviction, of the complete inadequacy of the training."

An imperfect instrument in the hands of an ill-trained man who believes that both he and the instrument are infallible can lead in only one direction—to the entrapment of the innocent. While polygraph experts like John Reid maintain that they err only in occasionally freeing a guilty man, never in ensnaring an innocent one, the evidence proves otherwise. Even Professor Inbau acknowledged it. "If you get an examiner," he testified, "who will browbeat everybody who takes the test hoping he will get a confession from the guilty ones and be able to report these people are lying, these things can happen."

A year ago, in an article written for the *American Journal of Psychiatry*, Dr. H. B. Dearman, a psychiatrist, and Dr. B. M. Smith, a psychologist, reported a case in which the polygraph had hurt an innocent subject. A young bank vice president, submitting to his firm's semi-annual routine lie-detector examination, failed the question, "Have you ever stolen any money from the bank or its customers?" He was given a test four times, and he failed the question each time. Convinced of the machine's infallibility, thoroughly confused, knowing that he had padded some expense accounts a bit, the young man finally broke down and confessed to the crime. He had stolen $1,000—a figure arrived at through some other questions on the polygraph tests. The bank books were audited. No money was missing. The bank president sent the young man to Dr. Dearman. The psychiatrist discovered that he was disturbed about his feelings toward his wife and mother, both of whom were customers of the bank, and that he felt guilty about some financial transactions with them amounting to approximately $1,000. Dr. Dearman decided that the young man's physiological changes, as recorded by the polygraph, reflected these emotional problems at home.

It is in personnel screening, however, not crime detection, that the polygraph can do the most damage. There is absolutely no recourse for a man who has failed a lie-detector test while applying for a job. He has no way of proving that the lie detector—which allegedly measured his future truthfulness and honesty—is wrong. He could do that only by staying truthful and honest on the job. But he has no job. Moreover, his failure on the lie-detector test may be noted in his personnel file and in government dossiers and scar him forever. Representatives of the polygraph industry estimate that lie detectors reject from 25 to 30 percent of the job applicants who take the examinations. These figures grow starker when the polygraph experts boast that these rejectees probably would have been hired if management had been dumb enough to screen them by the usual technique of interviews and reference checks.

"I would judge or estimate," Cleve Backster testified, "that about one out of every four that would undergo and have gone on the job by virtue of the conventional forms of screening would have disqualified themselves by their own assertions during the polygraph examination."

"Does this strike you as a high figure?" asked Rep. Ogden Reid (R., N.Y.).

"I would say initially it struck me as a high figure; yes, sir," Backster replied. "I am not shocked by it any more."

Since personnel screening is not designed to uncover a specific act, but only a tendency to act, polygraph operators can accomplish less and boast more in this field than in any other. The work can be sloppier than usual, the machine can take down less information—no one need know. A trade magazine, *Bus Transportation,* published an article in 1956 entitled, "Electronic Marvel Weeds Out Dishonest and Unfit Applicants," which described a new invention of Cleve Backster's. "With a special machine known as the Backster electronic evaluator it's now possible for a personnel executive to find out, in two hours if necessary, just about everything of importance in the background of a prospective employee," the article said. In its description of the "electronic marvel," the article said it comprised no more than the electrodes that measure the electric currents across the palm of the hand. Even Backster, in his testimony before the Moss subcommittee, acknowledged that this kind of measurement by a galvanometer alone would tell an examiner next to nothing about a subject. In fact, he told the subcommittee, an examiner would have to be at least "partially without sound reasoning" to depend on a galvanometer. Confronted with the *Bus Transportation* article, which he had reprinted and distributed for promotion, Backster said the writer had omitted the fact that his "marvel" measured breathing as well as palm sweating.

"You get these articles," Moss said at the hearings, "that say the scientific wonder, and with it all you have to do is set an employee down and ask him a series of questions and when you are finished you know if he has problems, you know if he is truthful, you know if he is honest, all of these things, you know. The fact is you know nothing. You may have many suspicions, but no more knowledge than when you started. . . . I suspect . . . that this little device has robbed many a person of an opportunity for employment or promotion."

Even harsher criticism of the use of the polygraph in personnel work came from Dr. Kubis, the Fordham psychologist who has spent much of his career experimenting with lie detectors. "The growing use of lie detectors in many vital aspects of our life is unwarranted, dangerous and degrading," Dr. Kubis testified. He condemned the lie detector, when used by inexperienced and unscrupulous men to check employees and prospective employees, as "a blindly probing instrument that can severely damage the inner life and reputation of the person tested."

Certain practices which have nothing to do with the machine itself, but which nevertheless have grown into the polygraph tradition, are distasteful to anyone concerned with the rights of American citizens. Most examination rooms, for example, have two-way mirrors behind which other investigators can watch the proceedings. Many rooms have hidden microphones.

Until very recently, the armed services never told a subject about the mirror and the microphone. One subcommittee witness, Maj. Gen. Ralph J. Roberts, the Army Provost Marshal General, didn't think it was necessary to tell a soldier anything. "It is my experience in thirty-six years in the Army that all of the soldiers that go into CID [Criminal Investigations Detachment] know that they are monitored and Big Brother is watching," he said. Similar testimony came from J. M. Barron of the Office of Naval Intelligence, who told the subcommittee that the Navy doesn't volunteer information about the rights of a citizen to a polygraph subject because "he is an American citizen. He should know." This brought a bristling reply from Congressman Reuss: "I would comment that I think the day will never come when the American citizens, as an incident of their citizenship, have to be aware of the fact that the room is bugged and the mirror is a device to enable Big Brother to see them. . . ." The anger from the Moss subcommittee persuaded Deputy Secretary of Defense Cyrus Vance to issue a new directive that ordered Pentagon polygraph examiners to tell their subjects of any mirrors and microphones. However, mirrors and mikes would stay.

But even without mirrors and microphones, there is serious question about the constitutionality of any polygraph test. The polygraph industry defends the use of the machine by pointing out that polygraph examinations are not admissible in most courts as evidence and that no one has to take the test if he does not want to. In this way, the industry maintains, the Fifth Amendment is not violated. But Rep. Cornelius E. Gallagher (D., N.J.) questions whether the examination violates the Fourth Amendment protection against unreasonable search and seizure: "Is not the Fourth Amendment violated if a condition precedent to employment is the subjection of a polygraph test, a test that seeks in some instances . . . to determine not only the veracity but to probe the very thought process of an individual?"

Dr. Dearman, the psychiatrist who handled the case of the harassed bank vice president, agrees with Representative Gallagher that the Fourth Amendment is violated, but adds that the Fifth Amendment is violated as well. "I am aware," he said in a letter to Congressman Moss, "that proponents of the use of the polygraph fall back on the statement that no one is forced to take a polygraph test. . . . However, this is of little or no avail because the examinee does not realize that not only will his conscious thoughts and his autonomic responses to them be recorded but his unconscious thoughts will also be delved into and consequently he will give autonomic responses to . . . thoughts of which he is totally unaware. . . . It is my opinion that the polygraph is used mainly as a mental blackjack to obtain a confession."

Whether unconstitutional or not, the polygraph is certainly unjust, imperfect and dangerous. It may have some value in the hands of a highly trained and competent criminal investigator who is seeking leads, but that is the limit of its usefulness. Even there, its scientific validity is so far from perfect and its potential for harm so great that any citizen—no matter how secure in his innocence—is well advised to refuse the test. As a personnel screening device, it can produce nothing but harm (and profits for polygraphists) and Congress should demand the end of its use in federal government personnel offices immediately and should exert all its pressure to persuade private firms to discontinue it. If necessary, it should pass legislation to that end.

The polygraph is a pernicious instrument that has been seized upon by a society obsessed with gadgetry. It should be relegated to a Smithsonian Institution exhibit case as a monument to an American craze.

Sam Dash
WIRETAPPING AND EAVESDROPPING

. . . One of the things that our study looked into was the reliability of tapes. It had been rumored that you can edit a tape easily and that the edition of the tape would not be detectible.

Portion of the statement of Mr. Sam Dash before the Sub-committee on Constitutional Rights of the Committee on the Judiciary, United States Senate, 86th Congress, 1st Session. Mr. Dash was formerly district attorney in Philadelphia, Pa.

We carried out an experiment with the help of Professor [Richard] Schwartz, [University of Pennsylvania] . . . who is my technical adviser, and through a private broadcasting firm in New York we taped an original message. I dictated a tape and it was the tape of a public official speaking in favor of God, for motherhood, and against communism.

We turned it over to the official of the broadcasting company and, using Ampex editing equipment, in 2 hours he changed this message so that my voice announced that I had stolen money from the Commonwealth of Pennsylvania, advocated the overthrow of the Government by force and violence, and confessed to killing an FBI agent—without additional words added to the tape, without doing anything other than cutting it up and putting it together again.

Now, one of the things that amazed me was that in addition to placing words in different positions, this editor, as all editors can do, was able to break up a word and take a syllable out of the word, to take the "l" sound or the "a" sound out and he could build a word out of a syllable he already had, so if you didn't have a word in the message because it had not been spoken, the editor could construct it out of the available syllables.

Senator HENNINGS. Sort of like the game Scrabble?

Mr. DASH. Scrabble with magnetic tapes.

The next question was, Could you detect the edition? People who listened to it—we ran it off on a new tape so you couldn't see the splices—people who listened to it could not detect through the ear the fact that it was edited.

We then played the tape through an oscilloscope, and, using a high-speed movie camera, took a picture of the images. We compared—Professor Schwartz, compared the image of the original tape against the image of the edited tape and Professor Schwartz states in our report that he was not able to tell which was the edited and which was the unedited.

It is his position today—this by no means is as thorough a research in this area as possible; it was our attempt to get into it. I think it would certainly be a very worthwhile study taken on by some electronics engineer or school to go into it more fully. But the present state of our investigation led Professor Schwartz to say that with the equipment he had, and with his own ability and experience, he was not able to detect an edited tape. It has provided quite a bit of amusement to people who listened to it, when you see how an innocent conversation can be turned into a guilty one as readily as it can. . . .

In theory . . . you can develop a device which will send a beam, a radio beam or supersonic beam, which makes contact with a metallic disk to pick up vibrations on the disk and return a signal which will, if recorded, give you conversation. But this has not been developed at the present time to a point where it is used by anybody that I know of.

Generally, the kind of investigations conducted by private detectives and police do not permit them to use the kind of expensive or large-size equipment. Most of this equipment is large.

For instance, the parabolic microphone, directional microphone, received a quite a bit of attention publicly. It is a microphone which can pick up sound a thousand feet away. It uses a parabola, a dish-shaped object, with a microphone in front, and it is directional so that it can be pinpointed, by use of a gunsight, on sounds a thousand feet away.

Senator CARROLL. Is this sort of listening device really on the market yet?

Mr. DASH. It is on the market and it has been developed by private detectives and they try to use it, but we found that although it is directional it is not discriminating. You would have to have an ideal situation. You would have to have no other noise in the area. If there is any noise in between the subject of the observation and the microphone, you are going to get it all. It will sound like a bunch of hubbub. Most of these detectives who talk about this device say it is excellent if you are on the shore of a lake and if you are seeking to get whispered conversation from two people in a boat in the middle of the lake. The times in which the detectives have that situation to investigate are rare indeed. . . .

Wiretapping is done by people actually making contact with the pairs on a telephone. Very little induction tapping is going on today. Bugging is pretty much being done by a microphone which we know about which is wired to a tape recorder. The advance in this field is in transmitters. It is true today that they have developed tiny transmitters, sir, about the size of your little matchbox there, using transistors which can be dropped in a wastebasket, and which will broadcast a signal about 50 to 100 feet away, or a flat transmitter about 5 inches by 4 inches which can be put in the back of a picture on the wall, in a hotel. They take the brown paper off the picture and put the flat transmitter there to broadcast 200 or 300 feet.

Senator CARROLL. Are you saying that they could take a transmitter the size of this matchbox that I hold in my hand and drop it without any wiring, just drop it in——

Mr. DASH. No wires, It will pick up sound. If it is left in the office, they will have parked on the street right below a closed truck with "Joe's Plumbing Supply" on the side, but inside there is a receiving set which would pick up the message and record it on a tape recorder.

Senator CARROLL. Would you be able to separate the other sounds that come from it?

Mr. DASH. This is broadcast, purely a broadcasting device. The reason why they have gone into this, is that the eavesdropper has a fear of being caught. A wired microphone can be traced to an eavesdropper. By the use of expendable transmitters—they will find the transmitter but not the fellow listening in.

Senator CARROLL. Is it a costly device?

Mr. DASH. It depends. I think it costs a few dollars if the person makes it himself and these small devices are being handmade. . . .

I can say that our study does show an almost untouched area, the area of electronic eavesdropping, that whereas so much attention has been put to wiretapping, the widest use of eavesdropping by private people and law enforcement today is through the use of microphones, transmitters, automatic cameras, closed-circuit television, and this is a new field.

In philosophy, or in the spirit of invasion of privacy, it is the same thing whether one listens to telephone communications or private communications in a room.

As I have indicated, New York has gone the farthest in developing an overall eavesdropping policy. I believe that the Federal Government could well get into it.

In those areas where it makes use of interstate communication, especially in the areas where broadcasting devices are used, or areas where telephone lines are used to carry the message, and that is very frequent—that would be a good area. . . .

Senator CARROLL. I have not been in this field, and that is why I asked you about the great scientific advancement. The law enforcement agencies are using these devices and techniques in aid of investigation.

Mr. DASH. Yes. I don't think, sir, you were here when I stated, I do want to emphasize that as an aid to investigation, law enforcement people who are using it are getting good results. People are in jail today for having committed serious crimes as a result of this technique.

Senator HENNINGS. Did you find any major city among those you surveyed, Mr. Dash, in which illegal wiretapping was not practiced?

Mr. DASH. No. Every major city we looked at, illegal wiretapping was practiced.

It was done on the theory that the community needed the protection, the law enforcement officer was given the job of doing the protecting and the people didn't know what was good for them. The law enforcement officers would have to do it anyway.

As I said, in those cities where it was illegal, it was done, as an aid to investigation and not for evidence and usually employing the aid of a private specialist. . . .

The area of illegal activity in New York, which is quite a bit because we come down to a figure, frankly, of 13,000 to 20,000 illegal wiretaps a year in New York City, is done by New York plainclothesmen, in violation of the law, and very often not for law enforcement. It is required that a law enforcement officer or a police officer get an order in New York before he wiretaps. Some of the excuses used by police officers for not getting orders is that when they are hot on the trail of a gambler they cannot take the time. One plainsclothesman told me that "I see a bookie or somebody go into a telephone booth and I know if I go to the police department and make an application to the legal division for a wiretap order and then have somebody go to the court to get the order, by the time I get back to the booth the conversation is over and he is not in the booth any more. So I am going to put that tap on, law or no law."

However, a good part of plainsclothes wiretapping is not done with that in mind, but too much of it was done with the idea of locating the bookie to get on the payroll rather than to make a law enforcement arrest.

We came to our figures briefly on the 13,000 to 20,000 taps by checking the amount of equipment held by certain divisions in New York and also by checking on the amount of people who were available to make the taps.

For instance, in the criminal investigation bureau, they had 77 pen registers on their shelves. The pen register is a device which is used in conjunction with a tap to record the dialed-out number. It is called in some jurisdictions a dial recorded. It has different names, but principally on a ticker tape it will either give a number or a dot or a dash indicating the dialed number.

We found through the statements made by the members of the criminal investigation bureau that in any 1 day only 12 pen registers might be left on the shelf; at least 65 were out. Therefore, using an approximation of a wiretap lasting usually a week—some can last a day—some can last half an hour—some can last a year—but taking the average amount of a week with the 65 pen registers, we came to, for that unit alone, 2,000 to 3,400 taps a year, and mind you, the pen register is a luxury-type tap that is not usually used on all taps. It is an additional piece of equipment to some taps, so that in from 2,000 to 3,400 cases pen registers were used.

I would think that in that unit alone there were many more taps.

This unit states that it only tapped 181 times that year but it was our belief that if all that unit was doing was tapping 181 times a year they certainly would not need 77 pen registers; 3 or 4 would be enough. There are approximately 400 plainclothesmen in the city of New York. We found through interviewing plainclothesmen that they were broken up into teams of two and usually one of each team knows something about wiretapping or owns equipment. Therefore, there are most likely about 200 wiretapping plainclothesmen in the city of New York. . . .

That the plainclothesmen, former plainclothesmen and former telephone company employees approximate that between 50 and 100 taps are installed by the 200 plainclothesmen a day and if you take that figure and multiply it by a 5-day week, you come out to between 13,000 and 26,000 taps a year. . . .

Leaving for a moment the police and law enforcement wiretapping, I think it is relevant, one of the things we did learn with regard to private wiretapping, private wiretapping is widespread throughout the country. We found it in every city. Private detectives are generally the persons who are called upon by lawyers to find somebody who will do a tap, install a tap. The private detective rarely, indeed, himself, installs a tap. He doesn't know how to do it.

A private detective usually gets the help of a police officer and we found in many, almost every city we looked into, certain police officers were willing to work for private detectives on their own for a fee to install taps, or a telephone company employee, or a special wiretapping specialist who does that type of work, and we found this in Philadelphia and Chicago, and this is new, certain sound recording companies or houses where they have this equipment ostensibly there for the purpose of making records or selling equipment, but they rent out the equipment for wiretapping and sometimes also provide the service of installing it.

Now, this area of private wiretapping includes the domestic relations activity which is a constant one, the jealous wife checking on the husband as well as the jealous husband checking on the wife.

By the way, the private detective who does this kind of wiretapping is generally unscrupulous. We found that a private detective hired by a wife will go to the husband and sell out for a higher fee to check back on the wife. . . .

In New York, there have been very few private detectives who have been prosecuted. There have been some. There have been three or four in the last 5 or 6 years, but generally private detectives know they can get away with it without prosecution. One of the reasons they get away with it is that the police department, the district attorneys, and even the Federal law-enforcement officers hesitate prosecuting private wiretappers because when they prosecute private tappers they bring into the open wiretapping. Since the law-enforcement officers themselves want to wiretap and don't want any scandal, they would rather not prosecute because the law will that way remain uninterpreted and they themselves are not involved in a prosecution.

This does not mean that there haven't been some prosecutions. In New York City and Kings County there have been prosecutions of private wiretappers. But again take Broady who installed this tremendous tap factory where he could tap 100,000 telephones, he has been convicted. I think his sentence was for 2 years. He is still on appeal. The only person who went to jail was Mr. Keating, the head of a private crime committee who informed everybody about it. He was the one who tipped off the newspapers that this thing was occurring and District Attorney Hogan called Keating before a New York County grand jury and asked Keating who was his tipster. Keating refused to tell and was sentenced there for contempt. In the most vicious and widespread wiretapping that has ever occurred in this country, as I repeat, only one man went to jail and he was the man who informed on it.

The private wiretapping goes beyond domestic relations cases. I think one of the wider users of private wiretapping are industrial concerns today. Businessmen have learned that for industrial, internal plant security, wiretapping and bugging is an excellent device. In New York, as in other cities, you will find plants putting in closed circuit television, recessed in the walls, to watch production personnel. Men's and women's, ladies' rooms have been bugged to find what the employees really think about the company. Buyers have been bugged to see if they are getting kickbacks from the seller.

This is being done, this is all being done through private detectives and specialists who sell a bill of goods to these industrial concerns that they can save thousands of dollars of money by checking on their own employees. This is a lucrative field for the specialist. . . .

Senator CARROLL. In your studies, did you examine whether in this industrial wiretapping or eavesdropping there was any conflict of action between the industrialist and the telephone company?

Mr. DASH. Very often the man who was hired to do the job had a telephone company contact. I won't say that it is the telephone company. It would be an employee of the telephone company. Very often when elaborate setups are made, multiple stations, so that the employer can listen in on a number of employees, he can legitimately, or was able in the past, or in some cities still today get the telephone company to install these multiple master listening devices which they consider are extensions only. But as extensions, they are really eavesdropping devices on the employees' calls.

Senator CARROLL. What about going into the homes of the employees? If they can go that far, do they have leased lines——

Mr. DASH. They were leased lines in the sense that they were extensions of telephones in their own plants.

Senator CARROLL. What about any evidence or any of your studies, whether they were permitted to go into homes of employees?

Mr. DASH. In certain cases we found certain employers did tap phones of employees they suspected in homes through private specialists. In such cases the fellow doing that tapping would have access to telephone company information.

Senator CARROLL. In other words, this illegality could extend into any phase of life where they are doing this wiretapping and eavesdropping?

Mr. DASH. What we found was this, sir. Once the industrialist or the plant owner started, his appetite was whetted. When he saw the results that he could get through eavesdropping, that is. Very often, his purpose was to his mind legitimate, protecting his investment. There was no limit to what he would do. He was sold on the devices. He was sold on the expert who was working for him. He would tap the home phones, tap a competitive's phone, or tap in his own plant.

The techniques, very briefly, I think it is important that people know this, the private wiretapper who does go out and do this tapping does not do it at nighttime, does not do it in the alleyways or skulk or hide. Your private specialist who taps a microphone does it in the open and right in front of your eyes. In this country, we are bedeviled by people who come to homes and check meters and car repair people, telephone company people, who legitimately have a right to check our lines—the private specialist fits himself right into that American picture. He has usually a green telephone company truck which he has bought used. Almost every one of them have it. He usually bedecks himself with wires and screwdrivers and pliers and has wire hanging all over him, the more the better. He will walk right up to a home and ring the doorbell and say, "Madam, I am from the telephone company; your line has been reported, trouble on the line."

The dear lady usually opens the door, shows him the telephone, and sometimes lends him a screwdriver, if he needs it.

We have one case where a wiretapper walked into a restaurant and told the owner that the telephone booth there was out of order and he had to repair it. The restaurant owner pushed back tables, made people leave to eat in another place in the restaurant, stood and watched him while he installed a wiretap and thanked him for his services as he left.

Wiretappers have worked on the top of poles in the presence of police and supervisors of the telephone company. One time a supervisor commented, "They have got you working up there pretty late."

His answer was, "Yes, it is a tough job." The supervisor replied, "Well, don't work too hard," and departed. Take the lawyers' offices, professional people's offices, any big office building—they have maintenance men who go in and out of the offices and I have been able to observe the telephone multiple box of a large office open and a man standing on the ladder working on it and no one questioning as to whether he was a maintenance man and had a right to be there.

They have walked in, as I said, to any office or any place and in the presence of the person who is being tapped installed the tap in the guise of a repairman. I think that this is quite noteworthy and might lead people to do a little more questioning as to the authenticity of a man who comes to their home.

Senator CARROLL. How do we stop this? This thing has grown to a wide extent—you talk about the industrial field, the law enforcement field? Have we become a nation subject to all these electronic eavesdroppers and wiretappers and buggers? How do we end it?

Mr. DASH. It has expanded in the labor field as well where the labor unions are tapping the management and management are tapping labor.

When labor and management are around the table holding a conference, management walks out to allow the union leaders to talk it over amongst themselves. They usually walk to an adjoining room where they have a listening device connected to a bug in the discussion room.

They explain that what they did is not eavesdropping but that the labor people really have a problem they have not been able to communicate to management, that if they could listen to the conversation they could see where the real problem lies and go back and adjust it.

Now, the closing rooms of automobile agencies throughout the country—it is an increasing practice—usually have a microphone in the room. So just as the husband and wife are about to buy the car and they are undecided because of certain things that they want, the salesman excuses himself and leaves to go to a listening device.

At that time, when they are alone, the wife might tell her husband that if it was only $10 cheaper, or if they only had undercoating thrown in for nothing, they would buy the car—he comes back knowing what the problem is and makes the sale. This is a widespread activity. . . .

Senator CARROLL. I have not listened to this for many years and I didn't dream that this thing is so widespread. We could easily, if we put the stamp of legal approval on this, we could become a Nation of eavesdroppers or stool pigeons; when you think of the devices that can be used in an industrial society, they could invade the homes.

On the other hand, they have this problem of how to meet organized crime and the syndicates and what has happened——

Mr. DASH. I admit that is—you have defined the problem. . . .

Robert F. Kennedy
THE CASE FOR WIRETAPPING

Mr. Chairman, I am here today to urge Congress to enact a wiretapping bill this session. The need for such action is very great.

This is a very controversial subject and the debate has continued for decades. While there is merit in the arguments on both sides, the result has been that the existing situation with respect to wiretapping is chaotic. Law enforcement has not kept pace with scientific advancement and individual privacy has not been protected. . . . The nation is being corrupted financially and morally by organized crime and racketeering.

There are over 100 million phones in the United States and the organized criminal syndicates engaged in racketeering activities involving millions of illicit dollars do a major part of their business over this network of communication.

The very fact that the telephone exists has made law enforcement more difficult. It permits criminals to conspire and carry out their activities without ever getting together and, therefore, without giving the police the opportunity to use other techniques of investigation.

The telephone is not only a means of facilitating crime, it may be an instrumentality of crime. It is used in bribery, extortion, and kidnaping, with the added advantage of protecting the identity of the criminal.

We submit that the Federal Government should be permitted to utilize wiretaps to investigate and to use the evidence so gained to prosecute for certain specified crimes and with appropriate procedural safeguards and centralized control. . . . In view of . . . the great gains that have been made by organized crime, the tremendous problems we have as espionage and treason and subversion are concerned, that under certain limited conditions wiretapping should be authorized.

I think there is obviously some opposition to this, but I think that there is certainly a general agreement amongst a good number of people that such authority should be given. . . .

I strongly believe that every citizen of the United States has a right not to have strangers listen in on his telephone conversations. But

Portion of the statement of the Hon. Robert F. Kennedy, at that time Attorney General of the United States, before the Committee on the Judiciary, United States Senate, 87th Congress, 2nd Session.

this right, like many other individual rights in our society, is not absolute or unqualified. Society also has a right to use effective means of law enforcement to protect itself from espionage and treason, from murder and kidnaping, and from organized crime and racketeering.

When these rights, both entitled to respect, come into conflict, a reasonable and fair accommodation must be found. The framers of the Constitution recognized this in the fourth amendment. They did not permit unlimited searches by police officers, nor did they prohibit all searches. They conferred a limited right of search.

Wiretapping is not a search within the fourth amendment, as the Supreme Court has held, since it does not involve a search of a man's person, home, papers, or effects. But, since wiretapping, like searches, does involve an invasion of privacy, we believe it should be only allowed under appropriate limitations and safeguards.

The proposed bill recognizes that in some respects wiretapping involves a greater invasion of privacy than does a search. Accordingly, in many respects it limits wiretapping more narrowly than searches.

Searches are permitted in connection with any offense, however trivial. Wiretapping would be permitted only in connection with enumerated offenses of major importance.

Searches are permitted in connection with various administrative actions by customs officials or State health officials, for example. Wiretapping would be permitted only in connection with crimes.

Searches may be made without a warrant, when incident to a lawful arrest, or involving a moving vehicle, or under the customs laws. Wiretapping would be permitted only on a court order, except in certain national security cases where it could be done on the personal authorization of the Attorney General.

A Federal search warrant may be applied for by any law-enforcement officer and issued by a U.S. commissioner or a State, Commonwealth, or territorial judge. Application to a court for a Federal wiretap order would have to be approved by the Attorney General or an Assistant Attorney General, and the order would have to be issued by a Federal district judge.

No limitations are placed on the use of evidence obtained by a lawful search warrant. Evidence obtained by an authorized wiretap under the proposed bill would be subject to important limitations on disclosure and use.

By eliminating the obstacles to law enforcement . . . and by adopting a clear-cut and realistic definition of what wiretapping is and is not permissible, the proposed bill, if enacted, would make individual rights of privacy far more secure than they are now, and that is an extremely important point. . . .

Herman Schwartz
THE CASE AGAINST WIRETAPPING

. . . An essential difference between the totalitarian state and the free society is that the totalitarian state completely deprives the citizen of his privacy. The state tries to observe all movements, words, and even thoughts. Fear and insecurity dominate every aspect of life and the pursuit of happiness is merely a phrase. . . .

Privacy does not, however, mean solitude. Each man must communicate and exchange thoughts and ideas with others—his wife, his children, his doctor, his lawyer, his priest, his business acquaintances and associates, his friends, his constituents. The growth and complexity of modern society have made the telephone probably the major instrument for such intercourse, for it provides instantaneous, direct, spontaneous, and ostensibly private communication.

To permit law-enforcement authorities to wiretap, even under limited circumstances, would seriously impair this privacy and security so necessary to a free society. Awareness by the public of the power to wiretap is alone sufficient to reduce drastically the sense of security and privacy so vital to a democratic society. The mere thought that someone may be eavesdropping on a conversation with one's wife or lawyer or business associate will discourage full and open discourse.

Indeed, officials who are in office for a period of time can build up a substantial body of information on other public officials and representatives, which can seriously impair the workings of representative democracy.

The rapid and multiple development of modern forms of electronic eavesdropping only aggravates the threat of this fundamental invasion of personal liberty. In *Silverman* v. *United States*, 365 U.S. 505 (March 6, 1961), a spike was inserted into a wall and became a giant microphone picking up all conversations on two floors of a house. The Supreme Court held that this violated the fourth amendment. This committee has heard testimony of other eavesdropping devices which can record conversations at great distances or behind closed doors. The

Portion of the statement of Mr. Herman Schwartz, Attorney at Law, New York City, Representing the American Civil Liberties Union, before the Subcommittee on Constitutional Rights of the Committee of the Judiciary, United States Senate, 87th Congress, 1st Session.

Supreme Court expressed shock and dismay at the microphone in the bedroom installed by California police in *Irvine* v. *California*, 347 U.S. 128 (1954). By these devices, the most private and intimate utterances, often deliberately confined to one's home, are exposed to the ears of listening police. Inevitably, miniature television and image recording instruments will soon be developed and the omnipresent telescreen of George Orwell's "1984" will be with us.

All such types of electronic eavesdropping directly violate the fundamental rights protected by the fourth amendment to the Constitution. The Founders established the protections of the fourth amendment because they had seen their homes subjected to unlimited invasions and searches by the authority of general warrants and writs of assistance. They sought to insure that such unlimited searches and general warrants would never be repeated and that Government officials would be allowed only specific warrants, particularly describing in the words of the fourth amendment, the "place to be searched" and the "thing to be seized." . . .

Electronic eavesdropping necessarily violates the spirit of the fourth amendment. Such eavesdropping cannot be limited in any way. Any authorization for such practices would necessarily be a general, rather than a specific warrant limited to specific objects and places, for it would necessarily permit a general exploratory search for evidence in aid of prosecution. This is because such devices inevitably pick up all the conversations on the wire tapped or room scrutinized, and nothing can be done about this. Thus, not only is the privacy of the telephone user invaded with respect to those calls relating to the offense for which the tap is installed, but (1) all his other calls are overheard, no matter how irrelevant and intimate; (2) all other persons who use his telephone are overheard, whether they be family, business associates, or visitors; and (3) all persons who call him, his family, his business, and those temporarily at his home are overheard.

The assumption that wiretapping and eavesdropping affect only criminals and outlaws of society is thus totally unwarranted and pernicious. The provisions of these bills and of the State enactments which authorize such practices do not limit the eavesdropping to phones of persons suspected of crime. Under such provisions, these eavesdropping devices may be installed wherever evidence of crime in general, or of specific crimes, may be obtained, whether it be on the home or business telephone of a witness, or merely an acquaintance of the suspect, witness, or victim.

Even as to the suspect himself, it must not be forgotten that we are dealing with the privacy of someone who is presumed to be innocent until proven guilty beyond a reasonable doubt. A large proportion of people suspected of crime are not even arrested, much less found guilty beyond a reasonable doubt.

Wiretapping's broad sweep is most apparent where public telephones are tapped, which is all too common. Of 3,588 telephones tapped by New York city police in 1953–54, for example, 1,617 were public telephones or almost half. It is inevitable that in these cases, only an infinitesimal number of the intercepted calls are even made by the suspect or by anyone remotely connected with him, yet, the privacy of numerous other callers is invaded, many of whom have resorted to a public telephone precisely in order to obtain a privacy not obtainable at their homes or businesses.

Because of this dragnet quality, wiretapping and other forms of electronic eavesdropping cannot be regulated by controls similar to search warrants; the object to be seized or the premises to be searched simply cannot be limited or even specified, because the very nature of a wiretap or spike microphone is to catch all calls and conversations. Indeed, the proponents of wiretapping themselves admit that the process is indiscriminate, because one of their proudest claims is that evidence of crime X has occasionally been uncovered when policemen were looking for evidence of crime Y. Carried to their logical implication, their claims would justify putting a tap on the line of anyone whom the police believe to be suspicious, which is exactly what is frequently done now. . . .

Despite the great clamor for wiretapping by prosecutors, there is serious doubt and disagreement as to the need for such authority in dealing with crime. Gambling and vice, which in New York, for example, are only misdemeanors, are the major crime areas where wiretapping is used. Even in these areas, the success and indispensability of wiretapping are dubious. Justice Samuel Hofstadter of New York declared in 1955 that his record of the fruits of wiretap orders "showed some arrests and fewer convictions and then rarely, if ever, for a heinous offense."

. . . Insofar as gambling and vice are generally operations of organized crime, the problem is not that the investigative techniques are inadequate but that the public is indifferent and law enforcement either inept or corrupt. A recent study in New York, although calling for wiretapping authority, attributed the ineffectiveness of efforts to suppress organized gambling primarily to the "absence of integrated effort" among law enforcement agencies, as well as to lax police work and public indifference. And the same causes seem operative elsewhere. . . .

In sum, the bill would only open the door to widespread uncontrolled eavesdropping on wholly innocent people, in their own homes, by the most modern and frightening devices. Because of the broad sweep of such modern devices, it is doubtful that the bill is constitutional. It is certainly undesirable as a matter of legislative policy.

In a free society the end of law enforcement does not justify any and all means. Even if far more convictions could be obtained through the use of such procedures as general warrants, for example, we should not choose to use them. Since the case for wiretapping and other forms of electronic eavesdropping is so weak and since great damage to the freedom and security of the individual is so obvious, there is absolutely no basis for passing any type of legislation to grant such authority. . . .

Jonathan O. Cole
DRUGS AND CONTROL OF THE MIND

Since I have been asked to give a paper on the relationship of psychopharmacology to human behavior in a conference which focuses its attention on the control of the mind, I must conclude that those organizing this conference believed explicitly, or implicitly, that drugs could be used to control the mind. An alternative hypothesis, of course, would be that the group organizing this meeting believed that drugs could be used to enhance the freedom of the mind. I will examine the evidence relating to both hypotheses.

I also believe I detect in this conference an implicit assumption that control of the mind is bad and freedom of the mind is good. B. F. Skinner, the father of the operant approach to the study of behavior, has seriously questioned this assumption, believing that behavior can be controlled effectively, or is about to be able to be controlled effectively, and that it is the duty of our society to actively attempt to control human behavior in such a way as to achieve effects which we consider desirable before some other group becomes more proficient at controlling behavior and directing it into paths which we consider undesirable. He assumes, of course, that human behavior can be controlled in an effective and precise manner, and that someone, somewhere, in this country or in the Western world, is capable of making value judgments concerning the kinds of behavior which are good and should be positively elicited and the kinds of behavior which are bad and should be suppressed. This, of course,

From *Control of the Mind: Man and Civilization*, edited by S. M. Farber and R. L. Wilson. Copyright, © 1961, McGraw-Hill, Inc. Used by permission of McGraw-Hill Book Company. Dr. Cole is Chief of the Psychopharmacology Service Center, National Institute of Health, U.S. Public Health Service, Bethesda, Md.

complicates the whole matter. We must consider whether drugs can be used to facilitate the control of "good" behavior and the abolishment of "bad" behavior, as well as the possibility that drugs may be used by enemies of our society to suppress desirable behavior and to elicit undesirable behavior. Can drugs do any of these things?

To answer this complex set of questions it would be necessary to define what kinds of behavior are bad and what kinds are good. This I feel uncomfortable doing, except in clinical situations, and will therefore retreat to the simpler question concerning the possibility of using drugs to control any behavior, noting in passing the effects of drugs on extremes of behavior which many people would unanimously consider to be clearly undesirable or clearly desirable. Skinner, of course, prefers to restrict himself to overt behavior. For the purpose of this conference, however, one must also consider less readily observable subjective phenomena, such as mood, creativity, imagination, etc.

Assuming one wished either to control or to free the mind, or to influence behavior, what classes of drugs are available for this purpose? Existing psychopharmacological agents fall rather nicely into five groups. First, one has the major tranquilizers, which include chlorpromazine and a variety of other phenothiazine derivatives, reserpine and a few related Rauwolfia alkaloids, and a few newer compounds such as haloperidol, which are chemically unrelated to the other two groups but appear to share certain properties with them. These drugs are relatively effective in the control of the symptoms of schizophrenia and other psychotic states.

The second group consists of the minor tranquilizers and sedatives, a group including such compounds as meprobamate (Equanil, Miltown) and methaminodiazepoxide (Librium), which may be effective in relieving neurotic anxiety at dosage levels that do not produce undesirable degrees of sedation, and sedatives such as the barbiturates and the bromides, whose clinically undesirable sedative properties may be more prominent than their anxiety-relieving properties.

The third discernible group is that of the stimulant drugs, including amphetamine. These drugs have a euphoriant action in some individuals. They also increase wakefulness, decrease fatigue-induced performance decrement under some conditions, and in addition sometimes causing jitteryness, tachycardia, and other relatively undesirable signs of central nervous system stimulation.

The fourth group is that of the antidepressive drugs, including iproniazid (Marsilid) and other monoamine oxidase inhibitors and imipramine (Tofranil). These drugs have some demonstrated effectiveness in the relief of depressive syndromes. In contrast to the stimulants, they are slow to act, requiring approximately 2 weeks for desirable clinical effects to manifest themselves. The monoamine oxidase inhibitors appear to share with the stimulants some euphoriant effect in some individuals and some capacity to speed reaction time, increase verbal productivity, and otherwise stimulate the organism. Imipramine does not seem to possess these particular properties.

The fifth group is that of the psychotomimetic drugs, including older compounds such as mescaline and LSD-25 and newer and more diverse compounds such as Sernyl and Ditran and psilocybin.

It may be that other classes or types of drugs with different, more discrete, more specific, or more varied effects will be found in the near future. Since all existing new types of drugs have been identified as having unique properties in man only on the basis of their observed effects in human subjects, rather than as a result of well-planned extrapolations from their effect in animals to their effects in man, it is extremely difficult to predict what kinds of drugs the future will bring. I suggest with some reluctance that it is unlikely, at present, that any chemical compounds with specific identifiable and predictable effects in human subjects can be developed on the basis of animal experimentation alone. In short, even if I felt that I could identify in man the psychological or behavioral function which I or anyone else wished to control, or for that matter to free, I would not be willing to predict that a rational and energetic attempt to create a drug which would have these specific effects would be particularly likely to be fruitful. This is not to say that investigation in man of compounds with new and different behavioral or neuropharmacological effects in animals may not lead to the discovery of drugs with new and surprising clinical properties, but I doubt that at this stage in our knowledge the discovery of such compounds can be systematically engineered. It is possible, of course, that having identified a drug with some specific desirable properties in animals one can by examining related compounds find one which possesses a particular property in greater degree while lacking some other undesirable or confounding properties. However, given the present state of drug development, it seems more appropriate to concern oneself with the effects of drugs we now have than to speculate further about the possible effects of possible drugs which might conceivably be developed to control specific mental functions or behaviors.

The physician, particularly the psychiatrist, is currently using the first four of the above five groups of drugs for the control of the mind. Most of the available evidence concerning the ability of drugs to control the mind or to control behavior comes from exactly this clinical use. The physician usually does not worry too much about the social goodness or badness of controlling behavior, since many patients come to him asking that their behavior, feelings, or thoughts be controlled. Other patients, of course, are brought to him by relatives or by society because their behavior is such that others feel it needs control. The need for such control is, in fact, not uncommonly legally certified by a court, and the patient is committed to a hospital for treatment until such time as the aberrant behavior has been brought under control. Physicians now have an extensive experience in using these drugs to control behavior, and I think most physicians would agree that the reliability with which existing drugs control specific behaviors leaves much to be desired.

Overwhelming doses of a barbiturate or an anesthetic will, of course, put anybody to sleep, and adequate doses of a drug like Metrazol will produce convulsions in anyone. Even with such clear-cut end-points, there is considerable individual variability in the doses required to produce these profound effects.

Moreover, our clinically most effective drugs, the phenothiazines and the antidepressives, appear to produce quite different effects in psychiatrically ill individuals from those they produce in normal subjects. Thus, a dose of chlorpromazine which renders a disturbed schizophrenic relatively calm and reduces the prominence of his delusions and hallucinations and improves the clarity of his thinking processes would leave a normal individual fatigued, lethargic, numb, and miserable. The evidence concerning the effects of the more potent antidepressives in normal subjects is very scanty, but again it seems likely that their effects are much less dramatic and much less desirable than they are in seriously depressed individuals.

The phenothiazines and Rauwolfia alkaloids could, of course, be used for the control of behavior in normal subjects by giving doses large enough to produce, in effect, a chemical straight jacket in which the individual had his muscles so stiffened by the Parkinsonianlike effects of the drugs and his energies so reduced by their anergic properties as to render him ineffective for most purposes. But I would judge that the use of drugs to induce the temporary states of physical incapacity is of less interest to this group than their use in producing less dramatic and more socially meaningful alterations in thinking and behavior.

The milder tranquilizers and sedatives can cause, in some individuals, a decrease in anxiety when anxiety is present to a discernible degree, and the amphetamines may prevent the occurrence of a fatigue-induced decrement in performance at monotonous tasks such as airplane flying or radar-screen watching, in addition to producing mild euphoria and some increase in talkativeness in some subjects. The sedatives and mild tranquilizers are likely to produce temporary decrements in psychomotor performance, and some evidence has recently been presented by Beecher to the effect that a barbiturate in athletes caused an impairment of athletic performance while causing the subjects to judge themselves to be doing much better than they usually did. Although it is suspected that the stimulants may also cause some alteration in judgment, this has not been clearly demonstrated.

All of the psychotomimetic agents can effectively impair behavior, if only through their autonomic side effects. Sernyl can produce a complete anesthesia in adequate dosage, while Ditran seems to be the one most capable of producing a severe and intense delirium with marked disorganization of thought, auditory and visual hallucinations, and complete loss of contact with reality.

The trouble with all existing psychopharmacologic agents as tools to be used in the control of the mind is that, even from the standpoint of the practicing psychiatrist, they are not completely satisfactory. Although both the phenothiazines and the antidepressive drugs may produce startling improvements, and even what appear to be complete remissions in some patients, these patients are usually in the minority. There is generally a larger proportion of patients in whom some change in the desired direction is produced, and such patients are usually classified as moderately improved, or slightly improved. There is always a residual group of patients, often in the neighborhood of 20 to 30 percent who are unchanged or worse. Worse, in this sense, means movement in the opposite direction from that desired. To date, clinicians have been notably unsuccessful in predicting which patients will respond in which ways. For this reason, even if one were only attempting to control the minds of a homogeneous group of psychiatric patients with a drug with which one had had considerable experience, the desired effect would not be produced in all patients, and one would not be able to plan specifically that any particular effect would be produced in a particular patient.

With the milder stimulants and sedatives one runs into great difficulty in predicting their effects on normal subjects or patients. Some patients become more active, stimulated, and euphoric when given sedatives; some normal subjects find the effects of amphetamine unpleasant and undesirable and experience no euphoria whatever. In hyperactive, hyperkinetic children, amphetamine often has a tranquilizing, slowing effect, and I have known adult depressed patients to take Benzedrine to go to sleep at night.

Particularly in normal and neurotic subjects, there is considerable evidence that the individual's expectations, the cues provided by the milieu, and the attitudes of the therapist may significantly alter the effectiveness of the drug. In a pilot study recently made at Denison University in collaboration with the Psychopharmacology Service Center on the response of normal college students to d-amphetamine, on some psychological measures there was a tendency for subjects who believed they were getting d-amphetamine and actually received d-amphetamine to have typical amphetaminelike reactions in both mood and psychomotor performance, while subjects who received Dexedrine and believed they were receiving a barbiturate showed a tendency toward barbituratelike reactions, at least in some aspects of psychological functioning. This study is in the process of being replicated to see whether these preliminary trends will be strengthened. Although further work may show that specific combinations of social influences and pharmacological effects may be very powerful methods for producing specific types of results, I know of no strong evidence that this is in fact the case.

There has been considerable discussion in recent years of the capacity of psychotomimetic agents, particularly LSD-25, mescaline, and psilocybin, to produce what may be described, in the context of this conference, as a "freeing" of the mind. Visual and auditory experiences may be made more vivid, and dramatic flights of fantasy, pleasurable or terrifying, may accompany the administration of these drugs. Artistic productions by persons in drugged states have elicited interest. These altered states of consciousness have also been reported to have been followed by profound and lasting changes in personality functioning and psychiatric symptomatology.

Two questions arise: First, do these psychotomimetic drugs "free" the mind in any useful manner during the period of their pharmacological activity? Second, do they have a useful effect in altering psychological functioning after the drug's acute effects have passed?

The first question is hard for me to answer. It is possible that artistic productions, poetry, or story plots conceived or executed under a psychotomimetic agent may, in some individuals, be superior to those produced in a drug-free or predrug state. I doubt this, being dubious that any interference with brain functioning is likely to produce an improvement in performance in a normal subject, but I suggest that the matter is susceptible to scientific test. A series of artistic productions by a series of artists produced predrug, during drug, and postdrug could be judged by other artists who were unaware of the conditions under which each production was executed. If the work produced during the influence of a drug such as LSD-25 were to be judged consistently superior, this would be powerfully convincing evidence indeed.

It should be noted, however, that the setting, including the expectations of the person administering the drug and the person receiving it, play a very powerful role here. There even is what I believe to be an artificial "geographical" effect on the response to the drug LSD-25. Workers in the East Coast, such as Malitz and Klee, do not appear to obtain from their subjects much in the way of bizarre fantasy material. Occasional subjects may become paranoid, and most experience visual illusions and autonomic side effects, but none of the subjects have reported self-revelations or other dramatic personal experiences. Hartman and Chandler and other workers in the Los Angeles area, on the other hand, seem to be able to induce most subjects to experience cosmic events such as union with the sun or death and rebirth with comparative ease. Other investigators such as Jackson and Savage report similar, though less dramatic, results. Since it seems unlikely that the subjects on the West Coast are organically different from those on the East Coast, it is more reasonable to assume that something in the test situation produces the striking difference in response. Does LSD-25 really increase a subject's suggestability? Is the West Coast phenomenon entirely physician-induced or due to cultural differences in expectations of patients, or do investigators in the East somehow manage to create a situation in which flights of fantasy and dramatic emotional experiences are effectively, and perhaps unconsciously, suppressed?

As possible additional evidence in favor of LSD-25 as a tool for eliciting a response desired by the administrator, one may note Abramson's utilization of it as a method for getting patients to work on their resistances in an approved psychoanalytic manner with an almost complete absence of more exotic or fantastic productions.

I view recent work on LSD-25 and psychotherapy with very mixed feelings. The drug may really be enabling patients to obtain startling new insights into their problems and may be able to cause them to strikingly alter their behavior, but I am at a loss as to how much of this to attribute to a drug-induced "freeing" of the mind and how much to attribute to a therapist-induced mystical experience similar to religious conversion. Either effect conceivably could be therapeutically valuable, but the whole area is now so highly charged with emotion and so lacking in adequately controlled research as to make firm conclusions impossible. I am also concerned with the possibility of prolonged psychotic episodes being precipitated by psychotomimetic agents and the possibility of suicidal attempts or other aberrant behavior occurring during the drugged state.

There remains the unpleasant possibility that psychotomimetic agents or other drugs may make individuals overly responsive to the demands of another person and therefore may be usable as a means of altering loyalties or changing moral attitudes or political beliefs. Certainly these drugs could be used to incapacitate individuals temporarily, but can they be used to establish long-term control over minds? The published scientific literature is not at all informative. Both experimental and clinical reports deal chiefly with volunteer subjects or amenable patients, and I know of no experimental attempts to specifically alter beliefs, attitudes, or perceptions during or after the psychotomimetic drug experience. Chronic schizophrenic subjects certainly appear to be very resistant to reporting any subjective effects of LSD-25, but whether this resistance is secondary to any inner will to avoid responding is impossible to say.

Other drugs, intravenous barbiturates or amphetamine derivatives, can certainly alter verbal behavior, increase talkativeness and emotional expression, and occasionally enable patients to recall repressed experiences or talk about subjects which they had previously consciously avoided mentioning. The extent to which such procedures are useful outside the combat-neurosis type of situation is difficult to assess. The fact that three such otherwise diverse drugs as sodium amytal, desoxyephedrine, and LSD-25 are all used to facilitate psychotherapy by increasing emotional expression and activating unconscious material is, in itself, evidence of the confusion in this area of psychiatric practice.

In summary, I advance the proposition that drugs are not, in and of themselves, useful tools for the control of the mind, nor are they particularly well suited to free the mind if one is primarily concerned with the subjective experiences, attitudes, or beliefs of relatively normal human subjects. Some drugs such as LSD-25 and psilocybin can enable subjects to experience bizarre and perhaps rewarding experiences, but usually only if the subjects are interested in having such experiences or if such experiences are expected by those administering the drug. Barbiturates or stimulants (or alcohol for that matter) may increase emotional displays or promote talkativeness, but again the drugs are probably only facilitating the expression of emotions or thoughts already present in the subject.

Drugs such as the phenothiazine tranquilizers or the antidepressives are often effective in altering psychiatric symptoms in some, but not all, patients presenting appropriate symptoms. These clinical effects, however limited, are the phenomena closest to specific drug effects on behavior and psychological functioning, but these effects are confined to psychiatrically ill individuals and do not have any obvious applications to the control of thought or behavior in normal individuals.

Large enough doses of almost any of these five groups of psychopharmacological agents can disorganize or suppress human behavior by generally incapacitating the subjects receiving them, but there is no real reason to believe that these acute effects would have any long-term effect on the minds of the subjects.

There remains the possibility that some drug or drugs combined with some structured situation, e.g., some type of brainwashing program, might make the latter more effective or might reduce the time or effort required to produce a desired effect.

Although published research even vaguely relevant to this last problem is almost totally lacking, I see no reason to believe any drug would be more effective than social and psychological pressures or physical discomforts in producing changes in an individual. The great interindividual variability in response to psychopharmacological agents in normal subjects and in patients makes it unlikely that any single drug would be a reliable aid in any planned program of mass thought control, although I accept the possibility that individual attempts at thought control may have something in common with psychotherapy, and skilled practitioners of such a black art may find drugs tailored to the practitioner and the subject of some use.

Furthermore, I consider it unlikely that current methods can be used to develop a new drug with any specific and reliable effect on either the freedom or the control of human mental processes, although I confidentially expect that new types of drugs with different effects on brain functioning and behavior will be uncovered by present drug-development methods.

In short, present psychopharmacological agents, though often chemically useful, have relatively nonspecific and quite variable effects on human behavior. How much of this variability is attributable to existing physical and psychological differences among human beings and how much variability is produced by the setting and by the behavior of the person administering the drugs is impossible to estimate. The difficulties in developing and evaluating drugs for the control of clinical psychiatric states are many; the difficulties in developing and/or evaluating drugs for the control of mental functioning or for the freeing of mental functioning in normal human beings appear to be well-nigh insurmountable.

Robert J. Lifton

THOUGHT REFORM OF CHINESE INTELLECTUALS

The Chinese Communist program of *Szu Hsiang Kai Tsao* or "thought reform" is unique both as a social experiment and as a laboratory for cross-cultural psychiatric study. Applied to Westerners and Chinese,

From Robert J. Lifton, "Thought Reform of Chinese Intellectuals: A Psychiatric Evaluation," *Journal of Social Issues*, 13, No. 3 (1957), 5–19. Reprinted with permission. Dr. Lifton is a psychiatrist whose particular interest is cross-cultural psychiatric research in relation to East Asia.

to professors, students, and peasants, it combines a remarkably widespread dissemination with impressive emotional force and depth.

It is a subject which has received much attention in this country (under the popular term "brainwashing") when involving such groups as American prisoners of war and other incarcerated Westerners. But there has been surprisingly little systematic psychological investigation of the thought reform procedures which the Chinese have employed with their own people, particularly with their intellectuals.

The most intensive of these all-Chinese thought reform programs for intellectuals is that conducted in the "revolutionary colleges"—set up all over China immediately after the Communist takeover. These were particularly active between 1948 and 1952, when they represented an ideological hard core for the entire thought reform movement, an extreme model for reform efforts throughout the population. Their techniques— which I will here attempt to describe and interpret—can give us a key to the understanding of all Chinese thought reform programs, whether applied to Chinese intellectuals, United Nations prisoners of war, or Western missionaries. . . .

Who attends a revolutionary college? Students are drawn from many divergent sources: former KMT officials and affiliates, teachers who had been associated with the old regime, Communist cadres who had demonstrated significant "errors" in their work or thoughts, party members who had spent long periods of time in KMT areas, students returning from the West, and finally, arbitrarily selected groups of university instructors or recent graduates. Many in these groups came in response to thinly veiled coercion—the strong "suggestion" that they attend; but others actively sought admission on a voluntary basis, in order to try to fit in with the requirements of the new regime, or at least to find out what was expected of them.

The college itself is tightly organized along Communist principles of "democratic centralism." One center may contain as many as 4,000 students, subdivided into sections of about 1,000 each, then classes of 100–200 each, and finally into six to ten man groups. The president of the institution may be a well known scholar serving as a figurehead; technically below him in rank are a vice-president and the section heads, who are likely to be Communist Party members, and exert the real authority at the center. Under their supervision are the class heads, each of whom works with three special cadres.

These cadres, usually long-standing and dedicated party workers, play a central role in the thought reform process; they are the connecting link between the faculty and the students, and it is they who perform the day-to-day leg work of the reform process. The three cadres of each class may be designated according to function: the executive cadre, concerned essentially with courses of study; the organizing cadre, most intimately involved with the structure and function of the small group and the attitudes of the individual students who make them up; and the advisory cadre—the only one of the three who may be a woman—offering counsel on personal and ideological problems which come up during this arduous experience.

I have divided the six-month reform course into three stages, which represent the successive psychological climates to which the student is exposed as he is guided along the path of his symbolic death and rebirth: The Great Togetherness, The Closing in of the Milieu, and Submission and Rebirth.

The Great Togetherness: Group Identification

New students approach the course with a varying mixture of curiosity, enthusiasm, and apprehension. When a group of them arrives, their first impression is likely to be a favorable one. They encounter an atmosphere which is austere, but friendly—an open area of low-slung wooden buildings (frequently converted from military barracks) which serve as living quarters and class rooms—old students and cadres greeting them warmly, showing them around, speaking glowingly of the virtues of the Revolutionary College, of the Communist movement, of the new hope for the future. Then, after a warm welcoming speech from the president of the college, they are organized into ten-man study groups. And for a period of from a few days to two weeks they are told to "just get to know each other."

Students are surprised by this free and enthusiastic atmosphere; some among the older ones may remain wary, but most are caught up in a feeling of camaraderie. Within the small groups they vent their widely-shared hostility towards the old regime—an important stimulus to the thought reform process. There is a frank exchange of feeling and ideas, past and present, as they discuss their background experiences, and hopes and fears for the future. There is an air of optimism, a feeling of being in the same boat, a high *esprit de corps*.

Next, through a series of "thought mobilization" lectures and discussions, the philosophy and rationale of the program are impressed upon the individual student: the "old society" was evil and corrupt; this was so because it was dominated by the "exploiting classes"—the land-owners and the bourgeoisie; most intellectuals come from these "exploiting classes" (or from the closely related petit-bourgeoisie) and therefore retain "evil remnants" of their origins and of the old regime; each must now rid himself of these "ideological poisons" in order to become a "new man" in the "new society." In this way, he is told, the "ideology of all classes" can be brought into harmony with "objective material conditions." Mao Tse-tung is frequently quoted in his references to "diseases in thought and politics" which require "an attitude of 'saving men by curing their diseases'."

At this time, and throughout the program, *thought reform is presented to the student as a morally uplifting, harmonizing, and therapeutic experience.*

Then the formal courses begin—the first usually entitled The History of the Development of Society (to be later followed by Lenin on the State and Materialistic Dialectics, History of the Chinese Revolution, Theory of the New Democracy, and Field Study—visits to old Communist workshops and industrial centers). The subject matter is introduced by a two to six hour lecture delivered by a leading Communist theorist. This is followed by the interminable *hsueh hsi* or study sessions within the ten-man group, where the real work of thought reform takes place. Discussion of the lecture material is led by the group leader who has been elected by its members—usually because of his superior knowledge of Marxism. At this point he encourages a spirited exchange of all views, and takes no side when there is disagreement. The other students realize that the group leader is making daily reports to a cadre or to the class head, but the full significance of these is not yet appreciated; they may be viewed as simply à necessary organizational procedure. Most students retain a feeling of pulling together toward a common goal in a group crusading spirit.

The Closing in of the Milieu: The Period of Emotional Conflict

About four to six weeks from the beginning of thought reform—at about the time of the completion of the first course—a change begins to develop in the atmosphere. With the submission of the first "thought summary" (these must be prepared after each course) there is a shift in emphasis from the intellectual and ideological to the personal and the emotional. The student begins to find that he, rather than the Communist doctrine, is the object of study. A pattern of criticism, self-criticism, and confession develops—pursued with increasing intensity throughout the remainder of the course.

Now the group leader is no longer "neutral"; acting upon instructions from above, he begins to "lean to one side," to support the "progressive elements," to apply stronger pressures in the direction of reform. He and the "activists" who begin to emerge take the lead in setting the tone for the group. The descriptions of past and present attitudes which the student so freely gave during the first two weeks of the course now come back to haunt him. Not only his ideas, but his underlying motivations are carefully scrutinized. Failure to achieve the correct "materialistic viewpoint," "proletarian standpoint," and "dialectical methodology" is pointed out, and the causes for this deficiency are carefully analyzed.

Criticisms cover every phase of past and present thought and behavior; they not only "nip in the bud" the slightest show of unorthodoxy or non-conformity, but they also point up "false progressives"—students who outwardly express the "correct" views without true depth of feeling. Group members are constantly on the look-out for indications in others of lack of real involvement in the process. Each must demonstrate the genuineness of his reform through continuous personal enthusiasm and active participation in the criticism of his fellow students. In this way he can avoid being rebuked for "failure to combine theory with practice."

Standard criticisms repeatedly driven home include: "individualism"—placing personal interests above those of "the people"—probably the most emphasized of all; "subjectivism"—applying a personal viewpoint to a problem rather than a "scientific" Marxist approach; "objectivism"—undue detachment, viewing oneself "above class distinction," or "posing as a spectator of the new China"; "sentimentalism"—allowing one's attachment to family or friends to interfere with reform needs, therefore "carrying about an ideological burden" (usually associated with reluctance to denounce family members or friends allegedly associated with the "exploiting classes.") And in addition: "deviationism," "opportunism," "dogmatism," "reflecting exploiting class ideology," "overly technical viewpoint," "bureaucratism," "individual heroism," "revisionism," "departmentalism," "sectarianism," "idealism," and "pro-American outlook."

The student is required to accept these criticisms gratefully when they are offered. But more than this, he is expected both to anticipate and expand upon them through the even more important device of *self-criticism*. He must correctly analyze his own thoughts and actions, and review his past life—family, educational, and social—in order to uncover the source of his difficulties. And the resulting insights are always expressed within the Communist jargon—corrupt "ruling class" and "bourgeois" influence, dervied from his specific class origin.

The criticism and self-criticism process is also extended into every aspect of daily life, always with a highly moralistic tone. Under attack here are the "bourgeois" or "ruling class" characteristics of pride, conceit, greed, competitiveness, dishonesty, boastfulness, and rudeness. Relationships with the opposite sex are discussed and evaluated, solely in terms of their effects upon the individual's progress in reform. Where a "backward" girl friend is thought to be impeding his progress, a student may be advised to break off a liasion; but if both are "progressive," or if one is thought to be aiding the other's progress, the relationship will be condoned. Sexual contacts are, on the whole, discouraged, as it is felt that they drain energies from the thought reform process.

The student must, within the small group, *confess* all the evils of his past life. Political and moral considerations here become inextricably merged; but especially emphasized are any "reactionary" affiliations with the old regime or with its student organizations. Each student develops a running confession, supplemented by material from his self-criticisms and "thought summaries"; its content becomes widely known to students, Some, recalling either stories they have heard or personal experiences, find revived in their minds images of the extreme measures used by the Communists in dealing with their enemies. All are extremely fearful of the consequences of being considered a "reactionary."

Students who show signs of emotional disturbance are encouraged to seek help by talking over their "thought problem" with the advisory cadre, in order to resolve whatever conflicts exist. Many experience psychosomatic expressions of their problems—fatigue, insomnia, loss of appetite, vague aches and pains, or gastro-intestinal symptoms. Should they take their complaints to the college doctor, they are apt to encounter a reform-oriented and psychologically-sophisticated reply: "There is nothing wrong with your body. It must be your thoughts that are sick. You will feel better when you have solved your problems and completed your reform." And indeed, most students are in a state of painful inner tension; relief is badly needed.

Submission and "Rebirth"

The last stage—that of the over-all thought summary or final confession—supplies each student with a means of resolving his conflicts. It is ushered in by a mass meeting at which high Communist officials and faculty members emphasize the importance of the final thought summary as the crystallization of the entire course. Group sessions over the next two or three days are devoted exclusively to discussions of the form this summary is to take. It is to be a life history, beginning two generations back, and extending through the reform experience. It must, with candor and thoroughness, describe the historical development of one's thoughts, and the relationship of these to actions. It is also to include a detailed analysis of the personal effects of thought reform.

The summary may be from five to twenty-five thousand Chinese characters (roughly equivalent numerically to English words) and require about ten days of preparation. Each student then must read his summary to the group, where it is subjected to more prolonged and penetrating criticism. He may be kept under fire for several days of detailed discussion and painful revision—as every group member is considered responsible for the approval of each confession presented, and all may even have to place their signatures upon it. The confession is the student's final opportunity to bring out anything he has previously held back, as well as to elaborate upon everything he has already said. It always includes a detailed analysis of class origin. And in almost every case its central feature is the denunciation of the father—both as a symbol of the exploiting classes, and as an individual. The student usually finds the recitation of his father's personal, political, and economic abuses to be the most painful part of his entire thought reform. He may require endless prodding, persuasion, and indirect threats before he is able to take this crucial step. But he has little choice, and he almost invariably complies.

The confession ends with an emphasis on personal liabilities which still remain, attitudes in need of further reform—and the solemn resolve to continue attempts at self-improvement, and to devotedly serve the regime in the future. When his confession is approved, the student experiences great emotional relief. He has weathered the thought reform ordeal, renounced his past, and established an organic bond between himself and the government. His confession will accompany him throughout his future career as a permanent part of his personal record.

It is no wonder that this period of the final thought summary is frequently referred to as "taking a bath." It is the symbolic submission to the regime, and at the same time the expression of individual rebirth into the Chinese Communist community. . . .

Viewed in its broadest perspective, thought reform represents an exaggerated expression of human emotions and psychological forces that are universal in nature. In its extreme character, it sets off in high relief things which cannot ordinarily be seen as clearly. It conveys to us valuable insights—of both an ethical and psychological variety.

It is, first of all, replete with important psychiatric data—concerning such issues as guilt, shame, and confession, change in identity and belief, relations between language and theory, the effects of group pressures, and techniques for controlling the environment. All of this may add to our knowledge of human emotions, and has great relevance to psychiatric illness and to treatment methods. Equally important is the manner in which thought reform gives us a test tube demonstration of the total manipulation of the human being, and a vantage point for further insights into Communist practices.

Thought reform also highlights the dilemma which we face in our own political, cultural, and educational institutions. Every society makes use of similar pressures of guilt, shame, and confession, and of milieu control, as means of maintaining its values and its organization. We must ask ourselves where we—inadvertently, and in less extreme form—could also be applying these in excess, to mould uniform identities, and to make men think and act in the conforming fashion. We are confronted with the problem of any democratic society—that of maintaining a balance which limits these forces sufficiently to allow its people a sense of individual freedom, creativity, and human dignity.

B. F. Skinner
FREEDOM AND THE CONTROL OF MEN

The second half of the twentieth century may be remembered for its solution of a curious problem. Although Western democracy created the conditions responsible for the rise of modern science, it is now evident that it may never fully profit from that achievement. The so-called "democratic philosophy" of human behavior to which it also gave rise is increasingly in conflict with the application of the methods of science to human affairs. Unless this conflict is somehow resolved, the ultimate goals of democracy may be long deferred.

I

Just as biographers and critics look for external influences to account for the traits and achievements of the men they study, so science ultimately explains behavior in terms of "causes" or conditions which lie beyond the individual himself. As more and more causal relations are demonstrated, a practical corollary becomes difficult to resist: it should be possible to *produce* behavior according to plan simply by arranging the proper conditions. Now, among the specifications which might reasonably be submitted to a behavioral technology are these: Let men be happy, informed, skillful, well behaved and productive.

This immediate practical implication of a science of behavior has a familiar ring, for it recalls the doctrine of human perfectibility of eighteenth- and nineteenth-century humanism. A science of man shares the optimism of that philosophy and supplies striking support for the working faith that men can build a better world and, through it, better

B. F. Skinner, "Freedom and the Control of Men," *The American Scholar*, 25 (1955–56), 47–65. Reprinted with the permission of the author. Dr. Skinner is Professor of Psychology at Harvard University. In addition to technical books and articles, he has published a utopian novel, *Walden Two*, and a general analysis of the implications of science for human affairs entitled *Science and Human Behavior*.

men. The support comes just in time, for there has been little optimism of late among those who speak from the traditional point of view. Democracy has become "realistic," and it is only with some embarrassment that one admits today to perfectionistic or utopian thinking.

The earlier temper is worth considering, however. History records many foolish and unworkable schemes for human betterment, but almost all the great changes in our culture which we now regard as worthwhile can be traced to perfectionistic philosophies. Governmental, religious, educational, economic and social reforms follow a common pattern. Someone believes that a change in a cultural practice—for example, in the rules of evidence in a court of law, in the characterization of man's relation to God, in the way children are taught to read and write, in permitted rates of interest, or in minimal housing standards—will improve the condition of men: by promoting justice, permitting men to seek salvation more effectively, increasing the literacy of a people, checking an inflationary trend, or improving public health and family relations, respectively. The underlying hypothesis is always the same: that a different physical or cultural environment will make a different and better man.

The scientific study of behavior not only justifies the general pattern of such proposals; it promises new and better hypotheses. The earliest cultural practices must have originated in sheer accidents. Those which strengthened the group survived with the group in a sort of natural selection. As soon as men began to propose and carry out changes in practice for the sake of possible consequences, the evolutionary process must have accelerated. The simple practice of making changes must have had survival value. A further acceleration is now to be expected. As laws of behavior are more precisely stated, the changes in the environment required to bring about a given effect may be more clearly specified. Conditions which have been neglected because their effects were slight or unlooked for may be shown to be relevant. New conditions may actually be created, as in the discovery and synthesis of drugs which affect behavior.

This is not time, then, to abandon notions of progress, improvement or, indeed, human perfectibility. The simple fact is that man is able, and now as never before, to lift himself by his own bootstraps. In achieving control of the world of which he is a part, he may learn at last to control himself.

II

Timeworn objections to the planned improvement of cultural practices are already losing much of their force. Marcus Aurelius was probably right in advising his readers to be content with a haphazard amelioration of mankind. "Never hope to realize Plato's republic," he sighed, ". . . for who can change the opinions of men? And without a change of sentiments what can you make but reluctant slaves and hypocrites?" He was thinking, no doubt, of contemporary patterns of control based upon punishment or the threat of punishment which, as he correctly observed, breed only reluctant slaves of those who submit and hypocrites of those who discover modes of evasion. But we need not share his pessimism, for the opinions of men can be changed. The techniques of indoctrination which were being devised by the early Christian Church at the very time Marcus Aurelius was writing are relevant, as are some of the techniques of psychotherapy and of advertising and public relations. Other methods suggested by recent scientific analyses leave little doubt of the matter.

The study of human behavior also answers the cynical complaint that there is a plain "cussedness" in man which will always thwart efforts to improve him. We are often told that men do not want to be changed, even for the better. Try to help them, and they will outwit you and remain happily wretched. Dostoevsky claimed to see some plan in it. "Out of sheer ingratitude," he complained, or possibly boasted, "man will play you a dirty trick, just to prove that men are still men and not the keys of a piano. . . . And even if you could prove that a man is only a piano key, he would still do something out of sheer perversity—he would create destruction and chaos—just to gain his point. . . . And if all this could in turn be analyzed and prevented by predicting that it would occur, then man would deliberately go mad to prove his point." This is a conceivable neurotic reaction to inept control. A few men may have shown it, and many have enjoyed Dostoevsky's statement because they tend to show it. But that such perversity is a fundamental reaction of the human organism to controlling conditions is sheer nonsense.

So is the objection that we have no way of knowing what changes to make even though we have the necessary techniques. That is one of the great hoaxes of the century—a sort of booby trap left behind in the retreat before the advancing front of science. Scientists themselves have unsuspectingly agreed that there are two kinds of useful propositions about nature—facts and value judgments—and that science must confine itself to "what is," leaving "what ought to be" to others. But with what special sort of wisdom is the non-scientist endowed? Science is only effective knowing, no matter who engages in it. Verbal behavior proves upon analysis to be composed of many different types of utterances, from poetry and exhortation to logic and factual description, but these are not all equally useful in talking about cultural practices. We may classify useful propositions according to the degrees of confidence with which they may be asserted. Sentences about nature range from highly probable "facts" to sheer guesses. In general, future events are less likely to be correctly described than past. When a scientist talks about a projected experiment, for example, he must often resort to statements having only a moderate likelihood of being correct; he calls them hypotheses.

Designing a new cultural pattern is in many ways like designing an experiment. In drawing up a new constitution, outlining a new educational program, modifying a religious doctrine, or setting up a new fiscal policy, many statements must be quite tentative. We cannot be sure that the practices we specify will have the consequences we predict, or that the consequences will reward our efforts. This is in the nature of such proposals. They are not value judgments—they are guesses. To confuse and delay the improvement of cultural practices by quibbling about the word *improve* is itself not a useful practice. Let us agree, to start with, that health is better than illness, wisdom better than ignorance, love better than hate, and productive energy better than neurotic sloth.

Another familiar objection is the "political problem." Though we know what changes to make and how to make them, we still need to control certain relevant conditions, but these have long since fallen into the hands of selfish men who are not going to relinquish them for such purposes. Possibly we shall be permitted to develop areas which at the moment seem unimportant, but at the first signs of success the strong men will move in. This, it is said, has happened to Christianity, democracy and communism. There will always be men who are fundamentally selfish and evil, and in the long run innocent goodness cannot have its way. The only evidence here is historical, and it may be misleading. Because of the way in which physical science developed, history could until very recently have "proved" that the unleashing of the energy of the atom was quite unlikely, if not impossible. Similarly, because of the order in which processes in human behavior have become available for purposes of control, history may seem to prove that power will probably be appropriated for selfish purposes. The first techniques to be discovered fell almost always to strong, selfish men. History led Lord Acton to believe that power corrupts, but he had probably never encountered absolute power, certainly not in all its forms, and had no way of predicting its effect.

An optimistic historian could defend a different conclusion. The principle that if there are not enough men of good will in the world the first step is to create more seems to be gaining recognition. The Marshall Plan (as originally conceived), Point Four, the offer of atomic materials to power-starved countries—these may or may not be wholly new in the history of international relations, but they suggest an increasing awareness of the power of governmental good will. They are proposals to make certain changes in the environments of men for the sake of consequences which should be rewarding for all concerned. They do not exemplify a disinterested generosity, but an interest which is the interest of everyone.

We have not yet seen Plato's philosopher-king, and may not want to, but the gap between real and utopian government is closing.

III

But we are not yet in the clear, for a new and unexpected obstacle has arisen. With a world of their own making almost within reach, men of good will have been seized with distaste for their achievement. They have uneasily rejected opportunities to apply the techniques and findings of science in the service of men, and as the import of effective cultural design has come to be understood, many of them have voiced an outright refusal to have any part in it. Science has been challenged before when it has encroached upon institutions already engaged in the control of human behavior; but what are we to make of benevolent men, with no special interests of their own to defend, who nevertheless turn against the very means of reaching long-dreamed-of goals?

What is being rejected, of course, is the scientific conception of man and his place in nature. So long as the findings and methods of science are applied to human affairs only in a sort of remedial patchwork, we may continue to hold any view of human nature we like. But as the use of science increases, we are forced to accept the theoretical structure with which science represents its facts. The difficulty is that this structure is clearly at odds with the traditional democratic conception of man. Every discovery of an event which has a part in shaping a man's behavior seems to leave so much the less to be credited to the man himself; and as such explanations become more and more comprehensive, the contribution which may be claimed by the individual himself appears to approach zero. Man's vaunted creative powers, his original accomplishments in art, science and morals, his capacity to choose and our right to hold him responsible for the consequences of his choice—none of these is conspicuous in this new self-portrait. Man, we once believed, was free to express himself in art, music and literature, to inquire into nature, to seek salvation in his own way. He could initiate action and make spontaneous and capricious changes of course. Under the most extreme duress some sort of choice remained to him. He could resist any effort to control him, though it might cost him his life. But science insists that action is initiated by forces impinging upon the individual, and that caprice is only another name for behavior for which we have not yet found a cause.

In attempting to reconcile these views it is important to note that the traditional democratic conception was not designed as a description in the scientific sense but as a philosophy to be used in setting up and maintaining a governmental process. It arose under historical circumstances and served political purposes apart from which it cannot be properly understood. In rallying men against tyranny it was necessary that the individual be strengthened, that he be taught that he had rights and could govern himself. To give the common man a new conception of his worth, his dignity, and his power to save himself, both here and hereafter, was often the only resource of the revolutionist. When democratic principles were put into practice, the same doctrines were used as a working formula. This is exemplified by the notion of personal responsibility in Anglo-American law. All governments make certain forms of punishment contingent upon certain kinds of acts. In democratic countries these contingencies are expressed by the notion of responsible choice. But the notion may have no meaning under governmental practices formulated in other ways and would certainly have no place in systems which did not use punishment.

The democratic philosophy of human nature is determined by certain political exigencies and techniques, not by the goals of democracy. But exigencies and techniques change; and a conception which is not supported for its accuracy as a likeness—is not, indeed, rooted in fact at all—may be expected to change too. No matter how effective we judge current democratic practices to be, how highly we value them or how long we expect them to survive, they are almost certainly not the *final* form of government. The philosophy of human nature which has been useful in implementing them is also almost certainly not the last word. The ultimate achievement of democracy may be long deferred unless we emphasize the real aims rather than the verbal devices of democratic thinking. A philosophy which has been appropriate to one set of political exigencies will defeat its purpose if, under other circumstances, it prevents us from applying to human affairs the science of man which probably nothing but democracy itself could have produced.

IV

Perhaps the most crucial part of our democratic philosophy to be reconsidered is our attitude toward freedom—or its reciprocal, the control of human behavior. We do not oppose all forms of control because it is "human nature" to do so. The reaction is not characteristic of all men under all conditions of life. It is an attitude which has been carefully engineered, in large part by what we call the "literature" of democracy. With respect to some methods of control (for example, the threat of force), very little engineering is needed, for the techniques or their immediate consequences are objectionable. Society has suppressed these methods by branding them "wrong," "illegal" or "sinful." But to encourage these attitudes toward objectionable forms of control, it has been necessary to disguise the real nature of certain indispensable techniques, the commonest examples of which are education, moral discourse, and persuasion. The actual procedures appear harmless enough. They consist of supplying information, presenting opportunities for action, pointing out logical relationships, appealing to reason or "enlightened understanding," and so on. Through a masterful piece of misrepresentation; the illusion is fostered that these procedures do not involve the control of behavior; at most, they are simply ways of "getting someone to change his mind." But analysis not only reveals the presence of well-defined behavioral pro- cesses, it demonstrates a kind of control no less inexorable, though in some ways more acceptable, than the bully's threat of force.

Let us suppose that someone in whom we are interested is acting unwisely—he is careless in the way he deals with his friends, he drives too fast, or he holds his golf club the wrong way. We could probably help him by issuing a series of commands: don't nag, don't drive over sixty, don't hold your club that way. Much less objectionable would be "an appeal to reason." We could show him how people are affected by his treatment of them, how accident rates rise sharply at higher speeds, how a particular grip on the club alters the way the ball is struck and corrects a slice. In doing so we resort to verbal mediating devices which emphasize and support certain "contingencies of reinforcement"—that is, certain relations between behavior and its consequences—which strengthen the behavior we wish to set up. The same consequences would possibly set up the be- havior without our help, and they eventually take control no matter which form of help we give. The appeal to reason has certain advantages over the authoritative command. A threat of punishment, no matter how subtle, generates emotional reactions and tendencies to escape or revolt. Perhaps the controllee merely "feels resentment" at being made to act in a given way, but even that is to be avoided. When we "appeal to reason," he "feels freer to do as he pleases." The fact is that we have exerted *less* control than in using a threat; since other conditions may contribute to the result, the effect may be delayed or, possibly in a given instance, lacking. But if we have worked a change in his behavior at all, it is because we have altered relevant environmental conditions, and the processes we have set in motion are just as real and just as inexorable, if not as comprehensive, as in the most authoritative coercion.

"Arranging an opportunity for action" is another example of disguised control. The power of the negative form has already been exposed in the analysis of censorship. Restriction of opportunity is recognized as far from harmless. As Ralph Barton Perry said in an article which appeared in the Spring, 1953, *Pacific Spectator*, "Whoever deter- mines what alternatives shall be made known to man controls what that man shall choose *from*. He is deprived of freedom in proportion as he is denied access to *any* ideas, or is confined to any range of ideas short of the totality of relevant possibilities." But there is a positive side as well. When we present a relevant state of affairs, we increase the likelihood that a given form of behavior will be emitted. To the extent that the probability of action has changed, we have made a definite contribution. The teacher of history controls a student's behavior (or, if the reader prefers, "deprives him of freedom") just as much in *presenting* historical facts as in suppressing them. Other conditions will no doubt affect the student, but the contribution made to his behavior by the presentation of material is fixed and, within its range, irresistible.

The methods of education, moral discourse, and persuasion are acceptable not because they recognize the freedom of the individual or his right to dissent, but because they make only *partial* contributions to the control of his behavior. The freedom they recognize is freedom from a more coercive form of control. The dissent which they tolerate is the possible effect of other determiners of action. Since these sanctioned methods are frequently ineffective, we have been able to convince ourselves that they do not represent control at all. When they show too much strength to permit disguise, we give them other names and suppress them as energetically as we suppress the use of force. Education grown too powerful is rejected as propaganda or "brain-washing," while really effective persuasion is decried as "undue influence," "demagoguery," "seduction," and so on.

If we are not to rely solely upon accident for the innovations which give rise to cultural evolution, we must accept the fact that some kind of control of human behavior is inevitable. We cannot use good sense in human affairs unless someone engages in the design and construction of environmental conditions which affect the behavior of men. Environmental changes have always been the condition for the improvement of cultural patterns, and we can hardly use the more effective methods of science without making changes on a grander scale. We are all controlled by the world in which we live, and part of that world has been and will be constructed by men. The question is this: Are we to be controlled by accident, by tyrants, or by ourselves in effective cultural design?

The danger of the misuse of power is possibly greater than ever. It is not allayed by disguising the facts. We cannot make wise decisions if we continue to pretend that human behavior is not controlled, or if we refuse to engage in control when valuable results might be forthcoming. Such measures weaken only ourselves, leaving the strength of science to others. The first step in a defense against tyranny is the fullest possible exposure of controlling techniques. A second step has already been taken successfully in restricting the use of physical force. Slowly, and as yet imperfectly, we have worked out an ethical and governmental design in which the strong man is not allowed to use the power deriving from his strength to control his fellow men. He is restrained by a superior force created for that purpose—the ethical pressure of the group, or more explicit religious and governmental measures. We tend to distrust superior forces, as we currently hesitate to relinquish sovereignty in order to set up an international police force. But it is only through such counter-control that we have achieved what we call peace—a condition in which men are not permitted to control each other through force. In other words, control itself must be controlled.

Science has turned up dangerous processes and materials before. To use the facts and techniques of a science of man to the fullest extent without making some monstrous mistake will be difficult and obviously perilous. It is not time for self-deception, emotional indulgence, or the assumption of attitudes which are no longer useful. Man is facing a difficult test. He must keep his head now, or he must start again—a long way back.

v

Those who reject the scientific conception of man must, to be logical, oppose the methods of science as well. The position is often supported by predicting a series of dire consequences which are to follow if science is not checked. A recent book by Joseph Wood Krutch, *The Measure of Man,* is in this vein. Mr. Krutch sees in the growing science of man the threat of an unexampled tyranny over men's minds. If science is permitted to have its way, he insists, "we may never be able really to think again." A controlled culture will, for example, lack some virtue inherent in disorder. We have emerged from chaos through a series of happy accidents, but in an engineered culture it will be "impossible for the unplanned to erupt again." But there is no virtue in the accidental character of an accident, and the diversity which arises from disorder can not only be duplicated by design but vastly extended. The experimental method is superior to simple observation just because it multiplies "accidents" in a systematic coverage of the possibilities. Technology offers many familiar examples. We no longer wait for immunity to disease to develop from a series of accidental exposures, nor do we wait for natural mutations in sheep and cotton to produce better fibers; but we continue to make use of such accidents when they occur, and we certainly do not prevent them. Many of the things we value have emerged from the clash of ignorant armies on darkling plains, but it is not therefore wise to encourage ignorance and darkness.

It is not always disorder itself which we are told we shall miss but certain admirable qualities in men which flourish only in the presence of disorder. A man rises above an unpropitious childhood to a position of eminence, and since we cannot give a plausible account of the action of so complex an environment, we attribute the achievement to some admirable faculty in the man himself. But such "faculties" are suspiciously like the explanatory fictions against which the history of science warns us. We admire Lincoln for rising above a deficient school system, but it was not necessarily something *in him* which permitted him to become an educated man in spite of it. His educational environment was certainly unplanned, but it could nevertheless have made a full contribution to his mature behavior. He was a rare man, but the circumstances of his childhood were rare too. We do not give Franklin Delano Roosevelt the same credit for becoming an educated man with the help of Groton and Harvard, although the same behavioral processes may have been involved. The founding of Groton and Harvard somewhat reduced the possibility that fortuitous combinations of circumstances would erupt to produce other Lincolns. Yet the founders can hardly be condemned for attacking an admirable human quality.

Another predicted consequence of a science of man is an excessive uniformity. We are told that effective control—whether governmental, religious, educational, economic or social—will produce a race of men who differ from each other only through relatively refractory genetic differences. That would probably be bad design, but we must admit that we are not now pursuing another course from choice. In a modern school, for example, there is usually a syllabus which specifies what every student is to learn by the end of each year. This would be flagrant regimentation if anyone expected every student to comply. But some will be poor in particular subjects, others will not study, others will not remember what they have been taught, and diversity is assured. Suppose, however, that we someday possess such effective educational techniques that every student will in fact be put in possession of all the behavior specified in a syllabus. At the end of the year, all students will correctly answer all questions on the final examination and "must all have prizes." Should we reject such a system on the grounds that in making all students excellent it has made them all alike? Advocates of the theory of a special faculty might contend that an important advantage of the present system is that the good student learns *in spite of* a system which is so defective that it is currently producing bad students as well. But if really effective techniques are available, we cannot avoid the problem of design simply by preferring the status quo. At what point should education be deliberately inefficient?

Such predictions of the havoc to be wreaked by the application of science to human affairs are usually made with surprising confidence. They not only show a faith in the orderliness of human behavior; they presuppose an established body of knowledge with the help of which it can be positively asserted that the changes which scientists propose to make will have quite specific results—albeit not the results they foresee. But the predictions made by the critics of science must be held to be equally fallible and subject also to empirical test. We may be sure that many steps in the scientific design of cultural patterns will produce unforeseen consequences. But there is only one way to find out. And the test must be made, for if we cannot advance in the design of cultural patterns with absolute certainty, neither can we rest completely confident of the superiority of the status quo.

VI

Apart from their possibly objectionable consequences, scientific methods seem to make no provision for certain admirable qualities and faculties which seem to have flourished in less explicitly planned cultures; hence they are called "degrading" or "lacking in dignity." (Mr. Krutch has called the author's *Walden Two* an "ignoble Utopia.") The conditioned reflex is the current whipping boy. Because conditioned reflexes may be demonstrated in animals, they are spoken of as though they were exclusively subhuman. It is implied, as we have seen, that no behavioral processes are involved in education and moral discourse or, at least, that the processes are exclusively human. But men do show conditioned reflexes (for example, when they are frightened by all instances of the control of human behavior because some instances engender fear), and animals do show processes similar to the human behavior involved in instruction and moral discourse. When Mr. Krutch asserts that " 'Conditioning' is achieved by methods which by-pass or, as it were, short-circuit those very reasoning faculties which education proposes to cultivate and exercise," he is making a technical statement which needs a definition of terms and a great deal of supporting evidence.

If such methods are called "ignoble" simply because they leave no room for certain admirable attributes, then perhaps the practice of admiration needs to be examined. We might say that the child whose education has been skillfully planned has been deprived of the right to intellectual heroism. Nothing has been left to be admired in the way he acquires an education. Similarly, we can conceive of moral training which is so adequate to the demands of the culture that men will be good practically automatically, but to that extent they will be deprived of the right to moral heroism, since we seldom admire automatic goodness. Yet if we consider the end of morals rather than certain virtuous means, is not "automatic goodness" a desirable state of affairs? Is it not, for example, the avowed goal of religious education? T. H. Huxley answered the question unambiguously: "If some great power would agree to make me always think what is true and do what is right, on condition of being a sort of clock and wound up every morning before I got out of bed, I should close instantly with the offer." Yet Mr. Krutch quotes this as the scarcely credible point of view of a "proto-modern" and seems himself to share T.

S. Eliot's contempt for ". . . systems so perfect / That no one will need to be good."

"Having to be good" is an excellent example of an expendable honorific. It is inseparable from a particular form of ethical and moral control. We distinguish between the things we *have* to do to avoid punishment and those we *want* to do for rewarding consequences. In a culture which did not resort to punishment we should never "have" to do anything except with respect to the punishing contingencies which arise directly in the physical environment. And we are moving toward such a culture, because the neurotic, not to say psychotic, by-products of control through punishment have long since led compassionate men to seek alternative techniques. Recent research has explained some of the objectionable results of punishment and has revealed resources of at least equal power in "positive reinforcement." It is reasonable to look forward to a time when man will seldom "have" to do anything, although he may show interest, energy, imagination and productivity far beyond the level seen under the present system (except for rare eruptions of the unplanned).

What we have to do we do with *effort*. We call it "work." There is no other way to distinguish between exhausting labor and the possibly equally energetic but rewarding activity of play. It is presumably good cultural design to replace the former with the latter. But an adjustment in attitudes is needed. We are much more practiced in admiring the heroic labor of a Hercules than the activity of one who works without having to. In a truly effective educational system the student might not "have to work" at all, but that possibility is likely to be received by the contemporary teacher with an emotion little short of rage.

We cannot reconcile traditional and scientific views by agreeing upon *what* is to be admired or condemned. The question is whether anything is to be so treated. Praise and blame are cultural practices which have been adjuncts of the prevailing system of control in Western democracy. All peoples do not engage in them for the same purposes or to the same extent, nor, of course, are the same behaviors always classified in the same way as subject to praise or blame. In admiring intellectual and moral heroism and unrewarding labor, and in rejecting a world in which these would be uncommon, we are simply demonstrating our own cultural conditioning. By promoting certain tendencies to admire and censure, the group of which we are a part has arranged for the social reinforcement and punishment needed to assure a high level of intellectual and moral industry. Under other and possibly better controlling systems, the behavior which we now admire would occur, but not under those conditions which make it admirable, and we should have no reason to admire it because the culture would have arranged for its maintenance in other ways.

To those who are stimulated by the glamorous heroism of the battlefield, a peaceful world may not be a better world. Others may reject a world without sorrow, longing or a sense of guilt because the relevance of deeply moving works of art would be lost. To many who have devoted their lives to the struggle to be wise and good, a world without confusion and evil might be an empty thing. A nostalgic concern for the decline of moral heroism has been a dominating theme in the work of Aldous Huxley. In *Brave New World* he could see in the application of science to human affairs only a travesty on the notion of the Good (just as George Orwell, in *1984,* could foresee nothing but horror). In a recent issue of *Esquire,* Huxley has expressed the point this way: "We have had religious revolutions, we have had political, industrial, economic and nationalistic revolutions. All of them, as our descendants will discover, were but ripples in an ocean of conservatism—trivial by comparison with the psychological revolution toward which we are so rapidly moving. *That* will really be a revolution. When it is over, the human race will give no further trouble." (Footnote for the reader of the future: This was not meant as a happy ending. Up to 1956 men had been admired, if at all, either for causing trouble or alleviating it. Therefore—)

It will be a long time before the world can dispense with heroes and hence with the cultural practice of admiring heroism, but we move in that direction whenever we act to prevent war, famine, pestilence and disaster. It will be a long time before man will never need to submit to punishing environments or engage in exhausting labor, but we move in that direction whenever we make food, shelter, clothing and labor-saving devices more readily available. We may mourn the passing of heroes but not the conditions which make for heroism. We can spare the self-made saint or sage as we spare the laundress on the river's bank struggling against fearful odds to achieve cleanliness.

VII

The two great dangers in modern democratic thinking are illustrated in a paper by former Secretary of State Dean Acheson. "For a long time now," writes Mr. Acheson, "we have gone along with some well-tested principles of conduct: That it was better to tell the truth than falsehoods; . . . that duties were older than and as fundamental as rights; that, as Justice Holmes put it, the mode by which the inevitable came to pass was effort; that to perpetrate a harm was wrong no matter how many joined in it . . . and so on. . . . Our institutions are founded on the assumption that most people follow these principles most of the time because they want to, and the institutions work pretty well when this assumption is true. More recently, however, bright people have been fooling with the machinery in the human head and they have discovered quite a lot. . . . Hitler introduced new refinements [as the result of which] a whole people have been utterly confused and corrupted. Unhappily neither the possession of this knowledge nor the desire to use it was confined to Hitler. . . . Others dip from this same devil's cauldron."

The first dangerous notion in this passage is that most people follow democratic principles of conduct "because they want to." This does not account for democracy or any other form of government if we have not explained why people *want* to behave in given ways. Although it is tempting to assume that it is human nature to believe in democratic principles, we must not overlook the "cultural engineering" which produced and continues to maintain democratic practices. If we neglect the conditions which produce democratic *behavior*, it is useless to try to maintain a democratic *form* of government. And we cannot expect to export a democratic form of government successfully if we do not also provide for the cultural practices which will sustain it. Our forebears did not discover the essential nature of man; they evolved a pattern of behavior which worked remarkably well under the circumstances. The "set of principles" expressed in that pattern is not the only true set or necessarily the best. Mr. Acheson has presumably listed the most unassailable items; some of them are probably beyond question, but others—concerning duty and effort—may need revision as the world changes.

The second—and greater—threat to the democracy which Mr. Acheson is defending is his assumption that knowledge is necessarily on the side of evil. All the admirable things he mentions are attributed to the innate goodness of man, all the detestable to "fooling with the machinery in the human head." This is reminiscent of the position, taken by other institutions engaged in the control of men, that certain forms of knowledge are in themselves evil. But how out of place in a democratic philosophy! Have we come this far only to conclude that well-intentioned people cannot study the behavior of men without becoming tyrants or that informed men cannot show good will? Let us for once have strength and good will on the same side.

VIII

Far from being a threat to the tradition of Western democracy, the growth of a science of man is a consistent and probably inevitable part of it. In turning to the external conditions which shape and maintain the behavior of men, while questioning the reality of inner qualities and faculties to which human achievements were once attributed, we turn from the ill-defined and remote to the observable and manipulable. Though it is a painful step, it has far-reaching consequences, for it not only sets higher standards of human welfare but shows us how to meet them. A change in a theory of human nature cannot change the facts. The achievements of man in science, art, literature, music and morals will survive any interpretation we place upon them. The uniqueness of the individual is unchallenged in the scientific view. Man, in short, will remain man. (There will be much to admire for those who are so inclined. Possibly the noblest achievement to which man can aspire, even according to present standards, is to accept himself for what he is, as that is revealed to him by the methods which he devised and tested on a part of the world in which he had only a small personal stake.)

If Western democracy does not lose sight of the aims of humanitarian action, it will welcome the almost fabulous support of its own science of man and will strengthen itself and play an important role in building a better world for everyone. But if it cannot put its "democratic philosophy" into proper historical perspective—if, under the control of attitudes and emotions which it generated for other purposes, it now rejects the help of science—then it must be prepared for defeat. For if we continue to insist that science has nothing to offer but a new and more horrible form of tyranny, we may produce just such a result by allowing the strength of science to fall into the hands of despots. And if, with luck, it were to fall instead to men of good will in other political communities, it would be perhaps a more ignominious defeat; for we should then, through a miscarriage of democratic principles, be forced to leave to others the next step in man's long struggle to control nature and himself.

9
The New Technology and the Future of Homo Sapiens

Today, biology is one of the most exciting areas of science. Rapid advances are being made in understanding human physiology; outstanding successes have been achieved in genetic analysis; knowledge of the functioning of the human brain is accumulating. What are the general implications of this new knowledge for the future of the human race? Can man improve himself so that his average life span will extend beyond the Bibical limit of three-score years and ten? If this is possible, does he wish to live, for example, to the age of one hundred and fifty years? Can he completely overcome disease? Can he improve his intelligence? In order to effect these ends, is it necessary for him to compromise other human values?

Joseph W. Still is optimistic about the possibility of our extending man's life span. He points out that, in the twentieth century, life expectancy has increased from forty to seventy years as a result of the curbing of infectious disease; and he predicts that these diseases will be totally wiped out in the future. At the present time, most attention is focused on the elimination of degenerative diseases, including aging; and Dr. Still is confident that biochemical research will eventually solve these problems to the extent that—although man may not live forever—life span will be extended substantially.

René Dubos does not share Still's optimism. Although age-old diseases have been eradicated, social change has brought new ones to the fore—vascular diseases, cancer, and mental diseases. In changing his environment, for example, by polluting the air and raising the level of radiation, man has brought upon himself new dangers to his health. In accelerating the rate of social change, so that old habits and values rapidly disappear, he has injected a feeling of rootlessness, thus increasing the frequency of mental illness. In basing his society on freedom from want and struggle, he has ignored his own need for strife and adventure. As Dubos says, man cannot escape his biological past.

Hermann Muller, after documenting the remarkable progress that has been achieved in the application of the principles of genetics to plants and animals, remarks that it would be strange if man left his own biological basis to chance. He points out that the social changes in the last few centuries must have been accompanied by a slackening of the genetic advancement of the human race and may even have effected a decline. Those who in the past would have died because of genetic defects are now kept alive and pass these defects on to their descendants. Cultural homogenization is blurring the lines between genetic pools. Muller warns that a continuation of the present situation spells genetic retrogression. But it is within man's power to direct his genetic progress; for example, reproductive cells can be stored and children can be produced without genetic defects and with inherited qualities that we value.

Theodosius Dobzhansky tends to agree with Muller that a program of eugenics would be desirable, but he doubts that genetics has reached the point where such a far-reaching program as Muller suggests is feasible. Further, he points out that not all genetic defects are equivalent. Myopia, for example, is a common defect; we could hardly expect to eliminate all myopics from the population. Dobzhansky stresses that it will be necessary to make a choice in any eugenics program as to what kinds of people we wish to produce in the future. This will go to the root of human ethics. But as a start in the prevention of the deterioration of the gene pool, he suggests that the spreading of biological information will help. If people who are genetically defective are made aware that their progeny will inherit their defects, they may not produce children.

Joseph W. Still, M.D.
WHY CAN'T WE LIVE FOREVER?

Death is regarded as the inevitable end result of living. No man can live forever is the assumption, and the history of mankind supports its validity.

But as a medical scientist who has been studying the most complex disease of mankind—the disease of aging—aided by the research tools of our atomic age, I have approached this question from an exactly opposite point of view: The only factor which prevents our living forever is death. This is more than a play on words.

In the past 75 years, science has been remarkably successful in preventing death from a great number of diseases. The result is that the average life span has increased from 40 years in 1900 to more than 70 years today. This is a 30-year gain within the present century in man's contest with death. It is just the beginning.

On the basis of all the medical research available on the subject, including my own, there is no absolute biological barrier to our greatly increasing the life span. We can increase it—and beyond the 150 years which a few people have already achieved.

It will help us to go back in the history of medicine to 1857. It was just 101 years ago that Pasteur reported the first experiments clearly proving that microscopic bacteria could cause disease. At that time, most deaths were caused by bacteria and viruses. Thousands and thousands of children and young adults were dying of tuberculosis, diphtheria, whooping cough, pneumonia, scarlet fever, and many other infectious and contagious diseases. Take one example: Infection and death during childbirth. Out of 9,886 deliveries in a Paris hospital of that day, 1,226 women died of "childbirth fever." In all the centuries before Pasteur, most children died before they reached adult life. The average length of life in Pasteur's youth was 40 years or less. And remember, France was then probably the leading nation of the world in medicine and science. By contrast, the average length of life in countries such as India was as short as 20 years.

Joseph W. Still, M.D., "Why Can't We Live Forever?" *Better Homes and Gardens* (August 1958). © 1958 Meredith Publishing Company. All rights reserved. Reprinted by permission. Dr. Still's area of research interest is physiology, and he is a consultant in the field of aging.

But in the past 100 years, the situation has changed almost unbelievably. Sanitation, antiseptics, vaccines, antibiotics, and related measures have prevented millions of deaths from infectious diseases. And the most startling of these victories over infectious disease have been won in *your* lifetime. The first antibiotic—sulfanilamide—was introduced in the late 1930s; penicillin during the middle 40s; the Salk vaccine only three years ago. Infectious disease deaths still occur, even with good medical care, since antibiotics and vaccines are not perfect weapons, especially for individuals who have low resistance, unusual body chemistry, or both. But the problem of infectious diseases has been so reduced for the average person that medical research can now concentrate, with optimism, on finding equivalent methods of helping those who need slightly different treatment.

The situation has changed so radically that today most deaths are the result of the so-called degenerative diseases—cancer, coronary thrombosis, cerebral thrombosis or stroke, and imbalances in endocrine glands such as diabetes. And these degenerative diseases may really be only variations of the master degenerative disease—aging itself.

We have confidence now that medical science will ultimately find ways to prevent every infectious disease of man and his domestic animals and plants. In fact, as far as human disease is concerned, this phase of infectious disease research is already in what might be called the "mop-up" period.

Medical research and practice have succeeded in almost completely changing the causes of death in the medically advanced countries of the world. Instead of the vast majority of deaths being due to bacteria and viruses, four out of five deaths today are due to degenerative diseases. Less than one out of 10 is due to infections. To see how far we have progressed, look at the causes of death in the United States in one year:

CAUSE OF DEATH	NUMBER OF DEATHS	PERCENT OF TOTAL
Infectious and parasitic diseases	112,513	7
Degenerative	1,216,309	80
(Cancers and tumors 245,849)		
(Cardio-vascular-renal 811,596)		
(Other degenerative		
diseases 158,864)		
Noninfectious diseases of		
newborn and infants	80,344	5
Maternal deaths in childbirth	1,901	–
Violent deaths (accidents,		
homicide and suicide)	117,650	8
TOTAL	1,528,717	100

So we see how wrong the people were who derided the germ theory, who called Pasteur a fool for believing germs were the cause of disease, and for believing that germs could be *prevented* from causing disease. Medical science must have time to study the degenerative diseases, including aging, before we say they can't be overcome. Granted, this is a greater problem than infectious diseases presented. But when people say, "You can't live forever," they are really saying, "Science can't discover and learn to prevent the cause of aging." I can't say that this statement will be proved wrong. I *can* say that a fixed belief of this kind is a handicap to intelligent research and to public support. Pasteur had to overcome this same sort of uninformed opposition.

But what about aging? Have we made any progress?

I think so. Research has now developed a few of the basic facts about aging, expressed in three principal theories:

1. The biological-clock theory
2. The cumulative-poison theory
3. The loss-of-control theory

The biological-clock theory, stated in its simplest form: People are born with a certain allotted time, a set number of heart beats, a fixed store of energy. The sand running from the top to the bottom of an hourglass symbolizes this theory. When the sand runs out, death occurs.

Ponce de Leon, searching for the "Fountain of Youth," must have believed this theory in its *energy* form. He searched for waters which would contain the essential energy of youth. He believed there was a "Fountain of Youth" some place in the world that would increase the quantity of youthful energy in his own body, thus prolonging life.

The clock theory is implicit in the three-score-and-ten notion— the fixed life span, the idea that once one has reached 70 he is living on borrowed time. Many similar false notions are still widely believed. Many of them are deep in our subconscious minds. They act as a sort of voodoo curse. Some people more or less simply decide it's time to die when they reach 70.

Pasteur's work literally destroyed the clock theory. Once it was proved that many people died from germs rather than "time," the fixed-span or heart-beat theories disappeared. But the theory lives on in a more subtle energy concept: that we are born with a fixed amount of special energy. This theory is not as easily disproved because the "special energies" are only hypothetical. No one has ever isolated or measured them. They have nothing to do with the chemical energy we derive from the food that powers the human organism. While these special-energy theories can't be disproved, the fact that they can't be measured keeps them from being very useful as a research tool.

The cumulative poison theories are of two general types: One is that our cells accumulate poisons from their environment. The other holds that metabolic poisons result from activity in our cells, and that these poisons gradually accumulate to cause aging. In either case, the assumption is that there are poisons which slow down the function of cells and ultimately kill many of them. When enough cells reach some critical state of poisoning, the organism collapses.

These theories are weakened by the wide range of longevity already achieved. Christian Jacobsen Drankenberg, a Dane who died in 1772, was 146 years of age. The little Indian brought to the United States from Ecuador recently to be examined scientifically was probably over 140. We have seen pictures of a Russian (usually on horseback), who is said to be over 140. There are several thousand people in this country who are over 100. The fact that it takes some people 140 years to collect enough poisons to die while others do it in 65 or 70 years hints at too wide a range of variation for the rather static cellular event these theories indicate. But, maybe so.

Such theories, at least in some forms, have quite a bit of evidence to support them. We see changes in some cells of old animals and old people which are not seen in the cells of young people. But we do not see these changes in *all* cells of old animals and old people. Even in subjects of advanced years, there are many cells which cannot be distinguished from those of youthful animals or people. Since aging and death is a universal phenomenon, any successful aging theory cannot permit exceptions of this kind to the data on which it depends.

Finally, let's consider the loss-of-control theory which seems to have the most facts to support it. One reason I favor this general theory is that it suggests physiological research problems. Those of us now following this theory are doing research to test it—research that should greatly advance our knowledge of degenerative diseases even if the theory is ultimately proved wrong as regards aging.

The loss-of-control theory is based on the idea that as we age, all our reactions, nervous and chemical, tend to slow down. For example, if something occurs which raises our temperature, it takes longer to return to normal levels in later years than in younger years. There is no exception to this generalization; we might say it is a law of physiology that all functional activities tend to slow down with increasing age. Look how our temperature varies at different ages of life. In childhood, temperature may fluctuate widely and rapidly. Every mother has seen how a child may have a fever of 104 or 105 degrees and is back to normal in a few hours. Very often the doctor finds little wrong even when the temperature is so high. In the middle years, temperature varies between narrower limits; the very old sometimes are incapable of developing a fever, even in the face of serious infection.

All of our internal body regulations, chemical as well as nervous, are controlled by the nervous-endocrine, or N-E, system. The central point for controlling the N-E system is in nerve centers in our brain. These nerve centers collectively are comparable to the headquarters of a large army or business. The control of our pulse rate, blood pressure, the rate and depth of breathing, the tension of all our muscles, the amount of salt and water retained in our tissues, the rate and quality of secretions of our various glands, and so on, stem from this headquarters in our brain. The number of factors controlled is fantastically large, and the efficiency of the headquarters which does the controlling is even more fantastic.

The cells of our bodies are organized by the headquarters of the N-E system. A constant series of messages comes into our N-E centers in the brain, and there is a continuous flow going out to the peripheral cells (which control the actions of muscles and secretory cells at the periphery, or "in the field"). Because these N-E controlled actions always tend to slow down with age, I feel this is the best of the three aging theories. Here is a universal event with a universal result which reflects some change in the cells of the nerve centers in the headquarters.

What could account for this change? Since all our internal N-E messages are chemical messages, the change must be of a chemical nature. There are chemical changes that occur with age in various materials, leading to chemical "stiffness" and "rigidity." Many chemical substances tend to grow brittle and less resilient with age. We see this not only in living materials such as hair, nails, or bones, but also in glues, jellies, and even metals. Not much is known about these slowly occurring chemical events, especially in living materials. Apparently, some kind of internal chemical bonding takes place which reduces the flexibility and increases the rigidity of some materials. We may think of this internal bonding and its effects in terms of traffic on a highway. As long as the cars have the proper amount of room, traffic moves normally. But if the road is narrowed, or the number of cars greatly increased, the cars get in each other's way and are forced to slow down. Eventually, they may become static—like sardines in a can or the New Year's Eve crowd in Times Square. We know that events analogous to this actually can take place among some chemical molecules. Whether this kind of event actually occurs with age in the cells of our brains—and, if so, whether it can account for aging as a chemical event, remains to be proved.

Until recently, this explanation of aging has been open to question. We thought that all the matter of our bodies was "turning over" all the time; that is, over a period of a few years, we were supposed to replace all the chemicals of our bodies. In essence, we thought that we were constantly being remade chemically. My own research and others' show that this is not true of all parts of our bodies. In certain cells, including those of our brain, there is a very slow "turn-over." It even seems possible that there may be some permanent chemical materials in our brain. It may be that in some of our cells—brain cells and muscle cells, both of which stop dividing early in life—there are cell parts which never are renewed. Experiments going on in my laboratory, aided by such atomic-age tools as radioactive isotopes, may settle this question.

If there are permanently stable chemical parts in brain cells, then we will certainly have a stronger reason than ever to look for internal chemical bonding changes which may occur in aging brain cells. Then we may ask, "If we can loosen or prevent such bonding rigidity—what then?"

Medical experience has taught us that when we fully understand a chemical event, we are able to manipulate and alter or modify it. For this reason, we can be skeptical about the assumption that "we can't live forever!" Already aging may have been brought into the realm of chemical research. A few years of intensive research in the causes of aging might give us some important answers. Aging may prove to be no more fatal or inevitable than smallpox, polio, pneumonia, or tuberculosis.

Learning the details of the N-E system will be no simple job. In fact, it is probably the biggest task research has ever tackled. Making the A-bomb or sending a rocket to the moon or even placing a platform in outer space are easier tasks than unraveling the whole endocrine complex. Yet, we have made important progress.

René Dubos
MODERN HORSEMEN OF THE APOCALYPSE

War, Famine, and Pestilence still commonly ride in advance of Death in most of the world today. But these time-honored allies of the pale rider are now less feared than they used to be. Men may not be happier, nor even fundamentally healthier, than their ancestors but in the Western world at least life expectancy is longer. The human mind has been freed of its obsession with death and disease caused by violence,

"Modern Horsemen of the Apocalypse," from *Mirage of Health* by René Dubos. Copyright © 1959 by René Dubos. Reprinted by permission of Harper & Row, Publishers. Dr. Dubos, a bacteriologist, is a member and professor of the Rockefeller Institute.

nutritional deficiencies, or infectious fevers, and it can now return with more confidence to some of its ancient dreams of eternal youth and long life.

Death, however, is now acquiring new allies that are taking the place of Famine and Pestilence. Horsemen of destruction that were rarely seen in the past are increasingly threatening the life and soul of modern man. Vascular diseases ruin his heart or brain; cancers run riot; mental diseases break his contact with the world of reason. As was the case for the great epidemics, two kinds of medical philosophy are guiding the approach to the control of these modern endemics. One is the search for drugs capable of reaching the site of the disease within the body of the patient. The other is the attempt to identify those aspects of modern life thought to be responsible for the disease problems peculiar to our times.

The search for magic bullets against cancer, vascular disease, and mental disease is made especially difficult by the fact that so little is known of the target that they must reach in the body. This problem epitomizes the dilemma encountered by medical scientists concerned with the search for cures. They try to apply rational methods to the discovery of drugs, but realize that this is a counsel of perfection rarely compatible with practical exigencies. Life is short, the art is long, the problems pressing. Even the most empirical approach is justified in medical research if it offers any hope of yielding results of practical usefulness. In the present state of ignorance the only possible method in most cases is the empirical hit-or-miss attack dignified in scientific circles by the expression "screening program."

While the search for the magic bullets continues, other studies are revealing that the environment in which the individual lives and his manner of living are of great importance in determining his susceptibility to the diseases of modern times. The cancerous ulcers of chimney sweeps probably constituted the first convincing demonstration that the incidence of tumors can be increased by certain chemical substances, in this case by certain components of coal tar. Many other substances have since been found capable of eliciting cancer, and one of the most disturbing aspects of this problem is that many of the carcinogenic effects reveal themselves slowly, often requiring years to become manifest. For example, workers who use benzine in the rubber industry often develop leukemia late in life, the solvent persisting long unnoticed in their bone marrow and ganglia. Awareness of these delayed effects is causing much alarm, of course, to those responsible for the safety of foodstuffs, as few of the dyes used in the food industry can be considered entirely safe from this point of view. Furthermore, many other hazardous chemicals find their way into food as thickeners, sweeteners, flavors, preservatives, etc. Unfortunately, the problem cannot be solved by restricting food additives to products of "natural" origin, for many constituents of plants and many other natural products have carcinogenic activity. In fact it has been suggested recently that the high incidence of stomach cancer in certain areas of Holland and England might be related to the composition of the water originating from the geological strata underlying those areas.

Radiations are another factor of the environment involved in the production of tumors. Thus, skin cancers are unusually frequent in fair-skinned people doing outdoor work in sunny countries, probably due to the carcinogenic effect of ultraviolet light in the range of 3,200 Å; maxillary sarcoma used to be common among women engaged in painting the dials of phosphorescent watches with radium. Of special interest at the present time is the high incidence of leukemias among persons exposed to excessive doses of certain radiations, whether they be physicians in their professional activities, patients receiving radiotherapy, or persons exposed to the effects of nuclear bombing. As in the case of carcinogenic substances, the effects of radiations are often delayed; witness the leukemias observed in the physicians who pioneered in the use of X rays are beginning to appear now among atomic physicists.

Many strange aspects of the distribution of cancers have recently come to light: the low rate for cancer of the breast in Japan; the high rates for cancer of the stomach and esophagus, with low rates for cancer of the lung, in Finland and Iceland; the effect of marriage customs on the ratio of breast cancer to cancer of the uterine cervix; the difference in occurrence of primary liver cancer in Africa, Indonesia, and Europe. In most cases it is not yet possible to trace the local occurrence of certain cancers to a particular determinant cause, but this is not surprising because so many different factors can play a role in cancer causation. In man, cigarette smoking and air pollution have been implicated in lung cancers; in experimental animals certain viruses can certainly pave the way for many different types of tumors.

Ill-defined as they are, all these observations suffice to suggest that the environment exerts a profound effect on the relative prevalence of the different types of cancer. In view of the fact that so many various agents can function as determinants of cancers—from the radiation of the sun to the constituents and products of the earth—it is futile to try to escape from the disease by returning to the ways of nature. But it is worth while to define more precisely the factors of the environment which contribute to cancer causation, since this knowledge bids fair to facilitate its control through prevention.

For a long time cardiovascular diseases were thought to be the inescapable consequence of aging, the natural manifestation of senescence with its decay of the body structures, more or less rapid but inevitable. In reality, however, arteriosclerosis is not a necessary accompaniment of aging, and blood vessels can remain "young" in structure and in function to a very old age. In 1635 there lived in Shropshire, England, one Thomas Parr who was reputed to be 152 years old. Old Parr was living quietly on his native heath when his fame reached the Constable of England, who ordered him to London. There he was presented to the King, well wined and dined—and thereupon promptly died. An autopsy was performed by none other than the great William Harvey, who found all the organs normal and healthy. No calcification was detected, no anatomical cause of death, and old Parr was declared to have died of a surfeit. He was buried in Westminster Abbey.

There are several other well-authenticated examples of centenarians whose arteries showed no trace of sclerosis. It seems to be a fact, furthermore, that arteriosclerosis does not strike at random, but occurs most commonly in certain parts of the world and certain social groups. Diets rich in meat and certain fats, absence of physical effort, and the pressure in everyday life imposed by highly competitive mores are among the factors which have been implicated as contributory to vascular diseases. Much has been made of the fact that the Neapolitans and other South Italians, with their starchy diet and far niente philosophy, suffer less from coronary diseases than do the Bolognese and other North Italians who eat more fat and exhibit a more aggressive behavior. Observations made during World War II seem to have provided further evidence for the view that abundant and rich diet bears a relation to cardiovascular accidents. In Norway and other occupied countries the deaths from coronary disease and thrombotic accidents became much less frequent when the Germans moved in and the calories and fats moved out, whereas these diseases resumed their prewar level shortly after alimentation became normal again after the war—the 3,600-calorie diet replacing the 1,800-calorie diet. But intriguing as these relationships are and useful in suggesting working hypotheses, they do not as yet constitute convincing evidence of the determinism of vascular disease. A rich table and easy living differ from austerity and hardships in many factors other than those concerned in blood levels of purines, cholesterol, or other lipids.

In addition to the killing diseases, like cancer and vascular disorders, which have monopolized public and scientific attention during recent years, there are many others which illustrate the effect that social habits exert on the state of health. As judged from the dentition in mummies, dental caries was rare in Egypt during the predynastic period and became more frequent with developing civilization, particularly among the wealthy classes. And subsequent periods of Egyptian history provide further evidence that every form of dental disease was more prevalent among the wealthy than among the poor people who had to be satisfied with a coarse, uncooked diet. Similar conclusions have been derived from studies on the children of African tribes. In a comparative investigation the caries rate was found to be 28 percent among the Luo children, who are town dwellers and eat manufactured foods, whereas it was only 11 percent among the Banyaruanda children, whose parents are poor and unable to buy European foods other than tea and sugar. Similarly, the aborigines of Australia, who live on kangaroo meat, which is tough and rubbery, have little caries and remarkably healthy paradontal tissues, capable of transmitting a biting stress far greater than those of more civilized man.

Gout has long been used to illustrate the deleterious effects of overindulgence in rich food. In reality little is known concerning the pathogenesis of this disease, despite the fact that the nineteenth-century caricaturists seem to have had well-established convictions on the subject. In countless cartoons they depicted the grimaces of the portly bourgeois or nobleman—especially English—paying for his rich fare of roast and port through excruciating pains in his gouty toe. It has been said in support of the caricaturists that gout became much less common in Great Britain after the war had imposed on all classes the discipline of austerity diets.

Men are naturally most impressed by diseases which have obvious manifestations, yet some of their worst enemies creep on them unobtrusively. For example, any significant addition to background radioactivity increases the mutation rate of all earth's creatures from plant to man, with results that will not be felt to the full for several generations. And, likewise, the continuously mounting pollution of the air and the inescapable contact with drugs and chemicals that are becoming part of everyday life carry threats which are less obvious than cancer or heart disease but at least as important.

Occupational diseases have long been recognized under a number of picturesque names such as chimney sweep's cancer, mule spinner's cancer, miner's phthisis, wool sorter's disease, etc., but it is only during recent decades that industrial processes have grown in variety and magnitude to an extent that affects the life of practically everyone.

The smoke and mist that evoke romantic moods in rural environments are replaced in industrialized areas by the dreaded smogs which kill many within a few days, cause painful irritation to the mucous membranes of all, and may be the source of much unforeseen disease that will become manifest only in the future. In the course of one single episode of smog that hung over London for 4½ days during late December, 1952, almost five thousand persons died—as well as the prize cattle in their stalls at the Smithfield Show.[1] This acute mortality was followed by a secondary and more prolonged plateau of deaths, some eight thousand above normal up to the end of February, 1953. In addition to the irritating substances of which everyone is aware, smogs contain other constituents that may well produce deleterious effects many years later. Smogs are the symbol of the new factors of the environment that man has created and that will constitute threats to himself and his race until he has learned to eliminate them altogether or has succeeded in reaching with them some sort of biological and social adaptation. In the modern industrial world smogs have become "the pestilence that walketh in darkness."

There is perhaps some symbolism, as yet incompletely deciphered, in the visions that St. John the Divine had on the island of Patmos. The first horsemen of the Apocalypse that he saw were Famine and Pestilence. Then another even more terrifying visitation was sent by the angered Deity. After the fifth angel had sounded his trumpet he opened the bottomless pit and "there arose a smoke out of the pit, as the smoke of a great furnace; and the sun and the air were darkened by reason of the smoke of the pit." And out of the bottomless pit came the scorpions that did not kill men but tormented them for five months before final destruction came "by the fire, and by the smoke, and by the brimstone." The time of fulfillment of the Apocalypse may not be far off.

From Madness to Boredom

In the United States during 1956, close to one million persons were hospitalized for mental disease, more than ten million were thought to be in need of psychiatric treatment, and there was reason to believe that a good percentage of the total population would spend at least part of their lives in a mental institution. In 1955, 16,760 persons were known to have committed suicide and not a few of those who had died a violent death had directly or indirectly been victims of abnormal or antisocial behavior. On the other hand, it was considered a great medical advance that tranquilizer drugs had become available to all. Three out of ten prescriptions were for these drugs in 1956, and more than a billion tablets of meprobamate alone were sold in a year!

---

[1] Although the prize cattle at the Smithfield Show were badly affected by the smog, ordinary cattle kept for slaughter were not. The former were kept in beautifully clean stalls, whereas the latter stood in the familiar barnyard atmosphere with a high concentration of ammonia. It has been suggested that this ammonia neutralized both the sulfur dioxide gas and the sulfuric acid mist which contributed much to the irritating character of the smog.

Psychiatric illnesses are not a problem special to the United States, but really constitute a burden of ever-increasing weight in most of the countries of Western civilization. Like all quantitative statements pertaining to human affairs, however, enumeration of disturbed persons or of psychiatric beds gives but a distorted impression of the change in incidence of mental diseases in modern times. It is true that the number of hospitalized persons has been increasing for many years. But it is also a fact that the village fool who used to be an accepted member of any rural setting, the semisenile oldster who was expected to spend his last years rocking on the porch of the family homestead, and even the timid soul who escaped competition by retiring into a sheltered home atmosphere are likely now to become inmates of mental institutions because they cannot find a safe place in the crowded high-pressure environment of modern life. Thus, the problem of our time may be less an actual increase in the numbers of mental defectives than a decrease in the tolerance of society for them. The sickness of the individual is not readily differentiated from the sickness of society.

Among mental diseases some can be traced to fairly well-defined organic damage, to general paralysis or alcohol psychosis, for example. Others result from individual stresses related to particular life situations. Still others, probably the largest number, correspond to group psychoses associated with certain cultural patterns. The dancing mania and tarantism of the Middle Ages, the madness of the New Guinea natives, and the ghost dances of the Plains and Ute Indians are among the many forms that have been well described. But whatever their origin, all forms of psychosis have a large social component and it is this aspect of the problem that we shall now consider.

Although mass psychoses have been observed all over the world, it is usually assumed that mental diseases are less common among primitive and semicivilized peoples than in highly evolved, complex societies. In reality there is little useful information on this subject. It is always difficult to dissociate ailments with an organic basis from those of psychogenic origin, even when the observer is dealing with people of his own culture, and the difficulty is still greater in the case of primitive people who rarely differentiate between the two classes of disease. The fact that medicine men and magicians so often achieve remarkable therapeutic successes through incantations and suggestions shows that much of disease in primitive societies has a large mental component.

On the other hand, it is likely that the incidence of psychiatric disorders tends to increase whenever a people begins to intermingle with a more complex civilization. It appears, for example, that mental diseases among the Kalmucks and the Kirghizes, who had in the past remained almost completely isolated, increased markedly after 1850 when these tribes first came into intimate contact with Western civilization. A similar state of affairs obtains presently among many tribes of North American Indians. One of its expressions is the alcoholism so prevalent among them when they pass from the protective atmosphere of their own culture into the no man's land that they must cross before achieving integration with the white people. The spread of the Peyote cult is probably another aspect of the same phenomenon. The consumption of the hallucinating drug and all the rites associated with it are attempts to replace by a new religion the social traditions lost as a result of disturbance of the ancestral Indian culture.

Psychotic disorders resulting from the process of acculturation are not peculiar to primitive people coming into contact with the white man's world. They occur wherever and whenever social changes are too rapid to allow for gradual, successful adaptation. If psychiatric illnesses are truly increasing in the Western world, the reason is not to be found in the complex and competitive character of our society but rather in the accelerated rate at which old habits and conventions disappear and new ones appear. Even the marginal man can generally achieve some form of equilibrium with his environment if the social order is stable, but he is likely to break down when the extent and rate of change exceed his adaptive potentialities. For this reason mental diseases are likely to become more apparent in areas undergoing rapid cultural transitions, and this means a large part of the world at the present time. Man in undeveloped countries is subjected to the strain of moving straight from a camel's back to a motor car or to an airplane without the intermediate experience of a stagecoach. In the most industrialized countries, also, electronics and automation are bound to cause maladjustment and social stress by revolutionizing from one year to the other the ways of life and the techniques of production, as well as the amount of leisure and the manners of entertainment. It probably took Western man long periods of relative stability before he could enjoy the peace of the Sabbath and the sociable evenings at the end of the day's work. The four-day week may be the cause of as many stresses as was the exploitation of labor a few generations ago.

Automation and dial watching eliminate the hardships of physical effort, but monotonous environments and mechanical operations have their own deleterious effects on the human brain. Recent studies have revealed that as a result of prolonged exposure to a monotonous situation "the individual's thinking is impaired; he shows childish emotional responses; his visual perception becomes disturbed; he suffers from hallucinations; his brain-wave pattern changes." In brief, the efficiency of industrial production is creating a pathology of boredom.

Man, furthermore, is a social animal, and intimate participation in the creative activities of his group constitutes a much-needed sense of fulfillment that he often had the opportunity to enjoy in the past. To a large extent this creative satisfaction is now denied him as a result of technological changes. Modern man has acquired the economic power to own things, but these are anonymously produced. He may even have some abstract knowledge of their nature and operations, but ownership and knowledge are not substitutes for direct experience and do not satisfy the ancient need for being a real participant in the act of creation. Failure to satisfy this need breeds at times despair, often boredom, or at least the listlessness so prevalent in modern societies.

The history of man, both racial and social, is a long saga of difficulties overcome, of emergencies that had to be met in order to avoid destruction. Dangers, real or imaginary, and fear of the unknown used to be part of everyday life, but the unexpected also contributed an atmosphere of adventure and expectancy—the type of exhilaration that helps man to free himself from bondage to matter and to reach for the stars. Accumulation of earthly goods does not make up for this exhilaration, without which the zest for life is readily lost. The indifferent and the outwardly satisfied are less likely to retain happiness and mental sanity than are those who sacrifice well-being and comfort for the sake of ideals or illusions.

The highly organized social structures of modern times try to provide the individual with security from the womb to the grave, but this security is often bought at the cost of boredom. The exhilaration of expectancy constitutes in large part the salt of life. Boredom is not easy to define or to recognize, and its onset is insidious. It often masquerades in the passive forms of entertainment, in the dreary hours of aimless driving, in anonymous holidays which have lost their meaning because they are no longer holy, as well as in the attitude of the person who "couldn't care less" about the events of the world around him. Its manifestations go from the various forms of escapism, such as addition to drugs or alcohol, to suicide, which relieves the victim of the need to care about anything.

According to statistics recently published, the highest rates of drug addiction, suicide, and death from violence occur in countries which enjoy material wealth and have the most effective social legislation and greatest political stability. The United States, Switzerland, Denmark, and Australia led the list for the period 1948–1951. With regard to both suicide and homicide (as well, of course, as to road accidents), the lowest rates occurred in countries where nature, economic circumstances, and inadequate social legislation seem to make life harder and more uncertain. Among these countries are Catholic Eire and Spain, Protestant Ulster and Scotland, and the Jewish state of Israel. It has been reported that, even under the worst and apparently most hopeless conditions, the rate of suicide was extremely low among the internees in German and Japanese concentration camps. It seems as if the will to live—the eagerness to overcome the varied and inescapable problems of existence—is often weakened by physical comfort and wherever the cushion of the welfare state has been made too soft and has provided shelters against most of the vicissitudes of life. The modern state is predicated on the assumption that happiness is best reached through freedom from want and from struggle, whereas evolution-wise life implies strife and adventure. Modern man is apparently finding it hard to escape from his biological past.

Hermann J. Muller
THE PROSPECTS OF GENETIC CHANGE

Our present generation has been brought to realize more vividly than any previous one the paltry dimensions of our earth and everything upon it, in comparison with the awesome reaches of the universe at large. To many persons this perspective has seemed a forbidding one, as though a great pall had arisen to overshadow and belittle the cherished world of familiar things that our forefathers had taught us to believe in.

However, these pessimists have failed to take sufficiently into their view one all-important aspect of the picture, that serves to illuminate and transfigure it. This lies in the conclusion, supported by many modern studies, that the natural processes of genetics have in the course of ages enabled primitive organic matter gradually to struggle upward and blossom out into the wondrous forms of us human beings and all the other living things around us. Equally significant, moreover, is the proposition, following as a corollary to the one just stated, that we humans—and we alone among all earthly creatures—have, through these processes of genetic change, gained the capacity rapidly to add a mighty cultural evolution on top of the stupendous biological endowment to which we are heir.

In terms of geological time, that is, of the time necessary for appreciable natural evolution of a genetic kind, this cultural evolution is

Hermann J. Muller, "The Prospects of Genetic Change," *The American Scientist*, 47 (1959), 551–561. Reprinted by permission. Dr. Muller is a biologist, a Nobel laureate in phsyiology, and a Distinguished Service professor at Indiana University.

only just beginning. Yet, in this biological moment we have risen from the mastery of fire to the governance of the atom, and from expletives through speech to electronic computors. At the same time, our cultural progress has become increasingly self-enhancing. Moreover, in addition to promoting its own operations it has even reached back into the course of biological evolution itself. That is, it has acted upon the genetic processes of other organisms so as eventually to reshape these organisms drastically in adaptation to human needs.

Empirically Controlled Breeding

True, the biological reshaping of earlier times was for the most part accomplished by means of a crude empiricism, ignorant of genetic principles, and acting one small step at a time without any realization of the magnitude of the accumulated series of steps. Yet, even so, the changes brought about within this period, most of them in less than 10,000 years, have proved to be far greater than any known to have taken place in natural evolution in an equal interval. Moreover, they have been so extraordinarily serviceable as to result in profound reorientations in the ways of life of the human groups involved.

Thus, the primitive hunting economy was raised to a much higher level not only by the development of weapons but, perhaps equally, by the making over of the nature of dogs so as to lead them to complement human efforts more effectively. Next, the success of an agricultural existence was enormously augmented by the remolding of primitive grains, tubers, beans, cucurbits, fiber-bearing plants, and so on, into those numerous high-yielding cultivated types that we today classify as species in their own right. And the genetic reconstruction of poultry, sheep, cattle, swine, horses, the camel family, and even carps, bees, and silkworms, has made possible further great advances, both quantitative and qualitative, in human living. In fact, cultures are often most aptly distinguished in terms of the type of remodelled organism, such as maize, wheat, rice, sheep, etc., upon which the livelihood of their peoples, their standards of living, and the size of their populations, chiefly depends.

It is evident that, if these revolutionary changes could have been wrought by such crude methods and with so little awareness of routes and goals, even though at the cost of centuries of effort, it should now be possible, with our understanding of the principles of genetic mutation, combination, and selection, to telescope into a relatively few years much more comprehensive transformations. Recent successes with the development of hybrid corn and poultry and of disease-resistant strains of many crops, give a substantial foretaste of such possibilities. These have already reduced greatly the acreage of cultivation that is necessary to support a given population. Yet in this field of conscious genetic engineering we have so far only scratched the surface.

The Methods Now Available

As the great Vavilov demonstrated, the centers of origin of cultivated species constitute vast reservoirs of genes already selected by both nature and man for very diverse conditions and purposes. The rational exploitation of these reservoirs requires the re-establishment, in assorted situations, of great, copious genetic "banks" of multitudinous strains and substrains, like those Vavilov founded but on a still more extensive scale. The potentialities of the types thus made available must then be tested out under varied conditions of climate and cultivation, both in their present forms and in many of the innumerable combinations obtainable by intercrossing and selection. This is an enormous, global task that calls for widespread cooperation of international scope.

It should be recognized from the start that this kind of work is long-term and ever-continuing. It seldom yields the quick and easy results falsely promised by the devotees of the naive doctrine of inheritance of acquired characters, who after gaining power allowed much of the fruit of the work of geneticists to be lost. As in the far more protracted experiments of nature, although in lesser degree, the great majority of the genetic trials can give only negative results. Nevertheless, the relatively few successes can open up permanent and expanding opportunities. They thereby yield immeasurable recompense in return for the expenditures.

While this work of making the most of what is already to be had is going on, there is also much to be gained by seeking out the individual variations that are continually arising within the strains presently in use, by testing them out and incorporating those that prove useful into ever more serviceable combinations. Beyond this, there is the actual induction of new mutations by means of radiation and chemical mutagens.

In considering the induction of mutations, it should be borne in mind that the great majority (ordinarily well over 99 percent) of induced mutations, as of spontaneous ones, are of a detrimental kind, but that mutations which have already existed in a population for a long time represent a more or less selected residue from which the detrimental types have tended, in proportion to their degree of detriment and the time elapsed, to be eliminated. Moreover, it would be unrealistic to bank on the dim and distant hope, unsupported by critical analysis of the situation, that it may, even if some centuries hence, be found possible to induce mutations of diverse desired types at will by specific treatments. We must for practical purposes, therefore, assume that among induced mutations an even smaller proportion will usually prove useful than among mutations already present in populations. This being the case, the profitability of inducing mutations, in comparison with that of discovering suitable spontaneous ones, varies directly with the expendability of the individual organisms of the given species, with the ease of breeding them, with the difficulty of culling already existing populations for mutations contained in them, and with the difficulty of transferring specified genes from their stock of origin into the strain in which it is desired to have them. By all these criteria smaller organisms, and more especially microorganisms, constitute the material in which the induction of mutations can most advantageously be practiced.

Objectives to Be Sought

The job of remodelling the genetic constitution of organisms is a never ending one as needs and conditions change and as the innovations in the organisms themselves open new routes to their progress. So, for example, the use of more effective insecticides, fungicides, and fertilizers allows more of the metabolic effort of the plant to be concentrated upon growth itself. Similarly, artificial aids and protection allow an increasing fraction of that growth to be concentrated in that portion—whether it be seed, fiber, tuber, fruit, or sap—which in the given organism is of special use to man. Thus, as our non-genetic techniques of raising and tending our organisms evolve, correlative genetic changes become not superfluous but advantageous. It therefore seems likely, in view both of our own inventiveness and of the almost unlimited genetic plasticity of organisms, that as their artificially directed evolution continues they will depart ever further from their present norms until they become quite unrecognizable, even as happened in their natural evolution but inordinately faster.

When such work becomes more advanced, it should become feasible to make blue prints for an ever larger number of generations ahead, just as, in some of the fruit fly experiments of as long as two decades ago, designs for genetic synthesis covering more than forty successive generations of precisely ordered crossings were successfully carried through. At present, however, we are in the stage of little more than feeling our way along in the improvement of types of economic importance and it would be rash to predict what only ten years might hold in store for such work on annual forms.

It should also be remembered that, although primitive man brought so many species under cultivation and must have tried out far more than those that he finally succeeded with, we with our longer-range breeding methods and our more analytical techniques for testing and utilizing organisms may find many still wild species to be promising candidates for conversion into cultivated forms. Some of these will be useful for the food, drugs, or industrial products they can yield. Others will be valuable for services of a less direct kind, such as promoting the fertility of the soil, preventing erosion or drought, facilitating the turnover of materials for the organisms of more direct importance, combating pests and parasites, and, in general, assisting in the maintenance of ecological conditions favorable for the immediately useful types or (as in the case of shade trees) favorable for man himself. Here a rational union of the ecological and genetic attacks appears to present rich possibilities. Such developments call for the pooling of much detailed familiarity with local types, conditions, and problems along with knowledge of general principles and advanced techniques. In this field again it is evident that the most effective efforts involve international collaboration.

Among the most promising of the organisms for future exploitation by man with the aid of genetics are those of microscopic dimensions. Yeasts and bacteria have been unwittingly employed by man for many thousands of years, but only recently have these and other microorganisms been knowingly cultivated and improved. The five- or more-fold stepping up of the yield of penicillin by the judicious application of radiation to the mold Penicillium for the induction of successive mutations having this effect is a case in point. Not only laboratory, factory, and hydroponically bred organisms but also those bred at large, in soils, in fresh water situations and even in marine waters present opportunities here for the production of food, food accessories and drugs, industrially useful materials, and fuels such as oils.

In this connection, nearly everyone nowadays has heard of the experiments with green algae, notably Chlorella, which seem to afford the possibility of supplying many times the yield of food per acre than higher plants, with their excess of inedible structural material, can offer us. It is not so generally known that, as Dean Burk has recently shown, a special "thermal" strain of Chlorella, adapted to growth at relatively high temperatures, gives several times the yield given by ordinary Chlorella. With the application of genetic methods to such organisms they could be molded to fit our requirements still better under the special artificially contrived conditions that we could make available to them, and diverse strains could be adapted for different purposes and for different situations. By such means, wide stretches of our planet, now unproductive, may be increasingly subjugated to supply human needs.

Some advocates of the chemical approach might interrupt at this point to say that long before any such union of genetics, ecology, industry, and food processing as is here in question has come about, photosynthetic and chemosynthetic reactions will have been mastered in the laboratory, and put into mass operation, that will free men from their dependence on living organisms. This may well be true. Certainly our present means of transportation and haulage by inanimate machines is already for most purposes superior to that by draft animals. Similarly, in the making of special organic substances, such as many drugs, hormones, and antibiotics, that form but a small part of the organisms containing them or that have evolved relatively recently in special groups of organisms, it is likely that organic chemistry, by the conversion of less specialized organic compounds, will soon prove more effective for us than biosynthesis and extraction.

However, the production of foodstuffs in general from inorganic materials involves an incomparably more intricate series of operations than has either transportation or the production of a given end-product by the conversion of organic precursors. For eons natural selection has been working to increase the efficiency of organisms in carrying out this great series of syntheses. As a part of this work they manufacture, maintain, and multiply their own superb organizations, in endless cycles, and only a minimum of tending on our part is needed, as compared with the services required of us for the replacement and repair of wholly artificial mechanisms. It therefore seems unlikely that men will in the "foreseeable future," that is, for some hundreds of years ahead, at least, be able to surpass in large-scale operations the potential efficiency of biological growth. At any rate, we must for a long time to come be prepared to exploit all available possibilities for supplying our material needs. In doing so we shall find that the world of living things, judiciously dealt with by a combination of genetic methods and artificial appliances, offers us enormous opportunities of the kind we are seeking.

Genetic Change in Early Man

It would be a strange incongruity if mankind instituted extensive alterations in the genetic constitution of his companion organisms in the interests of an ampler and better life for himself, while leaving his own biological basis entirely to the mercy of natural forces or to whatever genetic currents his present artificial ways of living unintentionally subjected him. Surely his paramount obligation, as regards applications of genetics, is to himself, not however under the delusion that he is already perfect in any respect but in the knowledge that he too has plenty of room for further progress. However, before undertaking to move forward consciously it is necessary for him to realize what direction was taken by his genetic evolution in the past, what factors decided that direction, and to what extent his present situation may have entailed changes in the direction or in the factors. It is also imperative for him to reach a solid conclusion concerning what direction he should consider "forward."

Studies of the remains of early man have made it increasingly evident that their most distinctive characteristic, that which enabled them so far to outdistance all other animals, was their capacity for cultural evolution. This is a complex capacity, requiring not only a modicum of intelligence (not necessarily much higher at its inception than that possessed by present apes) but also a social disposition that takes delight in cooperating and communicating. Important accessories were manipulating proclivities, that led to the use of fire, tools, etc., and vocalizing proclivities, that facilitated communication.

We need not here attempt to trace the development in apes of the preparatory stages of these faculties. Nor can we detail how men's transition to an erect ground-dwelling life, surrounded by both predators and potential victims, was conducive to an intensification of both defensive and aggressive group behavior, mediated by their hands, and thus forced human beings to act increasingly in concert both to protect themselves and to overcome their prey. This situation resulted in a natural selection that put a premium on intelligence both of the manual, thing-conscious type and of the type involving understanding of and communication with other persons. This selection favored at the same time the innate drives that led to the exercise of these faculties, and the disposition that derived satisfaction from exercising them in the service of others of the immediate group.

As these selective pressures resulted in the multiplication of the mutant genes that happened to be conducive to intelligence and cooperative behavior an ever better genetic groundwork was laid for the acquirement, dissemination, handing down, and consequent accumulation of the lessons learned through the experiences of many men in many generations, and of the innovations in techniques and mores based upon these lessons: in other words, for cultural evolution. Reciprocally, as cultural evolution developed, the conditions must for a long time have undergone an intensification that favored the survival of the individuals and groups who were more intelligent, more skillful, more cooperative, and better at communication. That is, genetic evolution and cultural evolution must have reenforced one another in a kind of zig-zagging fashion. Thereby along with the progress of techniques and mores, the genetic bases of intelligence, of the communicative propensities, and of the social impulses generally, became rapidly enhanced, so as to give that appearance of a discontinuity in evolution which is so striking a feature of man's emergence.

The genetic bases even of some features of men's physical structure became changed by natural selection as a result of the new conditions resulting from their social evolution. For example, the socially evolved use of weapons in hunting and fighting, and of fire, knives, scrapers, and pounders in the preparation of food, replaced the earlier natural selection for powerful jaws and teeth with conditions favoring their reduction and the improvement of hands. The adoption of clothing and other artificial protection from cold and rain allowed the advantages of relative hairlessness (greater opportunity for cleanliness and for eradication of ecto-parasites) to take precedence, in selection, over the advantages of a native coat of hair. Again, when men's advancing cultures made it possible for them to live in colder climates, a number of other bodily and physiological changes were favored by the types of natural selection thereupon ensuing. Thus, in varied ways men's present genetically determined constitution bears the unconscious imprint of the artificial ways of life that he himself developed.

Genetic Processes in Modern Man

With the further progress of culture, however, along the lines laid down by men's advancing techniques and group coordination in coping with their inanimate, human, and other biological environment, the conditions governing the natural selection of genetic traits among men have changed greatly. With the growth and the progressive merging of social groups and the concomitant reduction in the number of groups, there has been an inevitable reduction in the efficacy of that *inter*-group selection which, by favoring the more cooperative and more skillful groups, has tended to enhance genetically based social traits as well as intelligence. At the same time, the heightened efficacy of *intra*-group cooperation has lessened the competition for survival and reproduction among individuals and among families or the same group. Those who through physical, intellectual, or character defects are less well able to fend for themselves or to raise a family are increasingly supported by means of social aids to a degree that may even allow them, if they will, to leave more children than the others. Inevitably, then, the increases of the last several centuries in the size of human populations and in men's successes in their contests with outer nature must have been accompanied by a slackening of their genetic advancement and perhaps even by a genetic decline in some important respects.

The advanced technologies of the present day and the greater efficiency of social organization in ministering to need must be having the effect of making these anti-evolutionary tendencies much stronger. Genetic studies make it very probable that in technically advanced countries far more mutations, the great majority of them detrimental to health, mentality, or character, are arising in each generation than the number of genetically handicapped persons who are failing to survive or to reproduce. This situation spells a genetic retrogression that, if continued through a persistence of the same conditions, could not ultimately be compensated for by any conceivable advances in medicine, education, automation, or other cultural methods. Thus we are at present allowing our very successes to dig away the foundations from under everything most valuable in our own natures. The more advanced the peoples, the more is this the case.

Another circumstance affecting the genetics of modern man that merits our objective attention here is the recent reversal of the tendency of human groups to become genetically differentiated from one another. In earlier times the differences in conditions of life between different regions and the difficulties in traveling from one of these regions to another undoubtedly led to the selection of some special characteristics peculiar to and helpful specifically in the given regions. Examples are the darker skin that serves for protection against stronger ultraviolet, the narrowed eyes that reduce the threat of snowblindness, and the small stature that facilitates penetration through jungles. There is no reason to think that these essentially superficial characteristics connoted any parallel differences in the more basic human faculties previously discussed, that were developed as a result of the advantages accruing from intelligent cooperation against the forces of nature in general, but they did lead people of each group to emphasize their distinctivenesses.

Now, however, these special characteristics are losing their value, with the development of man-made expedients for meeting the special situations. These expedients are in effect replacing the natural environments with ever more artificial ones. At the same time, our generalized modern culture is diffusing ever more widely, rapidly, and deeply, and is increasingly bringing to all peoples alike not only its techniques but its ways of thinking, mores, ideals, and standards of appreciation. It is also promoting political mergers and economic cooperation between peoples. Along with all this cultural homogenization there is also an increasing physical movement and interbreeding that is progressively, as yet mainly at the edges, blurring out the lines between the age-old genetic pools. With the accentuation of all these factors by the progress of technology and education, mankind, barring a return to barbarism, will undoubtedly come to form one world community within which local differences of a genetic nature have largely lost whatever importance they may once have had.

This course of events is a very different one from that usually obtaining for successful species, which tend to split and split again into divergent groups, among which selection operates. Similarly, within each group, there has in man, unlike the successful groups of the past, been a tendency to obliterate the lines between the small semi-isolated subgroups that provided useful experiments in natural selection. We cannot say that this tendency to merge is bad, for it is a condition of human progress as we must think of progress. However, it, as well as the other peculiarities of the genetic processes of modern man previously cited, must be taken seriously into account in the consideration of future policies affecting human genetics. When trial and error are removed, foresight must be substituted.

Prospects of Future Genetic Progress in Man

In any such consideration of policies and prospects there is one, not strictly genetic, fact regarding human reproduction today that must not be overlooked. This is the fact that modern medicine combined with all our other artificial aids to living is so reducing the death rate as to result—unless there is a compensatory reduction in birth-rate much more drastic than any now occurring—in serious global overpopulation very soon. By no advances that we could conceivably make in the next 500 years in the production of food and other materials could we decently provide for the world population of some 15 trillion (more than 5000 times the present world population) that would theoretically be in existence if only the present rate of increase of a doubling every 40 years —an increase that applies to the present United States population and is not so very much higher than that in the world as a whole today—were maintained.

The slowing down of population growth that will undoubtedly prevent the attainment of this calculated plethora of people can come about only by the resumption of an increased death rate, brought about by the failure of civilization to achieve human betterment, or else by an adequate voluntary restriction of births. In the past such voluntary restriction has only developed among peoples who attained a high standard of living. There are some reckless optimists who think that this will happen again. However, it is very doubtful whether such a living standard can be attained by the populations that are at a low level of technology and grossly overcrowded already, unless the means and motivations for planned parenthood are brought to them with little delay. In other words, birth restriction should be initiated even while the standard of living is low, or it may never be able to achieve an adequate and stable rise. At the same time, enormous efforts should be put forth to effect the rise as rapidly as possible.

The voluntary restriction of births that will have to be adopted if civilization is to succeed implies a recognition of men's responsibility toward their children and descendants. It constitutes a break with the hoary tradition of having as many children as possible to honor oneself and one's ancestors. It opens the door to the recognition by modern men and women everywhere of their obligation to bequeath to the next generation the best conditions possible. With the spread of education, men will come to realize that not least in their ultimate importance, among such conditions, are the genetic ones. They will therefore develop the desire to do their bit in leaving humanity somewhat better off, even genetically, than it was in their own day.

The growing social conscience of men, developing along with their cultural progress in cooperation and understanding, will cause increasing numbers to regard the having of children as a service to mankind, not to be undertaken for purely personal vainglory. This reorientation can lead them to look upon the production of children who are likely to suffer from more than the average share of genetic defects as an act to be avoided while, on the contrary, it should be felt a special honor to produce children who are likely to be especially fortunate in their genetic endowment. This redirection of motivation can in itself turn the scales from genetic decline to genetic progress. It involves a way of looking at things that must not be imposed, but must represent an outgrowth of men's natural seeking for betterment. It can be materially aided by wise policies in education, economics, and law, that facilitate the courses of action that would follow from such motivation.

It is however naive to use such words as "betterment" unless one has some concept of what one means by "good." Yet, despite minor diversities in the ideals of different major cultures, they are in fundamental agreement in attaching especially high value to service to one's fellows, that is, to cooperative behavior, and to wisdom. As we have seen, these are the very qualities that are genetically as well as culturally most characteristic of man, and it is they above all others that have brought him to his present high estate as compared with other animals. At the same time, it is universally recognized that even in man the degree of their development is concerned, grounds have been cited above for inferring that, after human groups became larger and fewer, progress in these directions must have slackened, so that men were left inwardly stunted. It is still in the power of civilized men to remedy this situation, if only they will recognize it and act realistically upon it.

The task here confronting humanity is that of guiding our progress in genetic respects so as to allow it once again to parallel our cultural progress. Here the word "our" implies a feeling of unity of the individual with the species as a whole. This attitude of responsibility to all humanity is the very antithesis of that of the racists who not so long ago brought the world to the brink of ruin by their monstrous perversions of both genetic and cultural principles. Concentrating upon the fundamental human values regarding which all peoples can agree, men of modern outlook will seek to strengthen these values in every way possible, and to reduce the stress too often laid on superficialities. Given a peaceful world, joined in a universal cultural cross-fertilization, this is a logical development.

Acting on the same principle, good parents today seek to strengthen these same values by cultural means, in the process of educating their children. The same standards are needed in their attitude toward genetic matters.

As in all human activities, the rise of techniques can often act as a lever to implement a change in social practices and attitudes. So, for example, in the control of population the working out of substances that would readily and safely prevent overpopulation might be decisive. Similarly, in the sphere of positively planned parenthood, there is still much room for finding practicable ways for controlling the production of reproductive cells, for storing them, and for transferring them, that may bring radical possibilities within the reach of those who take these matters seriously.

Despite the progress that man makes, he finds many phases of his transitions painful, and is often reluctant to move. Yet he does move eventually. As he learns to control more powerful forces, no matter what their nature, he must also learn to apply them wisely in the light of his newer, wider knowledge. In this way he may at times proceed beyond the horizon, but he will be enabled to rise to heights hitherto undreamed of.

Men would indeed be ignoble if they, Narcissus-like, worshipped their present selves as the acmes of perfection, and reserved their efforts to bring about genetic betterment for their cattle, their corn, and the yeast that gives them beer. Not all men will continue to maintain such smugness of attitude. Those who look higher will find that, increasingly, they can put their ideals into corporeal form and help to create men worthy of the great new material opportunities that they have opened up. For such men, in their turn, still further advancement, cultural and genetic, will always be the major aims.

Theodosius Dobzhansky
MAN AND NATURAL SELECTION

Are Culture and Natural Selection Compatible?

. . . Several forms of natural selection operate in modern mankind. But they certainly do not operate as they did during the Stone Age

From Theodosius Dobzhansky, "Man and Natural Selection," *Science in Progress*, 13 (1963), 146–153. Reprinted by permission of Yale University Press. Dr. Dobzhansky is a zoologist and a member and professor of the Rockefeller Institute.

or even as they did a century ago. Neither does natural selection operate always in the same way in wild and "natural" species, quite "unspoiled" by culture. This is inevitable. Natural selection depends on environments, and environments change. Human environments have changed a great deal in a century, not to speak of millennia.

The real problem is not whether natural selection in man is going on, but whether it is going on toward what we, humans, regard as betterment or deterioration. Natural selection tends to enhance the reproductive proficiency of the population in which it operates. Such proficiency is, however, not the only estimable quality with which we wish to see people endowed. And besides, a high reproductive fitness in one environment does not even insure the survival of the population or the species when the environment changes.

Normalizing selection is, as we have seen, not the only form of natural selection; the relaxation of some of its functions is, however, a cause for apprehension. Medicine, hygiene, civilized living save many lives which would otherwise be extinguished. This situation is here to stay; we would not want it to be otherwise, even if we could. Some of the lives thus saved will, however, engender lives that will stand in need of being saved in the generations to come. Can it be that we help the ailing, the lame, and the deformed only to make our descendants more ailing, more lame, and more deformed?

Suppose that we have learned how to save the lives of persons afflicted with a hereditary disease, such as retinoblastoma, which previously was incurably fatal. In genetic terms, this means that the Darwinian fitness of the victims of the disease has increased, and that the normalizing selection against this disease is relaxed. What will be the consequence? The incidence of the disease in the population will increase from generation to generation. The increase is likely to be slow, generally no more than by one mutation rate per generation. It may take centuries or millennia to notice the difference for any one disease or malformation, but the average health and welfare of the population are liable to show adverse effects of relaxed selection much sooner.

The process of mutation injects into every generation a certain number of harmful genes in the gene pool of the population; the process of normalizing selection eliminates a certain number of these genes. With environment reasonably stable, the situation tends to reach a state of equilibrium. At equilibrium, the mutation and the elimination are equal. If mutation becomes more frequent (as it does in man because of exposure to high-energy radiations and perhaps to some chemicals), or if the elimination is lagging because of relaxation of normalizing selection, the incidence of harmful mutant genes in the population is bound to increase. And take note of this: If the classical theory of population structure were correct, all harmful mutations would be in a sense equivalent. For at equilibrium there is one elimination for every mutation, regardless of whether the mutation causes a lethal hereditary disease like retinoblastoma, or a malformation like achondroplasia, or a relatively mild defect such as myopia.

It would no doubt be desirable to eliminate from human populations all harmful mutant genes and to substitute for them favorable genes. But how is this end to be attained? A program of eugenics to achieve genetic health and eventual improvement of the human species has, in recent years, been urged with great eloquence, particularly by Muller, and many other authors: The fortunate few who happen to carry mostly "normal" or favorable genes should be better progenitors of the coming generations than are those who carry average, or heavier than average, genetic loads. Let us then take the semen of the superior males, and use it to produce numerous progeny by artificial insemination of women who will be happy to be mothers of children of the superior sires. Techniques will eventually be invented to obtain also the egg cells of superior females; indeed, the ovaries of human females are capable of producing numerous egg cells, most of which are at present wasted. It will then be possible to combine the finest egg cells with choicest sperms; the uteri of women who happen to be carriers of average or higher-than-average genetic loads will be good enough for the development of the genetically superior fetuses. But not even this would guarantee the best possible genetic endowments in the progeny. Very distinguished parents sometimes produce commonplace, and even inferior, children. The distant vista envisaged by Muller is tissue culture of (diploid) body cells of the very best donors, and a technique to stimulate these cells to develop without fertilization (parthenogenetically), thus giving rise to numerous individuals, all as similar to the donor and to each other as identical twins.

It may be doubted, however, whether modern genetics has progressed far enough to embark on a program as far-reaching as Muller suggests. Wright considers that the situation calls rather for research in what he describes neatly as "unfortunately the unpopular and scientifically somewhat unrewarding borderline fields of genetics and the social sciences." Although at equilibrium there may be one genetic elimination for every mutation, it is unrealistic to equate the human and social consequences of different mutations. The elimination of a lethal mutant which causes death of an embryo before implantation in the uterus is scarcely noticed by the mother or by anyone else. Suffering accompanies the elimination of a mutant, such as retinoblastoma, which kills an infant apparently normal at birth. Many mutants, such as hemophilia or Huntington's chorea, kill children, adolescents, or adults, cause misery to their victims, and disruption of the lives of their families. There is no way to measure precisely the amount of human anguish; yet one may surmise that the painful and slow death of the victims of so many hereditary diseases is torment greater than that involved in the elimination of a gene for achondroplasia owing to the failure of an achondroplastic dwarf to beget children.

Looked at from the angle of the costs to the society, the nonequivalence of different mutants is no less evident. Myopia may be inherited as a recessive trait. Increases of the frequency in populations of the gene for myopia are undesirable. Yet it may become more and more common in future generations. However, only a fanatic might advocate sterilization of the myopics or other radical measures to prevent the spread of this gene. One may hope that civilized societies can tolerate some more myopics; many of them are very useful citizens, and their defect can rather easily be corrected by a relatively inexpensive environmental change—wearing glasses. The effort needed to eradicate or to reduce the frequency of myopia genetically would exceed that requisite to rectify their defect environmentally, by manufacturing more pairs of glasses.

Diabetes mellitus is, given the present level of medicine, more difficult and expensive to correct than is myopia. Some diabetics may nevertheless be treated successfully by insulin therapy, helped to live to old age, and enabled to raise families as large as nondiabetics. The incidence of diabetes may therefore creep up slowly in the generations to come. Now, most people would probably agree that it is better to be free of diabetes than to have it under control, no matter how successfully, by insulin therapy or other means. The prospect is not a pleasant one to contemplate. Insulin injections may perhaps be almost as common in some remote future as taking aspirin tablets is at present.

Toward Guidance of Human Evolution

We are faced, then, with a dilemma—if we enable the weak and the deformed to live and to propagate their kind, we face the prospect of a genetic twilight; but if we let them die or suffer when we can save them we face the certainty of a moral twilight. How to escape this dilemma?

I can well understand the impatience which some of my readers may feel if I refuse to provide an unambiguous answer to so pressing a problem. Let me plead with you, however, that infatuation with oversimple answers to very complex and difficult problems is one of the earmarks of intellectual mediocrity. I am afraid that the problem of guidance of human evolution has no simple solution. At least I have not found one, nor has anybody else in my opinion. Each genetic condition will have to be considered on its own merits, and the solutions that may be adopted for different conditions will probably be different. Suppose that everybody agrees that the genes causing myopia, achondroplasia, diabetes, and retinoblastoma are undesirable. We shall nevertheless be forced to treat them differently. Some genetic defects will have to be put up with and managed environmentally; others will have to be treated genetically, by artificial selection, and the eugenic measures that may be needed can be effected without accepting any kind of biological Brave New World.

Let us face this fact: Our lives depend on civilization and technology, and the lives of our descendants will be even more dependent on civilized environments. I can imagine a wise old ape-man who deplored the softness of his contemporaries who used stone knives to carve their meat instead of doing this with their teeth; or a solid conservative Peking man viewing with alarm the newfangled habit of using fire to make oneself warm. I have yet to hear anyone seriously proposing that we give up the use of knives and fire now. Nor does anyone in his right mind urge that we let people die of smallpox or tuberculosis, in order that genetic resistance to these diseases be maintained. The remedy for our genetic dependence on technology and medicine is more, not less, technology and medicine. You may, if you wish, feel nostalgic for the good old days of our cave-dwelling ancestors; the point of no return was passed in the evolution of our species many millennia before anyone could know what was happening.

Of course, not all genetic defects can be corrected by tools or remedies or medicines. Even though new and better tools and medicines will, one may hope, be invented in the future, this will not make all genetic equipments equally desirable. It is a relatively simple matter to correct for lack of genetic resistance to smallpox by vaccination, or for myopia by suitable glasses. It is not so simple with many other genetic defects. Surgical removal of the eyes is called for in cases of retinoblastoma; this saves the lives of the victims, but leaves them blind. No remedies are known for countless other genetic defects. Human life is sacred; yet the social costs of some genetic variants are so great, and their social contributions are so small, that avoidance of their birth is ethically the most acceptable as well as the wisest solution. This does not necessarily call for enactment of Draconian eugenic laws; it is perhaps not overoptimistic to hope that spreading biological education and understanding may be a real help. Make persons whose progeny is likely to inherit a serious genetic defect aware of this fact; they may draw the conclusions themselves.

The strides accomplished by biochemical genetics in recent years have led some biologists to hope that methods will soon be discovered to induce specific changes in human genes of our choice. This would indeed be a radical solution of the problem of management of the evolution of our species and of other species as well. We would simply change the genes which we do not like, in ways conforming to our desires. Now, if the history of science has any lesson to teach us, it is the unwisdom of declaring certain goals to be unattainable. The cavalier way in which the progress of science often treats such predictions should instill due humility even in the most doctrinaire prophets. The best that can be said about the possibility of changing specific genes in man in accordance with our desires is that, although such an invention would be a great boon, it is not within reach yet. And it cannot be assumed to be achievable.

Let us also not exaggerate the urgency of the problem of the genetic management of the evolution of our species. Another problem, that of the runaway overpopulation of our planet, is far more immediate and critical. If mankind will prove unable to save itself from being choked by crowding it hardly needs to worry about its genetic quality. Although the problems of numbers and of quality are not one and the same, they may yet be closely connected in practice. As steps toward regulation of the size of population begin to be taken, and this surely cannot be postponed much longer, the genetic problem will inexorably obtrude itself. The questions, "how many people" and "what kind of people" will be solved together, if they will be solved at all.

Some people believe that all would be well with mankind if only natural selection were permitted to operate without obstruction by medicine and technology. Let us not forget, however, that countless biological species of the past have become extinct, although their evolution was directed by natural selection unadulterated by culture. What we want is not simply natural selection, but selection, natural and artificial, directed toward humanly desirable goals. What are these goals? This is the central problem of human ethics and of human evolution. Darwinian fitness is no guide here. If, in some human society, genetically duller people produce more progeny than the brighter ones, this simply means that, in the environment of that particular society, being a bit thick-headed increases the Darwinian fitness, and being too intelligent decreases it. Natural selection will act accordingly, and will not be any less "natural" on that account.

Human cultural evolution has resulted in the formation of a system of values, of *human* values. These are the values to which we wish human evolution to conform. These values are products of cultural evolution, conditioned of course by the biological evolution, yet not deducible from the latter. Where do we find a criterion by which these values are to be judged? I know of no better one than that proposed by the ancient Chinese sage: "Every system of moral laws must be based upon man's own consciousness, verified by the common experience of mankind, tested by due sanction of historical experience and found without error, applied to the operations and processes of nature in the physical universe and found to be without contradiction, laid before the gods without question or fear, and able to wait a hundred generations and have it confirmed without a doubt by a Sage of posterity."

Part Four
Science, Technology, and the Policy-Making Process

In the nineteenth century, military might and colonial possessions were the hallmarks of a nation's power; however, in our century leadership in science and technology has become the symbol of national prestige. Thus, our federal government has become increasingly involved in scientific research and development for military purposes and for such goals as resource conservation, public health, and the conquest of space. Our government is, therefore, responsible in great measure for the technological innovation that is transforming our society and for the scientific research upon which our society depends.

In this way, public-policy decisions which intimately involve science and technology have become an integral part of the political process. The directions in which science and technology proceed are deeply affected by political considerations; and, conversely, the structure and process of government is complicated by scientific and technological change. In this situation, where an ambiguous interplay between science and government is occurring, several major problems have arisen. Who is to make the decisions in matters that require scientific expertise? Should they be made by scientists, who are relatively inexperienced in the political process; or should they be left to our elected leaders, who, in the nature of things, know little of the implications of science for the future? Should there be an over-all science policy whereby the direction of science and technology is placed under firm control? And, more important, is the structure of our government, which was designed to fulfill the needs of the predominantly agrarian society of a century and a half ago, suited to meet the challenges and complexities of a scientific and technological age? Will the pressures of science and technology eventually provoke a crisis, resulting in the creation of a new form of government in the United States?

10
Science and Government

From the early days of the Republic, successive administrations have recognized that the search for scientific knowledge should be supported. This was the reason for the creation of agencies such as the Coast and Geological Surveys. Scientists were employed to do further research in the development of new crops and improved agricultural techniques. The various branches of the armed services used scientists for weapons and communications research.

Since World War II, however, the national government has become increasingly involved in promoting science and utilizing the results of scientific research to such an extent that the involvement implies a distinct change—of kind rather than of degree. Government support of science in 1940 amounted to approximately one hundred million dollars. In 1965 the total money spent by the federal government for scientific research and development amounted to about nineteen billion dollars. Previously the government aided science only in a few specific and well-defined areas that served the public interest or provided for its common defense. Currently there is *no* area of scientific research in which the government is not involved.

The selections in this chapter are designed to explore this new relationship of government and science. The original purpose of our national government was "to form a more perfect union, establish justice, insure domestic tranquillity, provide for the common defense, promote the general welfare, and secure the blessings of liberty to ourselves and our posterity.". . . In the twentieth century, Franklin Roosevelt stated that the social and political objectives of the American people were to ensure ". . . the freedom of speech and expression, the freedom of every person to worship God in his own way, the freedom from want, and the freedom from fear." How does the involvement of government in science —approximately one fifth of the yearly national budget committed to research and development—secure these goals? The expenditure of large sums to ensure military preparedness can certainly be justified, but can the appropriation of money (amounting to hundreds of millions) for linear accelerators and bevatrons be similarly justified as expressing national goals and values?

Berkner argues that new industries are required if we are to maintain a healthy economy and that new industries can be derived only from innovations emanating ultimately from basic scientific research. He recommends that the present government expenditure for basic research —about one billion dollars annually—be doubled. Bush, however, believes that the program of government support for science has been overextended; that trivial and mediocre projects are receiving financial aid. He thinks that basic scientific research should be carried on in the universities rather than in government laboratories. He doubts that there is a sufficient number of experienced and competent scientists to carry on relevant research at the present time. Holleman points to certain criteria by which government support may be justified: Is the program necessary? Is it desirable? Is it in the public interest? He thinks one question of national policy should be the extent to which government and private industry should share responsibility in certain programs. Further, he questions whether government support is adequately balanced between the civilian and military sectors of the economy.

The programs of the National Aeronautics and Space Administration, in particular, have been a subject of controversy among scientists and legislators. About one third of the total funds expended for research and development by the national government are channeled into this agency. Dryden justifies the space program principally on the basis that it will contribute immeasurably to the increase of scientific knowledge about the universe. Abelson, however, is sharply critical of the manned lunar project. He claims that the practical consequences of space exploration involve regions close to the earth and that scientific exploration of the moon and other planets can be done equally well (and at far less cost) by robots. Further, he states that the staggering sums expended by NASA have gravely disturbed the balance of scientific research and have drawn the best brains away from other areas of science where their talents are desperately needed.

Do such crash programs reflect valid national goals and values or do they reflect a lack of sound national policy with respect to science? Michael believes that this is the case and argues for a federal science policy. He describes the present conflict between scientific and non-scientific communities within the government and believes that the general public is quite unaware of what is at stake. He is most concerned that we are unable to predict the social consequences of increasing technological innovation.

Will a federal science policy restrict the freedom of scientific inquiry? What has been the experience of contemporary societies where a federal science policy has been established? Barber describes the German experience under the Nazi regime and concludes that, although government control weakens science, it will not kill it in a modern industrial society. Looking at science in the Soviet Union, he believes that the authoritarianism in Soviet society creates an impetus toward the sacrifice of basic science in the interests of applied science. It should be noted that Barber wrote this passage prior to Lysenko's removal from power in Soviet science. Rabinowitch, however, questions whether the discouragement of free inquiry inhibits the curiosity of the scientific mind. He argues that certainly in applied science long-range planning is useful and cites the success of the Manhattan project as a case in point. Thus, the case for a comprehensive and directed national science policy is by no means prejudiced by the Soviet example, and the question remains controversial.

Lloyd V. Berkner
SCIENCE AND THE NATION

. . . In responding to your request to evaluate our national program of scientific research, I think we should first view this program in the perspective of our national situation—our needs, and our objectives.

Portion of the statement of Dr. Lloyd V. Berkner, President, Graduate Research Center of the Southwest, Dallas, Texas, before the Select Committee on Government Research, House of Representatives, 88th Congress, 1st Session.

In short, why should we, as citizens, spend our tax money to support broad programs of scientific research? Is the expected return worth the cost? What would be the effect of cutting down such expenditures?

To answer these questions we must try to see our national situation clearly in the flow of history, and to identify the place and importance of scientific research with respect to that situation. First of all, what, basically, is our national objective. I found myself asking this question when I read your letter.

One can reply that it is to maintain a free and peaceful society under our constitutional system of free choice—a society that encourages the full diversity inherent among our citizens in the development of individual opportunity, with economic growth sufficient to reduce poverty continually, and to satisfy ever more fully the needs of our people.

Let me turn briefly to the elements of the present situation in our progress toward this objective:

First, our population is exploding at the rate of 2 percent per year. Where the doubling time for our population was 200 years at the time of the American Revolution, it has dropped quite suddenly in this century to 40 years. As a consequence of the new scientific basis for medicine, the life of the average man now surpasses the Biblical three score and 10 years.

Second, quite suddenly, at the midcentury, agriculture is becoming completely mechanized and industrialized. With the application of biology, chemistry, and mechanics to farming, agricultural productivity has increased a hundred times. Our food supplies can be maintained by a tiny fraction of our population, leaving great excesses for export. Where 70 percent of American population was occupied by agricultural pursuits in 1860, a century later, in 1960, only 7 percent were so employed, with estimates of 3 percent by 1980.

I might interpolate here, Mr. Chairman, that originally as a farm boy from Sleepy Eye, Minn., I am very struck by this change that has taken place over my own lifetime. At one time I could harness a team of horses. It is not necessary any more. I could pitch bundles. It is not done any more. So the change in agriculture to me is an exceedingly striking matter.

Third, the same situation is found in the natural resources industries—fuel and minerals. With the new technology sparkplugged by science, productivity of basic commodities is enormously enhanced.

Fourth, as a consequence of exploding populations, coupled with emigration from the land, our population growth is centering in just 100 or so major metropolitan areas which are bursting in size. Down in Texas, our population is growing 25 percent per decade. Yet of our 254 counties, all but 31 have lost population or have about stood still in each of the last three decades. Since 1950, more than a half million Texans have left the farming areas. Only 9 or 10 great metropolitan areas of Texas are getting all of the new and migrant population, thereby increasing their population more than 50 percent per decade. The example in Texas is typical of the whole Nation.

Fifth, the productivity of the industries that support the population of these cities is increasing enormously. A powerful technology, sustained by an equally powerful and progressive science, provides machines and computers that operate factories. Ever fewer, but very skilled men and women are required to produce larger quantities of superior products and services.

Sixth, with the improved productivity, the personal needs of the educated, highly skilled, and productive elements of our population are increasingly satisfied. On October 7, 1963, the New York Times noted:

> The family budget standard just issued by the Community Council shows that New Yorkers in the low-to-moderate income brackets are eating more meat, seeing more shows, walking on thicker rugs, and generally living better than they did 8 years ago.* * *.

What is true in New York is equally true throughout the country.

Seven, at the same time, however, chronic unemployment is increasing. This is the inevitable consequence of the sudden flooding of population to the cities and the coincident and equally sudden rise in individual productivity out of the application of science, through an ever improving technology, to every aspect of living.

These then are the basic elements of our national situation:

We are witnessing a technological revolution derived from the powerful science of our time, leading to vastly improving productivity and greater wealth of our population, but with a mass movement of people from the farms to flood 100 or so American metropolitan areas. While nothing ever happens instantly, I think we can date this mounting technological revolution as really beginning about the mid-20th century.

In a sense, at midcentury we moved almost abruptly from the traditional economy of scarcity which had plagued mankind since the beginning of history, into an economy of plenty. For the first time in history, man has acquired, out of science and technology, the power to produce adequately to supply all his needs, with a significant excess remaining.

Throughout history, man had struggled for the bare necessities— for the power to open his planet for his development and benefit. Then suddenly, at the midcentury he discovered that quick access to the whole planet had been gained.

After five millenniums of struggle in the economy of scarcity, we are not geared, in our thinking, to manage an entirely new kind of economy—this economy of plenty. For instance, we were all taught as youngsters the adages of Adam Smith that "labor is of equal value to the laborer" and that "labor is the basis for all value."

In this economy of plenty, controlled energy and highly developed applied brainpower seem to me to be the principal bases of value, with labor contributing only in proportion to its manipulative power over nature. So I suspect Adam Smith and Karl Marx, with all the other exponents of the economy of scarcity, can now be relegated to the museum of outmoded ideas acquired in the growth of human thought. For through exploitation of the opportunities offered by human diversity in our free system, widely applied to the science of our time and to the derived technology, we have created a wholly new basis for our national economy—an economy of plenty. But after living in the atmosphere of the economy of scarcity for five millenniums it is going to take some time to adjust our thinking to this new economic base where controlled energy and applied brain-power are the basic factors.

Up to a century ago, man's progress was characterized primarily by small improvements in obtaining his basic supplies of food, clothing, and housing. In the present century, as we move toward the new science-oriented economy of plenty, our progress is characterized by radically new and powerful industries that are not directly related to basic necessities. The automobile, the aircraft and other fast transportation, the communications and mass media, the computer and automatic control, the nuclear and the space industries are typical examples. These new industries have the characteristic, not of basic necessity, but of making the individual far more effective in his environment.

It has become quite clear that the fundamental industries related to basic necessity—food, shelter, agriculture, and basic materials in their traditional form—no longer have the potential for growth to overcome our increasing unemployment. New industries are required to provide new products and services, and with them, new sources for employment, and wealth, and human satisfaction.

Here we come to the crux of the situation. New industry can be derived only from innovation. Innovation is the altogether new resource that already provides for more than half of our economy. Today innovation arises predominantly from an ever-expanding science, under the command of men educated and trained to enlarge that science significantly. . . .

In particular, the funds for fundamental research, as contrasted to the funds for engineering, development, test, and evaluation, should be weighed carefully. I have heard quoted the figure of $16 billion for U.S.

research and development. Less than 10 percent of this figure—a little over a billion dollars—goes for true research. The remainder is involved in hardware in one way or another.

That billion dollars is the seed from which our enlarged economy must grow—we should not destroy that seed—it should be multiplied. Let us not confuse the massive, though necessary, engineering activities of our Government with the much tinier but imperative needs for basic scientific research from which can only be derived the innovation of the future. The serious cuts in the budget of the National Science Foundation this year will be reflected, inevitably, in the losses to our national economy, and, I might add, quite certainly, to more than equal losses to our Treasury in tax returns and payments to the relief rolls. Our experience now tells us this unambiguously. Consequently, I would estimate that our expenditures for basic research should be multiplied twice again, over the ensuing decade, a point which I amplify in my written statement, if you will accept this, Mr. Chairman.

Let us turn for a moment to ask: Just what are the points of impact of scientific research on our national situation?

I would emphasize five:

First, of course, is the innovation derived from an ever-growing knowledge of nature. As we solve the secrets of nature with precision, man acquires new means of commanding that nature, thereby adding to his effectiveness. The resultant industrial opportunity that science can provide has hardly been tapped, and we are on the threshold of immense future industrial opportunity if we but maintain a suitable scientific effort. We are within reach of abolishing poverty with its slavery of the human spirit. While, of course, our total production of goods and services cannot forever rise exponentially, the growth that is provided by our new resources can bridge the transition in human affairs, and in human thought, between the economy of scarcity and a stable economy of plenty. In the transition, the growth of productivity should be multiplied many times to satisfy the world's needs.

Second, is the part that scientific research must play in the graduate, or the postdoctoral, training of scientists. We cannot generate an adequate level of sound scientific research without a sufficient body of highly trained and creative scientists. You can't become a highly skilled military pilot by reading about flying in books—you must fly in airplanes with highly skilled instructors and then perfect your techniques for endless hours in advanced aircraft by yourself. In the same way, you don't become a scientist by merely attending classes or reading books. You have to work in the laboratory with skilled professors on creative and original problems to learn how to deal with novel situations, and to discover and recognize the significance of new knowledge. Parenthetically, I would add that just as training of pilots involves expensive duplication, so the Congress must recognize that training of scientists likewise justifies much similar duplication in research effort.

Third, the impact of scientific research on our national situation influences public attitudes toward new ideas, products, and services. No matter how useful a new idea or device may be, it will not create employment or wealth or opportunity unless the public will accept and buy it. The focus of public interest in scientific research, and the wonders of nature it discloses, unquestionably orients the public to acceptance of the new and more useful products and services that our new science-oriented economy can provide. Our space program has an enormous impact in this respect. . . .

It lifts a people from the horse-and-buggy age and accustoms them to the ideas of change and progress.

Fourth, the advancement of knowledge unquestionably lifts civilization in the cultural sense. The incredible brutality of the past, so aptly described by the late Hans Zinsser in "Rats, Lice, and History," is no longer tolerated in our age when knowledge with its consequent justice has lifted civilization above the dregs of animallike existence. Knowledge provides an ever higher richness of living within which we can more deeply enjoy and appreciate the opportunities that our scientific culture affords.

Finally, we cannot ignore the powerful relation of scientific research to the defense of our Nation. Only when we are at the forefront of science in every sector can we be certain that an enemy cannot immobilize our posture by some surprise discovery. . . .

Vannevar Bush

THE RELEVANCE OF SCIENTIFIC RESEARCH AND DEVELOPMENT

Your committee has before it a very heavy task, and I am happy to see it undertaken. I think it is time for a broad and intensive examination into the Government support of research.

Portion of the statement of Dr. Vannevar Bush, Honorary Chairman of the Corporation, Massachusetts Institute of Technology, before the Select Committee on Government Research, House of Representatives, 88th Congress, 1st Session.

After the war, and as a result of the success of our scientific war programs in developing new weapons, this country plunged into a broad program of Government support of research. A report to President Roosevelt, recommending such a course of action, summarizes the opinions of scientists at the time, and is worth review. It is well that this occurred, for the necessary size of the country's research program, to buttress our military strength, to insure rapid economic progress, and to give us our proper stature in the creation of new knowledge, was far too great to be supported by private funds. Those of us who recommended the program recognized the dangers, but felt they could be avoided. In general they have been, and the program has gone well and made sense. But the American people seldom do things moderately. The program has been overextended, and is still rapidly growing. I believe this is an opportune time for a thorough study by this committee. I trust, if your study indicates that we should now apply the brakes, we will not commit the converse error, and cut back really worthwhile efforts.

In the time available I will not be able to present fully any one aspect of your problem. I will hence confine myself to a number of brief statements of points I feel you should have in mind as you proceed. Some of my statements will no doubt be objected to vigorously. I could add many more, but have tried to pick out parts of what seem to me to be the important aspects of your overall program.

First, what is research? It is the search for new knowledge. But this includes a mathematician with a pencil and paper, sitting under a tree, and it also includes a hundred men designing a new type of aircraft.

Much of what we call scientific research is really engineering research, or even straight engineering. Putting a communications satellite in orbit, and working, is an engineering job, incidentally a magnificent one. I trust that when I say scientific research you will realize that I often mean to include engineering research.

A man sitting at a desk and thinking is not an expensive proposition. A scientist directing a team and operating an expensive array of apparatus is. The costs of research go up very rapidly when one gets into hardware. When money comes easily there is a tendency to rush into use of complex equipment too fast and too far. We may be making this mistake.

If the country pours enough money into research, it will inevitably support the trivial and the mediocre. The supply of scientific manpower is not unlimited.

Duplication in research can involve waste. But on really important problems duplication is inevitable, is even necessary for rapid progress. Competition among scientific groups is as important for producing outstanding researchers as competition among football teams is in producing great quarterbacks.

As has been said many times you cannot have great advances in applied research unless you have as a basis an extensive body of fundamental knowledge, developed over years by basic research. The development of an atomic bomb was possible only because of 50 years of basic work on the properties of the atom. We once leaned on Europe for our basic research, and Americans turned more naturally to applications. We are now doing better. But we should lead in every important field of fundamental scientific knowledge. Many of these will be hard to understand by laymen, or even by scientists in other fields.

It is impossible to calculate the efficiency of a research program. Having directed all three, I would, for effectiveness in basic research, rate universities and research institutes first, commercial laboratories second, Government laboratories third. One reason is that the scientist in a university can afford to make mistakes. Of course there are exceptions: outstanding basic scientific accomplishments in commercial and Government laboratories. But the normal home of basic research is the university.

When scientific programs are judged by popular acclaim we inevitably have overemphasis on the spectacular. That is just what we have today. The deeply important scientific advances moving today are not easy to understand. If they were they would have been accomplished long ago. Outstanding scientific progress, which will most affect the lives and health of our children, is not grasped by many. For example, I rate the program on interferon highly. Yet, if I tackled a hundred citizens at random I probably would not find one that knew what it is all about. I might even find the same situation among Members of Congress.[1] Yet it will do much more for us, a decade from now, than a probe of Venus.

In any broad program of research the key word in regard to any one aspect of the program is "relevance." It is a good word to have in mind in examining any research program. Competent directors of research know what it means. Probably "conducive to progress toward the main

---

[1] Later, in answer to a query from a Congressman who professed ignorance, Bush explained that British scientists had discovered that when an organism is attacked by a virus, it begins to manufacture something, which came to be called interferon, to protect itself. Interferon is a way in which the cell prevents the introduction of foreign nucleic acids into its structure. Bush pointed out that present work on viral disease concentrates on the discovery of specific anti-viral agents. If interferon proves to give a general protection against viruses, which appears likely, and some practical way is found to use it, there would be an end, for example, to all virus diseases of the respiratory tract, hence Bush's belief in its importance. Interferon is difficult to work on, because there is so very little with which to experiment.

object of a program" is as good a definition as any. Just finding out something new is not by itself sufficient justification for research. It needs to mean something when we find it.

It makes sense to ask a young researcher in basic research what he is trying to find out, what sort of knowledge he hopes to have at the end of his program which does not now exist. Surprisingly often the answer will be hard to extract. But it makes no sense to ask him just how he is going to do it, what it will cost, or how long it will take. If he knew the answers to these questions it would not be basic research.

In the nature of things the application of the physical sciences produces interesting gadgets of great popular appeal. The application of chemical science produces a new liquid in a bottle, or a stronger material, or a lowered cost of manufacture, and these are seldom spectacular. The application of biological science produces new drugs to cure our ills, or ingenious ways of combating insects without injuring birds. These may be very important, indeed, but, they involve little of the gadgetry which the American public enjoys. We need to use care, therefore, that our American love of gadgetry does not lead us astray in our emphasis.

The salaries of scientific researchers have gone up rapidly in recent years. This is good. They are still going up rapidly, which is also good. But one wonders what will set the ceiling. The dollar seeking a profit, the dollar from endowment has a tough time competing with the tax dollar. With many agencies using tax dollars and competing for men, I believe we are headed for trouble.

We are not doing too well in our rate of industrial growth. We have trouble on flow of gold, and our ability to compete and to export is part of this picture. It would be well to find out whether the pressure of Government-supported research is not now preventing industry from doing its research job well.

The spectacular success of applied research during the war led to a fallacy entertained by many. It is that any problem can be solved by gathering enough scientists and giving them enough money. To solve the problem of the common cold, assemble a great institution, fill it with scientists and money, and soon we will have no more colds. It is folly to thus proceed. The great scientific steps forward originate in the minds of gifted scientists, not in the minds of promoters. The best way to proceed is to be sure that really inspired scientists have what they need to work with, and then leave them alone.

Since the war we have avoided almost completely one of the great dangers of Government support of research in universities; namely, dictation to the universities on their programs. This has been due to a number of things; wisdom on the part of Government officials, for one.

Much of it is due to the fact that judgment of scientific programs has usually been made by competent committees rather than by individuals. This, too, has its dangers, but it is by far the best way.

It is a strange thing to have academic basic research supported by the military services. In my opinion, they have handled it very well thus far, but that does not prevent it from being unnatural.

I have said nothing about the social sciences, for one reason because I am not a social scientist. You gentlemen are in a better position to judge here in this field than I am. You are, at least, practitioners in one field of applied social science, or you would not be here.

I also have not said much about the space program. I think my attitude on that is pretty well known, and I doubt if the committee wants to plunge into this question now.

I have been speaking about nonclassified research, and especially about basic research. There is also the enormous field of military research. I have great sympathy for this committee in their task of judging our programs in the open research field. I suspect that sound judgment on military research is just as badly needed, and almost impossible to arrive at without far more effort than I believe is now contemplated.

Since the war, we have seen a strange and, to my mind, dangerous development. The armed services have called upon universities to manage great programs of research and development, involving secrecy, and often calling for business judgment. Some of this has been avoided by the creation of independent nonprofit organizations. We ought to find a better way. The universities will respond, when called upon by Government, to undertake burdens in the public interest, but management of secret programs is not their proper business, and they should not be thus utilized. We ought to be ingenious enough to avoid loading our universities with tasks which may interfere with their proper function of turning out educated men and women.

It should never be forgotten that the main task of the universities is to educate men. The country will need skilled professional men in the future as much as it will need new knowledge. As we now go we are not meeting this challenge sufficiently. Every research program placed in a university should be so ordered that its product is not only new knowledge but skilled, educated men.

I have suggested a broad range of inquiry. You have my sympathy, gentlemen, as you delve into it.

Thank you.

The CHAIRMAN. Thank you, Dr. Bush.

Dr. Bush, do you think we have reached the point where our support of research exceeds the supply of first-rank scientists?

Dr. Bush. I do; yes, sir.

Now, let me go back a bit. You mentioned that I was head of the Research and Development Board of the Armed Services after the war. At that time, and as Chairman of that body, I made a study to see whether the amount of money being spent on research by the military services was creeping up to the point where it was a greater burden than could properly be carried by the scientific personnel of the country, and I came to the conclusion that it was getting very close to it.

Yet, the amount of money at that time, I believe, was $800 million. . . .

J. Herbert Holleman
SCIENCE AND NATIONAL PRIORITIES

. . . With respect to basic research, I think we have to ask questions like: Is it competently performed? Are the people highly qualified? Are we supporting the maverick, the unusual genius? Have we provided a sufficient support for our basic institutions of learning?

Different and much more pointed questions can be asked about research and development activities supported for other objectives. Here we must first examine whether the program itself or the objectives which the program itself are aimed to serve are adequate. Is the program necessary, is it desirable and in the public interest? I think it is most important to determine the relative role of the private and the public sector and whether the benefit of the research exceeds its cost.

As an example, I think we might consider the national transportation system. Billions of dollars are authorized for Federal highway research. The U.S. subsidy for the maritime industry exceeds $300 million. The railroad industry in this country is declining from the standpoint of the total contribution to the national economy, and the aeronautical industry has obviously been partly dependent upon military expenditures.

But is the $25 million or so that we spend totally in the United

Portion of the statement of Dr. J. Herbert Holleman, Assistant Secretary of Commerce for Science and Technology, before the Select Committee on Government Research, House of Representatives, 88th Congress, 1st Session.

States for research and development supported by the Federal Govern-ment adequate for the improvement in the highway system, for the improvement of materials used in it, or for the improvement of the methods of highway design? How do the highways contribute to our economy? Does the Federal Government have the responsibility for elimination of smog, for optimum urban development?

I don't raise these questions because we know the answers. But is the $25 million or so that we aim at that purpose in the national interest?

With respect to the Maritime Administration, are our efforts to improve the automation of ships and obtain a more efficient merchant marine adequate, or are there stumbling blocks in the way of making a more efficient maritime fleet for the United States.

I think that there are certain programs in which both the private sector, private industry and Government have a joint responsibility. Here I think there are unanswered questions of national policy.

. . . I am convinced that we are inadequately supporting those things that have to do with the civil side of our society and the technology that relates to our economy.

But in these cases we must insure that the Federal Government participates without dulling the initiative of the private enterprise.

When the technology benefits the whole of the public, I think that Congress and the Government has in the past supported it.

Examples are agricultural research and development and water resources, where the results flow to the country generally.

Another reason for the partial support of research and develop-ment by the Government is that the cost of the technology is so great, and the risk is so high that a single firm cannot bear it. Current examples are support for communications satellites, and supersonic air transports.

Government participation is necessary when the technology is new and the results are far reaching. The early stages in the development of atomic energy and of aviation technology are examples. But when we consider the total national research and development effort of the Federal Government neglecting the part aimed at the military requirement, at space exploration, or health, we spent only $1 billion for all other purposes. Most of this is spent by the National Science Foundation adding to the scientific resources, for aeronautics, communications, and atomic technology.

We spend less than about $30 million of Federal funds aimed at the civilian economy and improving the capacity of our economy to function effectively and for that purpose exclusively.

The role of the Government in supporting industrial technology has historical precedent, but I don't think we have a rationale as to the participation of the Federal Government. . . .

Hugh L. Dryden
THE OBJECTIVES OF NASA

. . . Six years ago, before the Nation began to take space exploration seriously, and before NASA was formed to counter a grave Soviet threat, those of us who were directly concerned with such problems counted ourselves fortunate when the Nation managed, with a crash effort, to put a very small spacecraft with limited capability into orbit. It is comforting to contrast that and the concern we all felt then, with the situation today. Within the last week, because you and the other Members of the Congress have taken space exploration seriously, and have provided strong support for a vigorous effort in space research, this Nation was able to display to the world the most powerful rocket known to exist, overtaking, for the first time, the advantages in launch vehicle thrust so long held by the Soviet Union, and thus meeting one of the primary goals which was set forth at the very beginning of NASA.

However, . . . we are not only moving into a period of fruition, but one in which we must look to the refinement of the technology already developed and the scientific knowledge already gained. And most important, it is imperative that we look ahead to the things we must do now, or soon, to prepare for the space missions which the future will demand of us if we are to maintain leadership in space. . . .

The history of Federal participation in research and development is one of repeated preoccupation with the current requirements of the Nation at the expense of or to the neglect of the basic, long range efforts needed by any nation which hopes to maintain leadership in the vital areas of science and technology.

Because of the initiative and the daring of the Wright brothers, this Nation gave man the capacity for powered flight, freeing him forever from the bonds which for thousands of years of human existence had confined his activities to land and sea. The United States became the first country in the world to possess a military airplane when, in 1908, the Army Signal Corps contracted for a Wright biplane.

Portion of the statement of Dr. Hugh L. Dryden, Deputy Administrator, NASA, before the House Committee on Science and Astronautics, *Hearings on the 1965 NASA Authorization,* 88th Congress, 2nd Session.

Yet, prior to World War I this Nation was still so preoccupied with conventional weapons systems that it totally neglected the development of aeronautics—the force which was to dominate warfare for the next quarter century. In 1914, the United States possessed fewer military aircraft and of inferior types than the six leading aeronautical nations, including Mexico. The United States in 1914 was the only major nation in the world not to possess an aeronautical laboratory with an up-to-date wind tunnel. By November 1918, not one aircraft of American design and manufacture had entered combat operations during World War I.

In the thirties we were so preoccupied with refinement of conventional piston-driven aeronautical systems that we made little progress in jet propulsion. Meanwhile, the Germans set out to build a bigger and better NACA and to a large extent they did, developing jet-propelled military aircraft and 5½-ton V-2 rockets which almost spelled disaster in World War II.

In the late forties, despite the fact that Robert Goddard had demonstrated the feasibility of a liquid-fueled rocket engine in this country in 1926, and despite the memory of the V-2's raining on London during the blitz, we were so preoccupied with mating jet carriers to our exclusively held atomic bomb capability that we neglected missilery while other nations forged ahead. And finally, in the fifties, our A-bomb advantage gone, we were so preoccupied with the development of our ballistic missile program that we neglected a clear opportunity to become first in space.

Today, the Nation faces, we all face, this question: Have we learned enough from the often bitter and always costly experience of the last half century not only to carry out with determination this effort to meet the requirements of the present in space research and exploration, but to exercise the vision which is demanded if we are not, once again, to find ourselves lagging in the next phase of this most challenging effort?

It must be hoped that we have learned enough from the sequence of events which I have just described to put aside for all time any feelings of comfortable assurance that science and technology are areas in which the United States will remain firmly and forever supreme. It is not surprising that we should have felt such assurance in the past, for we did, as a Nation, establish an early techonolgical ascendancy over many other countries of the world. But it is equally clear that many other nations have overcome our early lead and that future leadership in this competition, which has such great economic, military, and political significance, will not be easily held or won.

Thus, while we may all glow with pride over the Nation's recent accomplishments in space, and our part in making them possible, we must not delude ourselves or the Nation with any thought that leadership in this fast-moving age can be maintained with anything less than determined, wholehearted, sustained effort.

I recall that as early as 1945 the Navy proposed the launching of an earth satellite. Subsequently, in 1946, Project RAND in an engineering report to the U.S. Army Air Force outlined the basis for rocket development which would have permitted the United States to place an Earth satellite in orbit in 1951—6 years ahead of the Soviet Union. I think the mere recollection of that fact makes a point which needs not be labored.

The present gap in manned flight activity is a direct consequence of a postponement of the decision to proceed beyond Project Mercury from September 1960 until May 1961 when President Kennedy recommended the present manned lunar landing project as a national goal.

The decisions which confront us today are those which will determine whether this kind of history will repeat itself a few years hence and whether we will once again experience a bitter awakening to the fact that others have seized the initiative in the more advanced space missions of the future.

Let me tell you some of the things which I believe must concern us now or in the near future if we are to have any assurance that the United States will retain the posture of leadership which we have gained through the difficult, demanding, and costly effort put into this program in its first 5 years.

In the scientific areas, we must begin looking forward to objectives in the next decade in three major areas: the lunar program, the planetary program, and the program for the study of the environment of space. The landing of men on the Moon is not an end in itself, but merely the beginning of an effort to extend man's knowledge of the planets, the solar system, and ultimately, the universe, and to relate what is learned to our existence here on Earth.

For example, we should in this decade establish priorities for scientific efforts to determine the geodetic properties of the Moon, for completion of topographic map coverage at reduced scales, and for preliminary geological exploration of the Kepler-Copernicus region by manned surface activities. Also in the offing are the establishment of a long-lived passive seismometer network on the Moon, in order to determine its internal structure, efforts to determine the chemical and mineral composition of major lunar rock types, and studies to determine the feasibility of a manned lunar astronomical observatory.

In the years ahead we should also be looking toward a detailed study of the Sun and solar terrestrial relations; to increasing our knowledge and understanding of the stellar process, and the evolution of the universe, through astronomical observations above the atmosphere; to determination of the figure of the Earth, and measurement of its gravitational field and to the mapping of interplanetary plasma and magnetic fields and the monitoring of radiation levels in space.

In the planetary program, the study of Mars offers great challenges. These include the study of the physical, meteorological, and topographic features of the planet and the investigation of the chemistry of the Martian surface and subsurface in relation to the evolution, metabolism, and survival of living forms.

If these efforts determine that life exists elsewhere in the solar system it will be the most profound and far-reaching discovery in the history of the human race.

In moving on to these objectives, we must also drive forward with the technology which will make their achievement possible. This involves achieving a higher order of reliability in the existing operational vehicles, surpassing the near perfect record of the past 2 years. It involves increasing existing vehicle performance through the use of a fluorine-oxygen combination, and the reduction of vehicle costs. It requires that the Atlas/Centaur be brought to operational status. And further in the future, it demands the development of a universal high performance upper stage for application to existing booster systems, and of a vehicle system capable of performing missions requiring solar escape.

Like its predecessor, NACA, the space agency, is a research and development organization which performs operational missions only to the extent that they acquire needed scientific knowledge or develop technology of value to the Nation.

If one looks at the history of NACA, it is apparent that the aeornautical research conducted by that agency not only brought this country to a position of leadership in civil aviation, but in military airpower as well. I well recall the statement of Frank Knox, the Secretary of the Navy in 1943, which pointed up the NACA contribution to airpower, and which, I am convinced, will apply with equal force to the NASA contribution to defensive strength in space. He said at that time:

> New ideas are weapons of immense significance. The U.S. Navy was the first to develop aircraft capable of vertical dive bombing; this was made possible by the prosecution of a program of scientific research by the NACA. The Navy's famous fighters—the Corsair, Wildcat, and Hellcat—are possible only because they were based on fundamentals developed by the NACA. All of them use NACA wing sections, NACA cooling methods, NACA high-lift devices. The great sea victories that have broken Japan's expanding grip in the Pacific would not have been possible without the contributions of the NACA.

Within recent weeks we have seen the first major example of the application of NASA research to military use, with the decision to employ

Gemini technology in the Air Force MOL project. But this is merely the forerunner of similar applications not only in manned operations, but in navigation, communications, and meteorology, as well.

NASA's own objectives in these latter fields include the establishment of the requirements for, and a national program to develop, the use of satellites for air-sea traffic control and navigation. In communications, they include development of such potentials as the provision of emergency communications to remote areas via satellites and small, highly transportable ground stations.

In meteorology, working with the Weather Bureau, we are looking toward an operational satellite system for global coverage on a daily basis. This would include developing a capability for continuous detail viewing of short-lived meteorological phenomenon, such as thunderstorms and tornadoes. Again, while NASA's objectives relate to the civilian application of such knowledge, its military value is obvious.

The point I am trying to make, Mr. Chairman, is simply this: The NASA effort is not confined, as so many seem to assume, to a single objective such as landing men on the moon. Rather, as was the case with NACA, it is a broad-based research and development effort which is designed to meet the needs of any agency of the Government having work to do in space. And the vigor with which we pursue this activity will determine how effectively those agencies can meet their responsibilities, and cope with their problems in space, in the years ahead. . . .

Philip Abelson
QUESTIONS CONCERNING THE SPACE PROGRAM

It is a privilege to appear before this committee to present views on the space program. Today I shall speak in part as an active research scientist but principally in the role of editor of Science. This journal is a publication of the American Association for the Advancement of Science. Members total about 76,000 and are drawn from every area of science and include about half of the top scientific talent of the Nation.

Portion of the statement of Dr. Philip Abelson, Director, Geophysical Laboratory, Carnegie Institution of Washington, Washington, D.C., before the Committee on Aeronautical and Space Sciences, Senate, 88th Congress, 1st Session.

Straw Poll against Present Manned Lunar Program

My comments will not be an official pronouncement of the organization, though they reflect what I believe to be views of our readers. As editor I am in touch with my audience by correspondence, by phone, and by personal contacts. I have conducted an informal straw poll among scientists not connected by self-interest to NASA. The vote was 110 to 3 against the present manned lunar program. This is a surprising result which I am loath to trust. However, I employ another indicator of sentiment, namely, the tone of correspondence to the editor. Our experience is that when readers disagree with us we get heated letters. When they approve, they usually don't bother to write. My recent stand questioning the manned lunar program drew 12 written commendations but only 3 mildly disagreeing. Two of those demurring were from persons connected with NASA.

Today I will evaluate aspects of space research and comment on some effects of the space program on availability of scientific manpower. In making a judgment as to the scientific potential inherent in space studies, it is desirable to evaluate these opportunities against the background of challenges in other areas of science and technology. . . .

Analogy to Columbus Is Poor

Enthusiasts have described space as an enormous frontier of vast potential and it has been stated frequently that we face an opportunity similar to that of Christopher Columbus when he sailed to discover a new world. The analogy is a poor one. Christopher Columbus was seeking economic returns; he wished to bring back the wealth of the Indies. He had no way of knowing that the Americas lay on his pathway—the Americas with their vast wealth and areas of habitable land. We are in a different position for with our great telescopes and astrophysical measurements we can look out at space and make an estimate of what is there—something that Columbus could not do. The high magnification of the Mount Palomar telescope brings the Moon within the equivalent of a few hundred miles of earth. The Moon has been weighed, its size is known, and the average density of its rocks determined. We already know that there will be no objects of economic value to be brought back from the Moon or any of the planets. These bodies consist of chemicals similar to those of common earth rocks.

We know that the other parts of the solar system are intrinsically less habitable than the most miserable spot on earth. Life on the top of Mount Everest would be sheer luxury in comparison with existence on the Moon, or even on Mars, the most habitable of the planets.

Practical Consequences Involve Near-Earth Regions

The practical consequences that may stem from space exploration principally involve regions near the Earth. Telstar and its successors seem destined to have important economic consequences. The weather satellites, Tiros and Nimbus, will surely lead to much better weather prediction which would have sizable economic value. A better understanding of solar-terrestrial relationships may permit us to understand how the Sun influences the weather and may also lead to better weather prediction.

Unmanned Vehicles Doing Important Scientific Work

Much of the science that is really important is already being done in the vicinity of earth using unmanned vehicles. Two very exciting prospects are the orbiting astronomical observatory and the orbiting solar observatories. These unmanned vehicles will permit a unique extension of observations that have been made from earth.

Most of the important scientific questions concerning the Moon and the other planets could be studied soon at relatively low cost employing unmanned vehicles. These questions, which are principally directed at an understanding of the origin and the history of the solar system, include the chemical composition of the solid bodies and of their atmospheres, if any; an investigation of surficial features; a determination of precise size and shape; and measurements intended to determine whether the solid object possesses a hot inner core.

From studies of meteorites, which give us a partial sample of the solar system, and from examination of the light emitted by the Sun we already can estimate that the chemical constitution of the Moon and Mars will not be strikingly different from that of the rocks at the surface of the earth.

Chances of Finding Extraterrestrial Life Are Small

Much has been made of the possibility of finding extraterrestrial life, but the chances that it exists are small. Reasons are simple—the Moon has no water or oxygen; Venus is too hot; Mars has virtually no oxygen and almost no water. There is about one-thousandth as much water in the atmosphere over Mars as there is in the air over the driest desert on this Earth. All terrestrial-type living things must have plenty of water in order to grow. If a form of life is present on Mars, it could not be related to life as we know it.

There has been talk of the scientific role of man in space, but the Mercury flights do not bear this out. A principal scientific value from the

Mercury program was to determine that man could function in space, but this was something that could have been predicted ahead of time anyway.

Including Man Has Two Important Drawbacks

Making man a part of the scientific exploration of space has two important drawbacks. It increases costs and it will probably slow down, at least for some years, the pace of getting valuable results. To provide life support for humans is expensive and vehicles employing them are heavier and cost approximately 100 times more than simple electronic probes. In the exploration of the planets the contrast is greater.

Our recent Mariner II probe to Venus cost a few tens of millions. To send men on a comparable mission might cost a hundred billion dollars and could not be done for many years.

The argument has been made that putting a man in space will open vast frontiers of knowledge. No one has delineated any impressive body of questions which are to be studied. Rather we are reassured by the statement that "Man can meet the unexpected."

Man Is a Poor Scientific Instrument

Unfortunately, man is a poor scientific instrument and in space his only natural observing equipment is his vision. The information which can be transmitted by optical wavelengths has been studied from the comfortable platform of earth using instruments such as the telescope at Mount Palomar. Man would be of limited usefulness in space unless reinforced by instrumentation. As a practical matter the apparatus he would employ would be part of the cargo of his space ship. Hence, it would be necessary ahead of time to decide what feature of the "unexpected" should be anticipated.

Hard advance thinking would be required to formulate experiments that could lead to definite answers. This is just the kind of consideration that precedes unmanned exploration.

Most of the creative thinking concerning space experiments will be done during preparation phases and after results have been transmitted back to earth. The one-man or multi-man crew will represent only a tiny fraction of the experimental and theoretical genius behind the effort.

Continued Failures in Moon Program Are Puzzling

One of the most puzzling aspects of the NASA program is the continued failure to land electronic equipment on the Moon. After a trajectory of more than 100 million miles Mariner II scored a fine success in exploring Venus. Why can't we hit the Moon, which is comparatively in our backyard? Why was there insufficient backup of the five Ranger vehicles which failed?

I have the feeling that scientific exploration of the Moon has been accorded a low priority, that the Apollo program is distorting scientific priorities and at least indirectly slowing progress.

NASA's Hiring of Scientists Is Disproportionate

Others have raised the question of whether excessive demands were being made by the space agency for personnel. Mr. Webb and his associates have reassured us by stating that only a few percent of the scientists of the Nation will be employed directly or indirectly by his agency. If the people he is hiring were drawn representatively from all the professions, there would be no present or potential problem. I have obtained some preliminary figures from the National Science Foundation concerning the number of scientists in the Nation. These total 438,000. Among them are 32,000 physicists and 30,000 psychologists. I doubt very much that NASA employs as many psychologists as physicists. The fact is that an overall percentage figure is meaningless and that the agency has hired heavily men trained in mathematics and physical sciences while recruiting a disproportionate few from the life sciences. The group that NASA is engaging is not representative in another way; namely, in the age group. I have seen relatively few scientists in the NASA organization of age 50 or older.

Physicists Contributing in Many Fields

The manpower requirements of NASA place the agency in strong competition for skilled scientists of special types. One such limited group are those whose basic training is physics. This discipline has attracted some of the Nation's best minds.

Although professional physicists are in great demand, their numbers are limited because few students are both willing and able to master this difficult discipline. Those who can, have knowledge that is applicable in many fields. Accordingly, these men have made and are making great contributions not only to the advancement of physics, but they are also active in all aspects of geophysics, including seismology, oceanography, meteorology, aeronomy, and space studies. They are important contributors to astrophysics and some of the great recent advances in biology have been made by men originally trained in physics. Physicists are also important to the civilian economy.

In addition, they are active in almost every area of military research and development and especially in all facets related to nuclear weapons. Thus, these men are engaged in almost all the areas of research and development for which Congress has voted large sums in recent years. They are involved in a very crucial way for they possess the kind of brains which can make great innovations, identify unexpected problems.

Funds for One Field Take Competent People Away from Others

In activities such as space research these men make their best contributions 10 to 20 years after they receive their Ph.D. degree. Van Allen, for instance, discovered the radiation belt some 19 years after his doctorate. The number of men that can make such contributions is limited and there is nothing the Congress can do now to increase their number now. A time lag of 5 to 10 years must intervene. When Congress votes to support an area such as space and to give it the funds necessary to hire personnel, it simultaneously votes to take competent people away from other and often important activities. Some of these men come from other civilian agencies but others come from activities vital to the defense of this country.

In the competition space has considerable advantages for it is new, glamorous, challenging, and exploration of the moon is a national goal. Perhaps the most severe competition comes from companies operating with reimbursable Government contracts who have little limitation on what they may offer as salaries when engaged in a recruiting drive.

Diversion of Talent to Space Is Damaging to Other Sciences

I believe that diversion of talent to the space program is having and will have direct and indirect damaging effects on almost every area of science, technology, and medicine. I believe that the program may delay conquest of cancer and mental illness. These opinions are difficult to document and highly controversial and I shall not insist on them. Rather permit me to indicate how damage is being done in an area where effects of personnel diversion are more clear cut and where this committee can elicit direct testimony. I refer to the impact that the space program is having on the technical resources of the weapons laboratories.

Consider the status of men working in weapons development. These scientists are grimly aware of the consequences of nuclear war. They feel keenly public antipathy for them and their work. They operate under necessity for complete secrecy and must watch their tongue and actions at all times. They have little opportunity to publish results of their research or to present those results for the approbation of colleagues at open professional meetings.

Since 1958 they have operated under a cloud of uncertainty as to when and whether nuclear tests would be made. In the light of these circumstances it has been difficult to maintain viable weapons establishments. The major motivation that has prevented gross deterioration has been the patriotic devotion of key figures in the laboratories.

Consider the new competitive factor that has entered in. Space is a national goal and one can be as patriotic working on the Moon project as in the weapons laboratory. A top man can get a salary increase amounting to as much as 25 percent by going to work for Government contractors. The weight of secrecy is removed, the scientist becomes socially respectable, and he can enjoy publication of his research results.

Crucial Bottleneck Is Brains—Not Money

Let me conclude by emphasizing once again that in many vital areas of science and technology the crucial bottleneck is brains not money. When Congress votes to expand an activity involving scientists or engineers of a type already in short supply, much damage can be done. There ensues a feverish and wasteful game of musical chairs in which men already working productively move to other spots. With them often departs special training and knowledge accumulated through years of experience. Dealing with this new development wisely is going to require a high level of statesmanship. . . .

Donald N. Michael
SCIENCE, SCIENTISTS, AND POLITICS

Anthropologists and historians tell us that a crucial juncture in the life of a culture occurs when the assurance that it has gained from an unchallenged world view of values, goals, and logic confronts the unchallenged world view of another culture. It is not easy for men to change their view of the world, for it is part of their view of themselves. The challenge of other values threatens all that has given them comfort and support. It takes strong men and felicitous circumstances for a society to ride out the storm of contact with another culture and learn and grow anew.

From *Science, Scientists, and Politics* (Santa Barbara, Calif.: Center for the Study of Democratic Institutions, 1963). Reprinted with permission of the Fund for the Republic, Inc., Center for the Study of Democratic Institutions.

It is by no means certain that this will happen. Some people are shattered by new experiences; so are some cultures. As segments of society splinter and converge, new institutions and new modes of thinking are generated. Some societies blossom in their revised form; others die.

Today we are faced with such a cultural crisis. The problems of making suitable policies for scientific work in the government arise chiefly from a profound cultural conflict. This conflict is the three-way confrontation among the scientific community, the non-scientific political governmental community, and the general public.

What is meant here by an adequate policy for federal science must be made clear at the outset. Such a policy would reconcile the needs of science and technology with the needs of the rest of society. Policy now springs from resolving disputes for priority among various projects. It is made in many places, from the Pentagon to the Department of Agriculture, as well as in those offices assigned part of the policy-making task. But nowhere do the social implications of science have a basic part in the formulation of policy.

Today, science and technology are not neutral. Not only does their development require vast social and human resources, but they are pursued because their powers for enhancing or degrading humanity are recognized. This non-neutrality demands an explicit relating of science and technology to the needs and processes of society. This relationship should be the foundation of federal science policy.

The one consensus among the three cultures—the scientific community, the non-scientific political community, and the public—is that the task of government is to serve the general public. There is no such agreement about the relationship of science to government and to the general public. There is no set of values mutually subscribed to by the three cultures that defines the proper purposes of science and technology and thereby the appropriate restraints and supports needed to fulfill those purposes. Nor is it clear that such a set of values can be deliberately produced. Values do not derive solely from rational considerations. They are historical products of emotion and plain accident as much as, or more than, reason. This is one weakness in the thesis that the scientific method by itself can solve society's problems.

Within each of the three cultures are men and institutions with different viewpoints and different goals. These dissimilarities are crucial. Some of them derive largely from training; some are induced by the preconceptions that each group has about the other two and about itself. Two of the three are contending for the power to insure that their particular values will prevail: the science community and the non-science governmental community. The general public has essentially no power.

The *science community* is represented at its upper levels by two types of scientists. The "traditional" type considers government to be synonymous with mediocrity and irrationality. These men feel that science must be left free to pursue its own ways. Their attitudes toward the rest of society are frequently ambivalent. They avoid involvement in social questions. Some of them perceive society as subject to, if not already operating along, logical lines. Others consider society as incorrigibly irrational and therefore unrelated to them. They are seldom asked to consider the social implications of their actions. By attending to their work, advising on the technical merits of this or that proposal, they can maintain the comfortable delusion that science can still be pursued without thought of the social consequences. Frequently they work for the university or for big industry, advancing the favorite programs of their employers.

Then there is the new breed of scientist around high Washington conference tables—the science entrepreneur, the "political" scientist. These men want to manage the bureaucracy to the extent necessary to make it behave the way they think it should. They have a sense of political technique, and they enjoy and seek power. Like the traditionalists, they feel that science is theirs, that no one else has the right to tamper with it. It is they who should decide which projects deserve emphasis. They believe a good dose of science would fix society fine, as C. P. Snow has so frequently tried to demonstrate. There are wise and modest men with social imagination in this sub-culture, but frequently the powerful members of this group are self-assured to the point of arrogance about their own abilities, about the over-riding rightness of scientific values and methods, and about the validity of their view of how society operates and what it needs.

The science entrepreneurs are supported by and in turn support big business, big publicity, big military, sometimes big academia and parts of big government. They are both the captives and the kings of these powerful coalitions—kings for obvious reasons, captives because in reaping the benefits of affiliation they capitulate in some degree to the operating principles of these institutions. They have climbed to power through conservative hierarchies and tend to hold conservative values. The infusion of émigrés from the disciplined institutions of Europe seems, in general, not to have been a liberalizing influence. The more powerful the "political" scientist gets, the more omnipresent he is at major deliberations on science policy.

The *non-scientific community* in Congress and the bureaucracies regards itself as the bones, meat, and brains of government and society. They resent the "woolly-headed" scientist who may be trying to change their ways or implying that these ways are inadequate. They are not about to be displaced by a new attitude or a new kind of knowledge. Scientific expertise is respected, but the political and social naïveté that is supposed to accompany it is regarded with disdain. A general feeling exists among these "non-scientists" that science must be controlled. Usurpation of power is feared, partly because of a conviction that science somehow cannot be stopped.

These men consider society a non-rational environment. They see the political process as subtle and changing, responsive to many pressures of which science is only one, and by no means the most important. They view science as a means, not as an end. But they are confused about means and ends in general, as well as about the implications of science, and have no clear view of the proper role of scientists in formulating policy.

These two cultures between them decide on national science programs. They are in deep conflict within and between themselves. There are great political and ethical splinterings in the science community alone. The entrepreneurs claim to speak for science, but speak only for their faction. The traditionalists are fearful and envious of the "political" scientists, upon whom they must depend for their survival, especially if they hope for accomplishment in fields requiring expensive equipment or team research. Both groups are dissatisfied with the workings of government.

Given this clash of cultures, how can a valid basis be found for policy-making in federal science? We must discover a common ground from which science and technology can be intelligently directed. We must be able to evaluate the social consequences of scientific innovation. We need to plan our economics to assure the effective and humane introduction of modern technologies. We must equip government to meet new regulatory and managerial tasks. It is not clear that these responsibilities can be met by any traditional form of government; nor is it certain that democracy can be preserved in doing so. What is clear is that we cannot continue to bumble along.

Already we are in desperate trouble over nuclear weapons. We are about to be overwhelmed by that terrible blessing of medical technology, overpopulation. The social implications of biological and psychopharmacological engineering are already evident. Cybernation is causing serious problems. What is more, our environment is being changed in ways no cybernetical system can cope with indefinitely. It must respond to a tremendous and growing range of information at increasing speed and with increasing accuracy. Instability of the system is the inevitable result.

In spite of these menacing developments we remain unable to forecast the social consequences of technology. This is partly because of the limited vision of both the non-scientists and the scientists. The first group does not have sufficient knowledge of technology to sense the potentialities of new developments and therefore cannot predict their social impact, and they are too preoccupied with conventional assessments of political issues and impacts. The second group is aware of the technological possibilities but is not sufficiently sensitive to their social implications. Some of the scientists care only about the success of their favorite projects. Some apply to these problems a personal pseudo-sociology made useless by its arrogance or naïveté. And still others dodge responsibility by arguing that technology itself is neither good nor bad, that its virtues are determined by its uses.

Another reason why the social repercussions of science are difficult to forecast is that we have too little understanding of the social processes. This limitation has been fostered by the disinclination of the natural scientist and the government operator to stimulate work in the social sciences. The bureaucrat feels threatened by the possibility that formalized knowledge will replace "experience" and "political know-how." Furthermore, the social sciences might demonstrate that the products of technology, or even science itself, need social control. This is an unhappy prospect for those scientists who are feeling for the first time the satisfactions of wielding power.

Since the consequences of scientific and technological developments are not fully predictable, it would seem impossible to establish priorities for individual projects on any sensible basis. Yet the forces of technological advance compel some kind of choice. Creative talent is a scarce resource, and the availability of money is a political, if not a real, limitation. "Political" scientists push their preferences vigorously, and the very existence of large programs influences selections in the absence of better criteria. Priority decisions today depend on political and economic pressures, personalities, and public relations.

The public relations juggernaut, in particular, imposes a crippling distortion on science and on those who would make scientific policy. From the laboratory to the launching pad science and technology are harried by promises about "product superiority" and the glamour of "breakthroughs." Commitments are quickly publicized and then science is pressed to maintain the "reality" of the commitments. The natural failures of science and the natural limits of accomplishment are covered by an ever-deepening layer of misrepresentation, deviousness, and downright lies. So pervasive becomes the aura of untruth that it is hard for anyone, from the man in the laboratory to the public, to know where reality lies.

A cliché of our political folklore is that somehow the *public* will make everything right. In its wisdom it will judge between the contending power groups, evaluate technologies, establish a scale for priorities. But the public, the third culture, hardly knows what is happening. Understanding or judging the conflicts and compromises now occurring between science and government is far beyond its capacity. The public is caught between a publicity-induced fantasy world where science knows all the answers and a frustrating actuality which it does not realize is caused at least in part by the inadequate or incorrect use of science and technology. The frustrations are blamed on someone else: Russia, the government, perhaps the intellectuals, seldom on science. The public still believes in the mad scientist working on bombs, or in the humble scientist laboring over polio vaccine. The member of government, civil servant or politician, is perceived no more realistically.

Rather than becoming able to resolve the problems of science policy, the public is likely to become increasingly alienated both from government and from science. As with many other groups in the past that have met cultures somehow superior to their own, the public may withdraw from the challenge of "adjusting up" to the new priests and the new power. How, in fact, can the ordinary citizen adjust up to a computer-run society and classified questions of life and death?

One segment of the public will not surrender without protest. This is the group of articulate, concerned laymen who are not solely scientists, politicians, or civil servants and who worry about the arms race, overpopulation, the ascendancy of the "political" scientist, and the inadequacy of non-scientific bureaucracies. These people might be the moderators, the synthesists, for a new culture. They do not have the trained incapacities of those solely immersed in the two contending cultures, and they do have perspective that the general public lacks. But these very characteristics may deny them the opportunity. The day of the technical specialist grows ever brighter. The scientist will not freely yield his newly gained power, nor will the government worker relinquish his long-held dominion. Neither is likely to give ground to a non-specialist who cannot build bombs or tread bureaucratic water, or otherwise play according to the rules of science and government.

The character of the coming generation of scientists is changing. The attributes attractive to laboratory directors interested in team-work are bringing a new personality into science. The old-guard traditionalists may be on the way out. Those who succeed will be those who are good at working with—or subverting—the non-scientific bureaucracy. Will these men be good scientists? This is not the important question. The real concern is for whom they will speak, and for what ends.

The problem in trying to resolve the ambitions of the two power cultures is that neither group has a clear view of what it wants in the way of policy for governmental science. As long as there is no community of values to guide judgment, basic policy decisions cannot be made, much less decisions on specific priorities for specific projects. Yet crises are arising on every hand. The evolution of a consensus cannot be awaited. If this society does not learn how to assimilate the changes that confront it, it will not survive.

Bernard Barber
SCIENCE IN MODERN SOCIETY

. . . Nazi Germany turned away, not completely, but in a degree which had harmful consequences for its science, from three of the conditions which are component elements of our "ideal type": the cultural values of universalism and of rationality, and the political condition of relative autonomy for science. It is impossible to measure these harmful consequences at all precisely, even now that we have been able to discover something of what was happening in Nazi Germany during the '30's and during the war years. While Nazi science was not utterly destroyed, as it was predicted it would be by some scientists in "liberal" societies in the first shock of their moral and emotional reaction to the Nazi revolution, still the damage done was quite considerable.

Consider, for example, the consequences of the Nazi denial of the cultural value of universalism. Positively, this denial meant the glorification of the particularistic virtues of "Aryan Germans" as scientists. As a result of this attitude, candidates for scientific teaching positions were required to meet certain "Aryan" standards of physical, moral, and "racial" fitness, standards which have no demonstrable connection at all with scientific talent. And negatively, of course, the denial meant a violent attack on German Jewish scientists and on something that devout Nazis referred to as "the Jewish evil" (*jüdischer Ungeist*) in science. The general consequences of the Nazi violation of the universalistic right of German Jews to continue as scientists or to train for the profession are evident in the serious losses of scientific personnel that Germany suffered during the '30's. Here are some rough figures. Between 1933 and 1938, 1880 scientific men of first-class distinction were exiled from the universities of Germany and Austria. Professor Needham, the English biologist, has estimated that more than 25% of Germany's Nobel Prize winners were among the 18% of all the men of scientific reputation who were banished.

Reprinted with permission of the publisher from *Science and the Social Order* by Bernard Barber. Copyright, 1952, by The Free Press. Dr. Barber is Professor of Sociology at Barnard College.

By 1937, the number of students in the natural sciences at the German universities was only about one-third of what it had been in 1932. Some of the special consequences of harm to German science should also be mentioned. By denouncing modern atomic and relativity physics as "the Jewish science," *par excellence,* the Nazis brought the whole subject so much into disrepute that it became unpopular at the universities. This, of course, was a great blow to the recruitment of new workers in the field and to continuing research.

The limitations placed upon universalism in Nazi society did not mean, however, that all social mobility into the profession of science ceased. But the attack on Jews and other "non-Aryans" destroyed a source of scientific ability that had hitherto been extremely important in German science. The roster of distinction in pre-Nazi German science had a great many Jewish names.

The German turning away from the cultural value of rationality was also, of course, and necessarily, only partial. It is easier for fanatic Nazis to recommend that Germans "think with their blood" than it is to run a complex industrial society on that precept. The esteem of irrationality probably was found more often in propaganda speeches than in everyday administration of the society. It was, to be sure, often found in the propaganda. Herr Bernhard Rust, Reichsminister of Education, for instance, said at the celebration of the 550th anniversary of Heidelberg University in 1936: "National Socialism is justly described as unfriendly to Science if its valuer assumes that independence of presuppositions and freedom from bias are the essential characteristics of scientific inquiry. But this we emphatically deny." Probably the most harmful consequences to science from the proud irrationality of the Nazi leaders were unintended by them, rather than deliberately sought. Hitler, it has been reported, often countermanded the advice of his assistants, advice based on rational investigation and planning, in favor of "hunches." Sometimes these half-irrational insights led to success; sometimes to failure. For instance, because of his irrational desire for miracle weapons, Hitler was susceptible to wild and quackish notions about scientific possibility. In the modern world, hunches are a weak foundation for decisions of state. National policy has to be right more often than hunches allow; it requires the best available rational empirical knowledge. Hence the importance of a strong value on rationality in the leaders as well as in the followers of modern industrial society.

The most directly evil effects upon German science came from the new political authoritarianism of the Nazi government. The great German universities, which had been the pride of the earlier society, were very quickly subjected to political control by the Nazis, who seem to have had an especial distrust for academic scientists. Not only were many "non-

Aryan" professors dismissed, but those who remained were put under the authority of men chosen for their party loyalty rather than for their scientific accomplishment. As a result, charlatans sometimes competed with competent scientists for funds and apparatus for research. Political authority could override knowledge established by scientific research and validated by scientific peers. From 1939 on, for example, all scientific theses for the Ph.D. degree had to be submitted to official Nazi censorship. Even earlier, from 1935 on, attendance of scientists at any scientific congress either in Germany or in some other country was subject to the approval of the Science Congress Center, an agency of the Reichsministry of Propaganda, whose chief we have quoted above. When delegations were sent to congresses outside Germany, they went under an appointed leader, "chosen for his reliability as a member of the Nazi Party." This is not . . . a satisfactory degree of autonomy for science; this is not the way in which science can operate effectively in the modern world.

Despite all the harmful consequences from the three sources we have treated, German science was far from extinguished, if we judge by its performance before and during the recent war. The particularistic attack on the Jews and political authoritarianism harmed some parts of science much more than others. For instance, though the Nazis had disparaged higher learning and pure science, "they may have strengthened the position of technicians and persons engaged in development." Research in the German Air Force was much better than that in the Army because Goering, head of the Luftwaffe, "before and during the war, employed pre-Nazi officials of known ability in technical capacities, even to the extent of having General Milch (a man of Jewish blood) as wartime head of the Air Forces Technical Office." Apparently there was always some conflict among and within Nazi officials between a pragmatic attitude toward the power of science and a moral disapproval of it for its rationality. Even the anti-rationalist Nazis, therefore, toward the middle of the war, under pressure of the impending loss of the war, favored a heavy subsidy for scientific research. It was, however, too late. Nevertheless, the summary picture we receive from accounts of German science during the war is that it was still very good science on the whole, although much less good than it had been twenty years before. It was a science living on the fat of basic research accumulated in the pre-Nazi period. It is hard to predict what would have happened in the future if Germany had won the war.

Now this variability in the quality of German science and this perpetuation of certain kinds of science at a fairly high level in Nazi Germany raise important sociological questions to which we can only suggest answers here. If German science was not utterly destroyed by the Nazis, but only seriously weakened, how long does it take to "kill" science? Indeed, can it really be extinguished in a modern industrial society? Probably not, and probably it cannot even be weakened beyond a certain point in such a society, as the Nazis seem to have discovered in the middle of the war. Their change of heart, based on expediency rather than on moral preference, to be sure, indicates that the sheer necessity for science in a modern industrial society may eventually cause a reaction against the social conditions which are harmful to it. In the short run, and what the short run is we cannot say at all precisely, a great deal of harm can be done to science by those who despise it and put it under too much political control. In the long run, another imprecise notion but also an important one, science could even be destroyed entirely. But this could only occur on payment of a very heavy social price, the loss of the ability to maintain an effectively functioning industrial society. This is not to say that even the harm done in the short run is tolerable to a modern industrial society. Especially in a world where powerful national industrial societies compete in peace as well as in war, the short run may be the significant time-span for social calculation. We cannot prove that this was so for the Nazis, but it does seem very likely that they greatly weakened themselves by changing those social conditions which are essential to a progressive science.

Soviet Russia is another modern "authoritarian" industrial society where we may find the harmful consequences of excessive political control of science. Here, in all accuracy, we must say that we still know very little about the details of these consequences; certainly we know even less than we do about what happened in Nazi Germany. For one thing, until quite recently, which is to say until after the late war, political control of science in Russia seems not to have been excessive, despite the great pretensions to such control that have existed "on paper." The freedom of science in Russia was once much greater than it is now. For another, not enough time has elapsed since the imposition of direct political control—as in the Communist party approval of Lysenkoism over neo-Mendelian genetics—to weigh carefully the harm that will be done to Russian science. But if the experience of Nazi Germany counts for anything, and if relative scientific autonomy is as necessary as we know it to be, then the Russians will have to pay a price for their direct political control of at least some, and perhaps all, parts of their science. For direct political control of science in Russia—for example, political control of the *particular theories* that should be held in a given scientific field—seems to be spreading from biology to other fields—most recently, to physics.

The spread of political authoritarianism in Russian science is all the more striking when we note how congruent with science in general other aspects of Soviet society are. In contrast with Nazi Germany, the Russians had not abandoned universalism, although of course there have been great violations against this value in practice, particularly against "resistant bourgeois" and "enemies of the state." More recently, unfortunately, an increase in strong Russian nationalism has diminished somewhat their support for social universalism, but this is an attitude in which they are not alone in the modern world. What is bad, though, is that they are now more and more speaking of "Russian science" and "bourgeois science," as if science were not an international unity. The Russians have not, however, lessened the emphasis the modern world places on the cultural values of rationality and utilitarianism. Indeed, in these two respects, the Russians are in the main stream of development of Western society, and if anything, they have pushed their approval of rationality and utilitarianism to an extreme. "More than one observer," says President Conant of Harvard, "in the course of the last two decades has been impressed by the deep concern for science manifested by the Kremlin." The Russians have glorified science, quite self-consciously, as an instrument of social revolution and social planning, and they have given it great support both directly and through the enlargement of their whole educational system. During the first five-year plan, for example, beginning in 1929, the Russian government expanded the number of scientific academies, research institutes, research workers, and "aspirants," or scientific recruits. To take only the planned expansion of the latter, the aspirants: in 1930, there were to be 1,000; in 1931, 2,600; in 1934, 6,000; and in 1935, 4,000. This shows the order of planned increase in all scientific activities. "According to an authoritative statement," says Leontieff, "in 1942 there existed 1,806 research institutes: 452 devoted to fundamental research in natural sciences and mathematics; 570 in various fields of industrial research; and 399 in agricultural research." Their whole social creed, the Russians constantly remind us, is not just "Marxism," but "*scientific* Marxism." This creed, they feel, has the rational solution for every empirical physical and social problem, and therefore it is considered to be the most potent instrument for realizing the value they attach to social progress and social meliorism. Hence the veritable cult of science among all classes in Russia today. Hence also the great Russian striving for rational mastery over Nature in man's interest. The idea of this struggle (*borba,* as the Russian word has it) permeates all Soviet activities.

The changes that have occurred in several parts of the Soviet social structure have also been of the kind that is favorable to the development and maintenance of a high level of scientific activity. The aspect of the great industrialization of Soviet society that most interests us here is the vast increase in the specialization of scientific and other occupational roles. The specialization in science and the specialization in industrial technology have been mutually fruitful, as they always are in modern industrial society. This transformation of Soviet society has been possible, of course, only because of the practically unlimited social mobility which has occurred, only because of the selection of scientific and other talent from all groups in the society, wherever it may be found. Although the amount of this social mobility now seems to be decreasing somewhat, as inevitably it had to, it still seems to be the equal of what occurs in American society, and it is highly conducive to the recruitment of competent scientific personnel.

Yet against all these changes that are favorable to science, the change toward greater political authoritarianism over science works its contrary effects. To quote further from President Conant's shrewd observation: "That a wholehearted acceptance of science by politicians can lead to the curtailment of the work of scientists seems to have been clearly demonstrated" in Russia. How these opposing influences are to be weighed against one another, no one can yet say. But we may predict certain possible consequences. Since science is to some extent an interconnected web of activities and theories, the several parts stimulating or retarding one another, political control of even a few areas of science may diffuse its harmful effects to other areas. The deterioration of Soviet genetics has already spread its influence to biochemistry and neuropsychiatry. More immediately, perhaps, political intervention in any given scientific area undermines the stability of established scientific control in that area. Scientific fanatics and quacks—men like Lysenko in genetics—take over when political authority demands what competent scientists cannot conscientiously give it—particular substantive theories or results "on order." Where scientific authority is endangered or destroyed, competent men fear to take a position on scientific theory itself, for the demands of political authority are changeful and make almost any position insubstantial. Even further, in such a situation, competent men avoid a scientific career altogether. In all societies, men seek a *relatively* "safe" occupational career. A "flight from science," perhaps only to the more applied branches of scientific technology, as was the case in Nazi Germany, may be one of the unintended consequences of the extension of political control of science in Russia.

Not one, but two different pressures in Soviet society are apparently responsible for the recent extension of political control over science. The first pressure is the one which is the more commonly remarked, the need of an authoritarian political system to include within its direct control *every* activity in the society in order to have effective power over *any* activity. Analysis here runs as follows: in order to keep the Soviet educational system "in line," for example, the Communist Party must impose its organizational control even into the far reaches of "pure" science. The second kind of pressure that is evident in Soviet society is perhaps a more satisfactorily specific and identifiable one. That pressure comes from the great need the Russians have for immediate "results" from *all* activities in the society, science included as much as industry. The pressure for usable scientific theories in their agriculture and in their industry tends to force them toward demanding such theories from science, or, in the case of apparently competing theories, to choose that theory which is more immediately useful. This seems to be one of the causes for the Communist Party's support for Lysenkoism in genetics. Lysenko promises immediately useful scientific theories for the improvement of agriculture; for example, that he can create stable genetic changes in plants and animals and thereby produce breeds and species "on order" as required by Soviet society. The Russians are probably not completely unaware of the necessity to let "pure" science have its head to some extent, but their determinist philosophy and the immediate needs of their agricultural and industrial system, including planned advances of course, push them towards the sacrifice of "pure" for "applied" science. Sometimes the push delivers them into the hands of scientific incompetents. In this perspective, Lysenko is not unique but only a prototype of the men who may come increasingly to wield authority over Soviet science. . . .

Eugene Rabinowitch
SOVIET SCIENCE—A SURVEY

. . . Whether or not the general discouragement of free inquiry in Soviet academic and public life also inhibits the inquiring mind in science, there is no doubt that other forces at work in the Soviet Union are powerfully assisting scientific progress.

In the first place, Soviet secondary education introduces youth to the ideas and techniques of mathematics and science. The curriculum itself—except for the emphasis on ideological studies and the disappearance of classical languages—is not very different from that offered by high schools in prerevolutionary Russia (or for the matter in many other countries now). What is, of course, radically different from prerevolutionary days is the enormous spread of secondary education and the opportunity given to gifted children to qualify for further training in scientific careers.

From "Soviet Science—A Survey," *Problems of Communism*, VII (March–April 1958), 8–9. Dr. Rabinowitch, a research professor at the University of Illinois, is editor of the *Bulletin of the Atomic Scientists*.

Two other factors favoring the development of science are more uniquely typical of Soviet society. The first is the prestige with which science is endowed, and which finds expression both in the financial rewards of a successful scientific career and in the high standing of scientists in public opinion. The second is the lavish support the government gives to institutions of higher learning and to research institutes. The facts relevant to these considerations have been widely discussed since the launching of the first satellite: they include the larger numbers of scientific and engineering graduates in the USSR compared to the US; the relatively high salaries and other benefits in science; the conviction of Soviet scientists that "money is there for the asking"—so different from the often precarious financial status of the most important research projects in the United States.

There is another factor which deserves more attention than it has received from the West: that is the Soviet glorification of science as a way to achieve happiness and prosperity for the peoples of the USSR and of the whole world. This faith in science as a creative force in society is, perhaps, even more important in attracting the best minds to science than the expectation of financial rewards and social recognition. Soviet youth grows up in a world of poverty and privation. It is not hard to instill in them the desire to transform society, through science, into something much happier and more prosperous. Small wonder, then, that in publicizing the aims of scientific development, the regime puts less emphasis on the enhancement of Soviet military might than on such attractive and appealing aspects as the exploration of space and inter-planetary travel, which are calculated to arouse the enthusiasm of youth.

While world attention remains glued on Soviet successes in producing thermonuclear weapons, ballistic missiles, and space satellites, there is a tendency to forget that this is only one aspect of the broad development of Soviet science. The regime aims at making the USSR, through science and technology, not only the most powerful but also the most productive country in the world, and to induce other nations to accept its technical and scientific help and leadership. It is to this wider aim that the enormous organization of scientific research in Russia is directed.

The direction of this effort is centered in the Soviet Academy of Sciences. In contrast to similar institutions in the US and Western Europe, the Soviet Academy is not merely the leading learned society in the country; it is also the operating agency for much of the research done in the USSR. According to a recent study by A. Vucinich of Stanford University, the Academy now has 118 institutes in the various natural sciences. Besides sixteen local branches of the central academy, there are twelve affiliated academies in the constituent republics of the USSR.

In viewing the work of this vast institute, Western scholars are inclined to note primarily its subordination to party control and to the political aims of the regime. If they are sociologists (like Professor Vucinich), they are impressed by the low scholarly level of the historical, sociological, and economic sections of the Academy, and the subservience in all these fields to the current party line. Attention is called to the hollowness of the autonomy of the Academy, the powerlessness of its supposedly supreme General Assembly, and the influence of its party-dominated Presidium and permanent secretariat.

All this is undoubtedly true. However, in most of its important *scientific* functions, the Academy is a highly competent and largely independent body. It is composed of a fair selection of the best minds in Soviet science, including a considerable number of older men with prerevolutionary education. Those who owe their membership to considerations other than scientific prominence (such as Lysenko) are small in number. While Nesmeyanov, the present head of the Academy Presidium, and Topchiev, the chief scientific secretary, are both Communist Party members, they are also prominent scientists, not party hacks or bureaucrats (both are organic chemists).

The academy has been described as the "general staff" of a scientific army, throwing its columns to this or that decisive segment of the "scientific front," in response to the directives of the Communist leadership; in fact, this is the picture that the Presidium itself likes to paint in official reports. Science is visualized as a centrally planned activity; its most spectacular achievements are interpreted as results of planned concentration on a few "targets."

This is only partly true. Efforts in *applied science* can be planned; if considered of national importance, they can be speeded up by a crash program. The United States' "Manhattan Project," which produced the atom bomb in 1945, is an example. It is quite likely that the Soviet space satellites were the result of a similar crash program.

The advance of fundamental science is much more difficult to plan. It has been reported that when the requirement of planning was first imposed on the research institutes, the directors presented, as the "plan of research for the next year," the actual results of the previous year's research in order to assure 100 percent fulfilment. As in other fields, probably a good deal of this type of deceptive manipulation of the plan goes on, but this is not to say that central planning is totally ineffectual. To cite an example, in 1946 a conference was called by the Academy to review the state of photosynthesis research; it was found to be backward, and a decision was taken to promote it. By 1957, a second conference on photosynthesis saw the presentation of about 150 research papers as against ten at the earlier gathering. In a similar way, research in electronic computers and automation has been spurred by resolutions of the Academy.

However, pressures of this type are much more likely to spur progress in fields where Soviet science is recognized as backward compared to the West than in forays into new, unexplored regions. They can bring up the rear, but not lead the van. Resolutions proclaiming the necessity of achieving breakthroughs into unexplored areas of physics or biology are bound to remain mere words until a creative scientific mind shows the way, usually in an unexpected direction.

All attempts at central planning notwithstanding, the decisive determinant of new achievements in science remains the personal interest and dedication of individual scientists—and this cannot be planned. The recent development of areas of science which require expensive instrumentation and the cooperation of large groups of researchers has not invalidated the fact that science is what individual scientists make it. Particle accelerators were developed in America, not because a central agency had planned it, but because of Ernest Lawrence; Soviet science owes its success in the same area largely to Wechsler. In short, the development of fundamental science in Soviet Russia proceeds in about the same way as in the West, through the interplay of individual talents.

As to the alleged "unevenness" of scientific progress in the Soviet Union, attributed to planned concentration on a few sectors—this again, if true at all, affects *applied* science only. If one takes wide classifications (such as "nuclear physics," "molecular physics," "atomic physics," "organic chemistry," "enzymology," *etc.*) and counts the numbers of papers in these classes published in the USSR and in the United States, one finds a more or less constant ratio, indicating that Soviet science—insofar as broadness of coverage is concerned—has generally caught up with Western science. One does find wide differences in special areas, but differences are easy to find in the scientific record of every country. What is significant is that this kind of statistics, extended over several recent years, reveals continuous increase in the relative contribution of Soviet research to most if not all areas of science—an increase that will probably become more and more conspicuous in the years to come. However, scientific leadership does not consist in numbers—be it numbers of scientists or of scientific papers; it is based, above all, on great individual achievements (Holland and Denmark, for example, have played a role in science out of all proportion to the numbers, not only of their population, but also of their scientists and scientific publications). Whether such achievements will come in increasing numbers from the USSR, because of the growth of its total scientific manpower and resources, or whether they will remain disproportionately small because of the general prevalence of conformism and discouragement of unorthodox thinking, only time can tell.

11
The New Technology and the Future of Democracy

The selections in Chapter 10 described the increasing involvement of government in science and explored some of the problems that have been created. Voices are being raised more and more, warning that the increasing pace of scientifically based technology will eventually destroy democratic society as we know it, unless we keep the applications of science under firm control. At first, these predictions were contained in fictional literature—Butler's *Erewhon*, for example, and in this century Aldous Huxley's *Brave New World* and George Orwell's *1984*. More recently, they have been raised by scholars and authorities in sociology, history, political science, and economics. What are the indications that trouble lies ahead? Are there any forces at work to prevent the decay of our democratic institutions? What can we do to assure that we do not lose control of our future?

Jacques Ellul believes that the question of control is now academic; we have already lost our ability to control the direction of scientifically based technology, which he terms "technique." The four restraints on innovation—morality, public opinion, social structure, and the state—favor technique and offer no restriction on its reckless and

373

purposeless advance. The system has become independent of man; man is now unable to limit or direct the process. Ellul complains that scientists naïvely speak about a future utopia; however, they fail to realize that implied in reaching this utopia is a worldwide totalitarian dictatorship, which will allow the new technology its full scope.

Reverend Clarke rejects Ellul's position. He views the progress of technology as both natural and essential but believes there must be proper rational control of the rate and timing of technological development. He sees a growing realization of the need for controls and thinks that there are certain laws of equilibrium and self-correction at work.

Edward Chase is convinced that the nation is becoming aware that a fundamental political crisis is developing because of technological change. The government is increasingly facing situations brought about by technological change, where current popular practices (sanctioned by our present economic system) must be revised. Awareness brings about discussion which will bring the situation into focus. Many Americans, Chase believes, still have a blind faith that the old market system will correct any ills, but he feels that our dedication to freedom will see us through the crisis.

Max Ways rejects the idea that government should control change. He believes that a "middle-tier" of institutions—business corporations, local government services, voluntary organizations, labor unions, philanthropic foundations, and universities,—possess collectively the necessary power and constitute the proper group to assess and control technological change. He thinks that from these institutions, new values and purposes can emerge, if they assume sufficient responsibility.

Nigel Calder, although admitting that politicians must become more enlightened, believes that debates concerning the implications of technological change in the political arena would be useful and valuable. In this way, complex technical and social issues would be brought to the attention of the public. Politicians should realize that the issues of technological change have a definite relationship to political beliefs and should question these issues as a part of their political life.

Aldous Huxley views the problem largely from the point of view of the individual in our present society. People living a normal life in this society are to a large extent de-individualized. There is a desire to conform, to gain the status of the "organization man." The majority of individuals could rebel against the system if they wished; they could refuse to cooperate. However, Huxley sees no widespread indications that people question, care, or have any awareness of what our future society may be like in terms of human freedom. Although he does not accept Ellul's view that nothing can be done, Huxley is pessimistic about the future of democratic society.

Jacques Ellul
THE TECHNOLOGICAL SOCIETY

. . . At present there is no counterbalance to technique. In a society in equilibrium, every new cultural tendency, every new impulse, encounters a certain number of obstacles which act as the society's first line of defense. This is not due to the interplay of conservative and revolutionary forces in general, nor in particular to the play between the means of production and the organs of consumption. It is rather due to the simple fact that every new factor must be integrated into the cultural framework, and this process requires a certain period of time because it entails modifications of the two interacting elements. It is never initially clear that the new factor will be acceptable to the cultural complex. On one hand is a kind of process of selection and, on the other, a resistance that gradually abates. A number of different forces play this restraining role. I shall discuss four of them.

The first is morality. Every civilization has rules of precise conduct, which are covered by the term *morality* in either its French or its Anglo-Saxon meaning. They may be conscious and thought out, or unconscious and spontaneous. They determine what is good and what is bad and, consequently, admit or reject a given innovation.

Very close to morality, public opinion comprises a set of much more irrational reactions which are not necessarily related to good and evil. For reasons still poorly understood, public opinion may be impelled in a certain direction under the influence of a given impulse, or it may remain refractory. Obviously, public opinion is decisive in the interaction between morality and a new factor. It can render morality obsolete or lead it to triumph.

A third restraining force is social structure, which includes both social morphology and economic or legal structure. The social structure reacts strongly whenever new factors threaten to modify it. (This, incidentally, is the only one of the four factors retained by Marxism.) Systems or ideas are no longer the sole operative factors; economic

From Jacques Ellul, *The Technological Society* (New York: Alfred A. Knopf, 1964). Reprinted with permission. Dr. Ellul is a professor in the Faculty of Law at the University of Bordeaux.

relations or sociological factors can disturb the equilibrium even of a situation the stability of which was previously thought assured.

Finally, there is the state, the special organ of defense of a society, which reacts with every means at its disposal against all disturbing forces.

We may now ask what position we are in today with respect to these factors insofar as technique is concerned. Let us put aside the problem of morality and concern ourselves with public opinion. It is completely oriented in favor of technique; only technical phenomena interest modern men. The machine has made itself master of the heart and brain both of the average man and of the mob. What excites the crowd? Performance—whether performance in sports (the result of a certain sporting technique) or economic performance (as in the Soviet Union), in reality these are the same thing. Technique is the instrument of performance. What is important is to go higher and faster; the object of the performance means little. The act is sufficient unto itself. Modern man can think only in terms of figures, and the higher the figures, the greater his satisfaction. He looks for nothing beyond the marvelous escape mechanism that technique has allowed him, to offset the very repressions caused by the life technique forces him to lead. He is reduced, in the process, to a near nullity. Even if he is not a worker on the assembly line, his share of autonomy and individual initiative becomes smaller and smaller. He is constrained and repressed in thought and action by an omnivorous reality which is external to him and imposed upon him. He is no longer permitted to display any personal power. Then, suddenly, he learns that the airplane his factory manufactures has flown at 700 miles an hour! All his repressed power soars into flight in that figure. Into that record speed he sublimates everything that was repressed in himself. He has gone one step further toward fusion with the mob, for it is the mob as a whole that is moved by a performance that incarnates its will to power. Every modern man expresses his will to power in records he has not established himself.

Public opinion is all the more important in that it is a two-pronged element. In the first place, there is modern man's collective worship of the power of fact, which is displayed in every technique and which is manifested in his total devotion to its overwhelming progress. This adoration is not passive but truly mystical. Men sacrifice themselves to it and lose themselves in the search for it. In this sense Mussolini was right in speaking of men realizing themselves in and through the state, the collective instrument of power. The martyrs of science or of the air force or of the atomic pile give us the most profound sense of this worship when we see the deference the crowd pays them. "I have faith in technique," declared Henry Wallace, the former Secretary of Commerce of the United States. His faith indeed dwells in men's hearts. Man is scandalized when he is told that technique causes evil; the scourges engendered by one technique will be made good by still other techniques. This is society's normal attitude.

In the second place, there is the deep conviction that technical problems are the only serious ones. The amused glance people give the philosopher; the lack of interest displayed in metaphysical and theological questions ("Byzantine" quarrels); the rejection of the humanities which comes from the conviction that we are living in a technical age and education must correspond to it; the search for the immediately practical, carrying the implication that history is useless and can serve no practical ends—all these are symptomatic of that "reasonable" conviction which pervades the social hierarchy and is identical for all social classes. "Only technique is not mere gab." It is positive and brings about real achievements.

In these two ways, the mystic and the rational, public opinion is completely oriented toward technique. And at present another precise technique molds public opinion with reference to any given question. This technique has never been fully exploited because public opinion is favorable enough to technique without it. But if a sudden change should occur and public opinion should turn against technique, we would see the propaganda machinery set into motion to re-create a favorable atmosphere, for the whole social edifice would be at stake.

As to the third traditional restraining force—the social structure —the question is whether the social structure of our world acts as a brake on technical evolution. By way of answer, I have shown that progress has been rapid only because social morphology has favored it. This phenomenon has not fluctuated very much; and at present we are witnessing the penetration of social structure by techniques. The life of the modern world is to an ever greater degree dominated by economics, and economics in turn is more and more dominated by technique. The whole of the material world in which we live rests on this technical base. (It is a commonplace of science-fiction writers to imagine what would happen if the use of technical instruments were to be suddenly stopped.) Likewise, our analysis has led us to recognize that as technique progresses in a given society, it tends to reproduce in that society the social structures that gave birth to it.

The individualist and atomized society of the nineteenth century was, from the sociological point of view, favorable to technical development. Today we are witnessing a kind of technical reconstitution of the scattered fragments of society; communities and associations flourish everywhere. Men seem overjoyed at this creation of new social frameworks independent of the state. The social solidification of today contrasts sharply with the fluidity of the nineteenth century. Does this phenomenon then present an effective opposition to techniques? The answer must be in the negative. If we examine these new sociological forms in detail, we find them all organized as functions of techniques. We hardly need to examine industrial associations, but the same applies to all other twentieth-century associations. They may be associations for sport or for culture, the goal of which is clearly recognizable. They may be labor unions, which have their characteristic relation to life through the economy, this last being conditioned by technique. They may be communities like the *Kibbutzim*, whose object is to exploit techniques while allowing man a normal life. In every kind of modern society there is a predominance of techniques. The social morphology of these societies indeed differs radically from that of traditional societies. Traditional societies were centered upon human needs and instincts (for example, in family, clan, seignory). Modern societies, on the other hand, are centered on technical necessity and derivatively, of course, on human adherence. Man, in modern societies, is not situated in relation to other men, but in relation to technique; for this reason the sociological structure of these societies is completely altered. There is no longer any question of autonomous collectivities or groups with specific values and orientations. Modern collectivities and groups have no existence beyond technique—they are representative of the major tendency of our time.

In the transition from the individualist to the collectivist society, there are then two stages of evolution, both of which are favorable to technique, not two different attitudes of society toward technique. Comparably, it is clear that collectivist society cannot be established, or even conceived of, except as growing out of an extreme technical development. This might not be true in a communal society (although the communities that exist today are markedly dependent on technique); but we do not seem to be moving in the direction of such societies.

Hence, we must conclude that our social structures, viewed in any light whatsoever, are unanimously favorable to technique and could hardly act as a check upon it.

Only the state remains, then, as a possible brake upon technique. But . . . the state has abdicated this function, renouncing its directive role in favor of technique. Indeed, since the nineteenth century every social element which traditionally acted as a restraint on innovating forces has been overthrown as far as technique is concerned. *Inverted* might be a better term; the factors which formerly acted as hindrances have today become powerful auxiliaries to technique. (We have only to reflect on public opinion and the expansion of the economy to realize this.) Technique, therefore, encounters no possible obstacles or checks to its progress. It can advance as it will, since it encounters no limiting factors other than its own powers (which seem unlimited and inexhaustible).

A technique without limits is not in itself disquieting. If we look at our technical society without our idealist spectacles, what seems most disquieting is that the character of technique renders it *independent of man himself*. We do not mean by this that the machine tends to replace the human being; that fact is already well-known. The important thing is that man, practically speaking, no longer possesses any means of bringing action to bear upon technique. He is unable to limit it or even to orient it. I am well acquainted with the claims of those who think that society has technique under firm control because man is always inventing it anew. I know too of the hopes of those who are always prescribing remedies for this sorcerer's apprentice whom they feel free to invoke without discernment. But these claims and hopes are mere words. The reality is that man no longer has any means with which to subjugate technique, which is not an intellectual, or even, as some would have it, a spiritual phenomenon. It is above all a sociological phenomenon; and in order to cure or change it, one would have to oppose to it checks and barriers of a sociological character. By such means alone man might possibly bring action to bear upon it. But everything of a sociological character has had its character changed by technique. There is, therefore, nothing of a sociological character available to restrain technique, because everything in society is its servant. Technique is essentially independent of the human being, who finds himself naked and disarmed before it. Modern man divines that there is only one reasonable way out: to submit and take what profit he can from what technique otherwise so richly bestows upon him. If he is of a mind to oppose it, he finds himself really alone.

It has been said that modern man surrounded by techniques is in the same situation as prehistoric man in the midst of nature. This is only a metaphor; it cannot be carried very far, even though it is as exact as a metaphor can be. Both environments give life but both place him in utter peril. Both represent terrifying powers, worlds in which man is a participant but which are closed against him. In the joy of conquest, he has not perceived that what he has created takes from him the possibility of being himself. He is like a rich man of many possessions who finds himself a nonentity in his own household. The state, man's last protector, has made common cause with alien powers. . . .

In 1960 the weekly *l'Express* of Paris published a series of extracts from texts by American and Russian scientists concerning society in the year 2000. As long as such visions were purely a literary concern of science-fiction writers and sensational journalists, it was possible to smile at them. Now we have like works from Nobel Prize winners, members of the Academy of Sciences of Moscow, and other scientific notables whose qualifications are beyond dispute. The visions of these gentlemen put science fiction in the shade. By the year 2000, voyages to the moon will be commonplace; so will inhabited artificial satellites. All food will be completely synthetic. The world's population will have increased fourfold but will have been stabilized. Sea water and ordinary rocks will yield all the necessary metals. Disease, as well as famine, will have been eliminated; and there will be universal hygienic inspection and control. The problems of energy production will have been completely resolved. Serious scientists, it must be repeated, are the source of these predictions, which hitherto were found only in philosophic utopias.

The most remarkable predictions concern the transformation of educational methods and the problem of human reproduction. Knowledge will be accumulated in "electronic banks" and transmitted directly to the human nervous system by means of coded electronic messages. There will no longer be any need of reading or learning mountains of useless information; everything will be received and registered according to the needs of the moment. There will be no need of attention or effort. What is needed will pass directly from the machine to the brain without going through consciousness.

In the domain of genetics, natural reproduction will be forbidden. A stable population will be necessary, and it will consist of the highest human types. Artificial insemination will be employed. This, according to Muller, will "permit the introduction into a carrier uterus of an ovum fertilized *in vitro*, ovum and sperm . . . having been taken from persons representing the masculine ideal and the feminine ideal, respectively. The reproductive cells in question will preferably be those of persons dead long enough that a true perspective of their lives and works, free of all personal prejudice, can be seen. Such cells will be taken from cell banks and will represent the most precious genetic heritage of humanity. . . . The method will have to be applied universally. If the people of a single country were to apply it intelligently and intensively . . . they would quickly attain a practically invincible level of superiority . . ." Here is a future Huxley never dreamed of.

Perhaps, instead of marveling or being shocked, we ought to reflect a little. A question no one ever asks when confronted with the scientific wonders of the future concerns the interim period. Consider, for example, the problems of automation, which will become acute in a very short time. How, socially, politically, morally, and humanly, shall we contrive to get there? How are the prodigious economic problems, for example, of unemployment, to be solved? And, in Muller's more distant utopia, how shall we force humanity to refrain from begetting children naturally? How shall we force them to submit to constant and rigorous hygienic controls? How shall man be persuaded to accept a radical transformation of his traditional modes of nutrition? How and where shall we relocate a billion and a half persons who today make their livings from agriculture and who, in the promised ultrarapid conversion of the next forty years, will become completely useless as cultivators of the soil? How shall we distribute such numbers of people equably over the surface of the earth, particularly if the promised fourfold increase in population materializes? How will we handle the control and occupation of outer space in order to provide a stable *modus vivendi?* How shall national boundaries be made to disappear? (One of the last two would be a necessity.) There are many other "hows," but they are conveniently left unformulated. When we reflect on the serious although relatively minor problems that were provoked by the industrial exploitation of coal and electricity, when we reflect that after a hundred and fifty years these problems are still not satisfactorily resolved, we are entitled to ask whether there are any solutions to the infinitely more complex "hows" of the next forty years. In fact, there is one and only one means to their solution, a world-wide totalitarian dictatorship which will allow technique its full scope and at the same time resolve the concomitant difficulties. It is not difficult to understand why the scientists and worshippers of technology prefer not to dwell on this solution, but rather to leap nimbly across the dull and uninteresting intermediary period and land squarely in the golden age. We might indeed ask ourselves if we will succeed in getting through the transition period at all, or if the blood and the suffering required are not perhaps too high a price to pay for this golden age.

If we take a hard, unromantic look at the golden age itself, we are struck with the incredible naïveté of these scientists. They say, for example, that they will be able to shape and reshape at will human emotions, desires, and thoughts and arrive scientifically at certain efficient, pre-established collective decisions. They claim they will be in a position to develop certain collective desires, to constitute certain homogeneous social units out of aggregates of individuals, to forbid men to raise their children, and even to persuade them to renounce having any. At the same time, they speak of assuring the triumph of freedom and of the necessity of avoiding dictatorship at any price. They seem incapable of grasping the contradiction involved, or of understanding that what they are proposing, even after the intermediary period, is in fact the harshest of dictatorships. In comparison, Hitler's was a trifling affair. That it is to be a dictatorship of test tubes rather than of hobnailed boots will not make it any less a dictatorship.

When our savants characterize their golden age in any but scientific terms, they emit a quantity of down-at-the-heel platitudes that would gladden the heart of the pettiest politician. Let's take a few samples. "To render human nature nobler, more beautiful, and more harmonious." What on earth can this mean? What criteria, what content, do they propose? Not many, I fear, would be able to reply. "To assure the triumph of peace, liberty, and reason." Fine words with no substance behind them. "To eliminate cultural lag." What culture? And would the culture they have in mind be able to subsist in this harsh social organization? "To conquer outer space." For what purpose? The conquest of space seems to be an end in itself, which dispenses with any need for reflection.

We are forced to conclude that our scientists are incapable of any but the emptiest platitudes when they stray from their specialties. It makes one think back on the collection of mediocrities accumulated by Einstein when he spoke of God, the state, peace, and the meaning of life. It is clear that Einstein, extraordinary mathematical genius that he was, was no Pascal; he knew nothing of political or human reality, or, in fact, anything at all outside his mathematical reach. The banality of Einstein's remarks in matters outside his specialty is as astonishing as his genius within it. It seems as though the specialized application of all one's faculties in a particular area inhibits the consideration of things in general. Even J. Robert Oppenheimer, who seems receptive to a general culture, is not outside this judgment. His political and social declarations, for example, scarcely go beyond the level of those of the man in the street. And the opinions of the scientists quoted by *l'Express* are not even on the level of Einstein or Oppenheimer. Their pomposities, in fact, do not rise to the level of the average. They are vague generalities inherited from the nineteenth century, and the fact that they represent the furthest limits of thought of our scientific worthies must be symptomatic of arrested development or of a mental block. Particularly disquieting is the gap between the enormous power they wield and their critical ability, which must be estimated as null. To wield power well entails a certain faculty of criticism, discrimination, judgment, and option. It is impossible to have confidence in men who apparently lack these faculties. Yet it is apparently our fate to be facing a "golden age" in the power of sorcerers who are totally blind to the meaning of the human adventure. When they speak of preserving the seed of outstanding men, whom, pray, do they mean to be the judges. It is clear, alas, that they propose to sit in judgment themselves. It is hardly likely that they will deem a Rimbaud or a Nietszche worthy of posterity. When they announce that they will conserve the genetic mutations which appear to them most favorable, and that they propose to modify the very germ cells in order to produce such and such traits; and when we consider the mediocrity of the scientists themselves outside the confines of their specialties, we can only shudder at the thought of what they will esteem most "favorable."

None of our wise men ever pose the question of the end of all their marvels. The "wherefore" is resolutely passed by. The response which would occur to our contemporaries is: for the sake of happiness.

Unfortunately, there is no longer any question of that. One of our best-known specialists in diseases of the nervous system writes: "We will be able to modify man's emotions, desires and thoughts, as we have already done in a rudimentary way with tranquillizers." It will be possible, says our specialist to produce a conviction or an impression of happiness without any real basis for it. Our man of the golden age, therefore, will be capable of "happiness" amid the worst privations. Why, then, promise us extraordinary comforts, hygiene, knowledge, and nourishment if, by simply manipulating our nervous systems, we can be happy without them? The last meager motive we could possibly ascribe to the technical adventure thus vanishes into thin air through the very existence of technique itself.

But what good is it to pose questions of motives? of Why? All that must be the work of some miserable intellectual who balks at technical progress. The attitude of the scientists, at any rate, is clear. Technique exists because it is technique. The golden age will be because it will be. Any other answer is superfluous.

W. Norris Clarke, S.J.
CHRISTIANS CONFRONT TECHNOLOGY

Both the need and the aptitude for technology are rooted deep in human nature. Man simply cannot live with security and dignity in this material environment of physically superior forces unless, by means of tools, he extends and intensifies the power of his own comparatively feeble body so that it can cope with nature. Thus we find that as far back as the presence of man is discernible in history it is accompanied by the use of tools. And the use of even the simplest tools is a rudimentary technology, differing only in degree from the technology of the great machines of today.

Nor is it merely a question of decent survival. If man is made as a living image of God, he must imitate in his own way the life of his Father in heaven. Now in relation to the material universe God is both its thinker

W. Norris Clarke, S.J., "Christians Confront Technology," *America*, 101 (1959), 761–762. Reprinted with permission from *America*, The National Catholic Weekly Review, 920 Broadway, New York, New York 10010. The Rev. Clarke is Professor of Philosophy at Fordham University.

and its maker—the supreme Artist. Hence man, His adopted son, must first strive to rethink the handiwork that his Father has thought up. (This is the fundamental justification for all pure science.) He must then strive to remake or transform creatively, by his own God-given powers, the world that his Father has made for him out of nothing and given him as his workshop. (This is the fundamental justification for all technology and art.)

The goal of all technology, then, is to make matter serve the human spirit as the most pliant instrument possible for authentic human growth. This involves both the gradual liberation of man from all inhumane, degrading, purely animal-like drudgery and subservience to matter, and also the positive transformation of matter to express man's own spiritual vision of the meaning and purpose of the universe.

Secondly, the unfolding of this basic aptitude is of its nature dynamic and progressive. Each successive achievement in technology builds upon what has gone before and opens up in turn new developments beyond it. As the range of possibilities constantly expands, the rate of development is able to advance more and more rapidly. This dynamic dialog of man with nature is inherent in the very presence of man as a rational animal in a material universe. To attempt to freeze this process, which by its very nature is developmental, at some supposed point of ideal equilibrium (determined by whom and on what evidence?) would be like trying to immobilize the growth of art or of human intelligence itself—indeed of any living thing, which dies when it can no longer put forth new fruits. The conclusion of all this is that progressive technology in some form or other is both natural and essential—hence basically good —for man if he is to fulfill his God-given destiny in the universe.

So much for the credit side of the account. On the debit side it must also be admitted that there are grave dangers inherent in the pursuit of technology, as in the use of all natural human aptitudes. These perils arise, it seems to me, from two main sources: first, lack of subordination to the higher spiritual good of man; second, lack of the proper rational control of the rate and timing of technological development.

The danger of the first is that what should be a mere means, at the service of the spiritual growth of mankind, may become so all-absorbing that it will upset the proper hierarchy of values and reduce the spiritual intelligence of man to the role of a mere servant of technological progress pursued for its own sake. Technology would then become like an overdeveloped organ or the runaway growth of cancerous cells—a threat to the basic cultural and spiritual health of mankind.

The second main danger is that the tempo of technological development be allowed to follow unchecked its own inner dynamism, independently of its relation to the balanced over-all good of the people it is supposed to serve. Too rapid a tempo of change can produce an atmosphere of such constant flux and severe social dislocation that the people subjected to it will be in grave danger of becoming culturally rootless and deprived of all fixed landmarks as they are whirled hectically along by the racing current of "progress." Thus the ever increasing mobility made possible by the automobile (though not so much, strange to say, by the airplane) has so far proved to be a very mixed blessing, whose dissipating effects we have not yet learned to control.

Another form of the same danger is the so-called "enslavement of man to the machine." The harsh rhythms of the machine and its artificial environment will, it is said, dominate or destroy the heathy natural rhythms of the living body in harmony with nature as God made it. The example of the assembly line, with its impoverishment of creative ability and subjection of the workers to a monotonous, repetitive routine, is sufficient warning of where technology can lead.

All of these dangers are real and serious, in addition to the very special and obvious perils connected with the use of the immense power now at our disposal. I have no intention of trying to conjure them away by general optimistic affirmations of the "inevitable forward march of progress." The latter is a dangerous modern myth, a secularized distortion of Christian hope. Uncontrolled technology can certainly bring down disaster, perhaps irreparable, on our race. The only protection against it is a growth in man's spiritual and moral maturity proportionate to his growth in technical skill and power. Either we grow in both dimensions or we perish, like the overgrown monsters of our prehistoric past. But this is already a law in the development of every individual personality (for example, scientific geniuses with a child's knowledge of religion and morality). If individuals can solve it there is no reason why people generally cannot either. Actually, it seems to me that there is already a rapidly growing recognition on the part of both scientists and political leaders—who are also the ones most able to do something about it—of the urgent necessity of greater moral control over the exploitation of scientific and technological advances.

Furthermore, as technological development proceeds along its course among a people still endowed with basic biological, social and moral vitality—as I believe our people still is—certain laws of equilibrium and self-correction seem to be constantly and unobtrusively at work. Thus, losses in one area are compensated for by gains in another, or exaggeration in one direction generates its own counterreaction in the other direction. Thus the very mobility which seems, at least temporarily, to be weakening our roots in the family and the local community is at the same time strengthening our bonds with the rest of the world. The very increase in perfection of the means of communication at a distance, as in television, may eventually make it neither necessary nor desirable to move about so feverishly on a small scale as we now do. We may end up by visiting our friends and clients relaxedly on a two-way television circuit rather than by transporting ourselves physically to them along over-crowded highways or airways. Or by the mysterious providence of God it may happen that the insistent challenge of outer mobility may succeed more effectively than pulpit sermons in making us turn within and discover that it is possible to achieve a sense of permanence, self-identity and rootedness in more interior, supramaterial and universal values than we now believe capable of winning our allegiance.

What of the threatened enslavement of man to the machine? The danger is real. But I am convinced that it is limited by the very inner logic and laws of equilibrium of technology itself to certain transitory types of techniques and local or temporary abuses during periods of transition. The whole innate drive of technology is to substitute machines for man in all areas where monotonous, repetitive actions are the rule, and to leave man free for more intelligent, creative or supervisory work. The supposed threat of a constantly increasing slavery to the machine, as some kind of inexorable drift inherent in the process of technology itself seems to me to be largely a myth, without solid historical, psychological or sociological foundation. The true danger lies in the moral dispositions of those who use technology. The far greater peril is that men may become slaves to their fellow men rather than to their machines.

I believe, therefore, that if we have the courage to assume with full moral and intellectual maturity the responsibility of actively guiding and controlling the mighty power of technology that is now in our hands, far from being ruined by it, we shall be able rather to turn it into a profoundly beneficent instrument for the authentic growth of the human family. And no one has greater inner resources for rising to this challenge, nor more urgent motives for doing so, than the Christian.

Edward T. Chase
POLITICS AND TECHNOLOGY

At last there is a dawning realization that in the United States it is rapid technological change rather than ideological strife or even econom-

From Edward T. Chase, "Politics and Technology," *The Yale Review*, LII (1963), 321–326; 335–339. Copyright 1963 Yale University. Reprinted with permission. Mr. Chase, vice president of Cunningham & Walsh (advertising), is a member of the Advisory Council of the Society for the History of Technology.

ics that is building up a fundamental political crisis. This realization is evidenced in several recent symposiums involving a number of the outstanding thinkers of the times and by recent executive acts and legislation with far-reaching implications. What is happening is that technology's effects are suddenly calling into question the viability of our political institutions to a degree unknown at least since the Civil War.

There is a growing awareness that tomorrow's political convulsion will be different from what doctrinaires, obsessed with dated rhetoric about socialism vs. capitalism, have led us to expect, because it derives from the cumulative impact of technology, an impact that is impersonal, nonideological, relentless, and possibly overwhelming. Above all else our political adaptability and inventiveness are being challenged by technology. This point has seldom been demonstrated more dramatically than by last summer's Senate filibuster growing out of the dispute over whether AT&T or the government should dominate the control of the communications space satellite. Such perplexity and passion were fomented by the power problem created by this particular technological triumph as to immobilize the political process for days, until cloture was invoked in the Senate for the first time in 35 years.

Examples of political consternation provoked by technology are becoming pervasive. They range from the familiar to the esoteric. How, for instance, does a free society force human and land resources out of agriculture to adjust to the realities of modern scientific farming? And does a free society make the massive, explosive problem of retraining workers displaced by automation the responsibility of state governments or the national government or industry, or some ingenious combination of all? Again, when technological unemployment in combination with scientific medicine produces a growing population of "retired" elderly persons in an urbanized, wage-based industrial society, how will their heavy medical costs for the inevitable chronic ills of old age be financed? Or when an essential public service is threatened with extinction as a paying proposition, owing to fatal competition from more advanced technology, is the government helpless, as in the case of the New Haven Railroad, or will our political leaders devise some successful expedient without incurring a constitutional crisis? Again, is our incapacity to adjust politically such that we must forego manifest social gains from technological progress—as almost happened in the Hanford, Washington, atomic power plant case, where an invaluable supply of reactor-generated steam for creating electricity would have been wasted had there not been an eleventh hour political resolution of the conflict between private and government ownership? When completed in 1965, this will be the world's largest nuclear power plant. The plant will be the locus of further political controversy soon over the question of what particular industries the electric power will be used for. Use in one category of industry will result in 5,000 new jobs; use in another in 10,000 new jobs; and in still another category 36,000 new jobs. Not the "market" but a conscious deliberation by officials will resolve the issue.

This Hanford example, like the communications space satellite debate, introduces problems with political implications of a new order of complexity for American society. Yet already it is being widely sensed that they are only the beginning. To be sure, man has long had to make gradual social adaptation to technological change. It is the exponential rate of change today that is uniquely challenging to our political super-structure.

What is perhaps most conducive to political controversy is the fact that advancing technology is beginning to promise immediate practi-cal solutions to hitherto insoluble frustrations, if it is given the chance. As a practical matter there must first be expensive studies of the feasibility of technological innovations and then funds appropriated for research and development. If, as is increasingly the case, these funds must be substan-tial and there is no promise of relatively quick profit, then the market mechanism simply does not become engaged. Only the government can undertake the enterprise. It is true that in a modern mixed economy this does not invariably create a political dilemma. But in the United States it does more frequently than not. There may be no immediate political repercussions from the unusual amount of attention President Kennedy has been giving to conquering the problem of turning brackish and sea water into usable water. Seventy-five million dollars is being spent by the Office of Saline Water to ascertain the best of a number of competing commercial processes. Nor would there be a formidable political problem in governmental support, say, for eradicating malaria from the world (3 million deaths annually, 300 million people afflicted), which is something distinctly within reach at a cost of only $50 million spread over a ten-year period.

But consider the political reverberations should the government undertake the rescue operation that could be consummated for our moribund textile industry if technology were subsidized—as is being seriously considered in Washington—to master the task of applying high speed electronic computers to our textile looms, thus rendering American textiles competitive in the world market. Comparable practical achieve-ments are within reach in a score of areas, were it not for the political obstacles—for instance, the revival of our East Coast shipping industry by the use of fast hydrofoil ships now anchored on drawing boards for lack of developmental money, ships quite capable of out-performing trucks (hence offering some relief to the traffic problem); or, for another example, creating a major new source of high protein food by making a systematic effort to harvest the ocean.

The questions posed by these considerations are ultimately and essentially political. They go to the heart of the political problem of how a democratic government, one that is both responsive and responsible, reconciles technological promise with the will of the public. For decisions have to be made as to what public resources are to be devoted to what technological ventures—and who is to make the choice. Throughout the lifetime of the United States, our tradition has been to depend upon the market mechanism to register the people's choices. It is the doctrine of consumer sovereignty, the revered "invisible hand" (which economist Robert Heilbroner usefully characterizes as a system "to mobilize and allocate human energies and to distribute the social produce in a manner to assure society of its continued existence.") However, the evidence is now becoming overwhelming that the traditional market mechanism of supply and demand, for all its uncanny power to articulate the public will, simply is not up to reflecting the long-range values that have to be weighed if a rational use is to be made of the new technology. The point is that this is not a doctrinaire matter, a sly triumph by creeping socialists; it is a result of technological change.

The underlying dilemma arises from the fact that a democratic government must be responsive to the present electorate, yet, since it makes decisions that determine the impact of technology upon the environment of succeeding generations, it must also be responsive to future electorates. Government is now facing situations with increasing frequency where currently popular practices sanctioned by the market system (exploitation of natural resources is an obvious example) must be modified for the sake of this future. Rachel Carson's *Silent Spring,* about the devastating ecological impact of pesticides, has wonderfully dramatized this issue.

This is to put the matter negatively, however. The political problem is not so much a matter of placing restraints on technology. It stems more from the fact that positive forces are now building up that urge us to circumvent the market mechanism and apply public funds directly to technology, as traditionally we have done only in wartime. What is slowly being realized is that the support of technology cannot any longer be confined to what the public wants. After all, the public can only choose alternatives among things it knows; it simply does not know enough to project its wants into the future, with the result that the market mechanism cannot be depended upon to nourish technological development. For the first time in our history the government has set up a unit, called the Panel on Civilian Technology, responsive to this fact. This little-known operation was established strictly for the purpose of encouraging technological innovation on the premise that new technology, as much as or more than new plant and equipment investment, is what stimulates economic growth. The 18-man panel, composed of industrialists, academics, and bureaucrats, is especially concerned with four industries suffering from technological lag—textiles, coal, housing, and transport. It reports to science adviser Jerome Wiesner, to economic adviser Walter Heller, and to Commerce Secretary Luther Hodges. It has already become a center of controversy in certain planning circles because of its first report, on urban transportation, in which it argues against support for rail transit and instead favors express buses on exclusive rights of way.

The political inhibitions to direct government subsidy on any substantial scale remain enormous, of course. Suggestions such as those made at a Brookings Institution symposium on "The Uses of Economics" —suggestions for revitalizing our lagging economy by having the government finance research and development in areas like communications, transport, food, and industrial production—are still widely judged as heresy. In business circles they are viewed as the sure road to Communist despotism.

"To what extent should government finance or subsidize industrial research in general, or for certain industries as it has already done so productively for agriculture and defense?" asked Charles J. Hitch, former Chairman of the Research Council of the RAND corporation, at the Brookings meeting. Now an Assistant Secretary of Defense, Hitch went on to say that "relatively small expenditures" for deliberately planned research and development in the military sector "have been staggeringly, alarmingly, productive. . . . I have tried to think of any reasons why the military area should be unique in this respect; I can think of none. That it is not is suggested by our somewhat similar experience in agriculture, though on a much smaller scale. I suspect that there has been a serious misallocation of resources and that it corresponds to economists' misallocation of their effort between problems of investment and problems of technological change." Coming from so highly placed a representative of the power elite, these are words calculated to give pause. Hitch was impressively seconded in his main sentiments by Francis M. Bator, of M.I.T., whose cool disparagement of laissez-faire markets as an effective allocator of resources went unchallenged. . . .

In his testimony to Congress pleading for more money to pay for scientists, Wiesner said that the step-up in government-subsidized research and development was bound to accelerate quite apart from defense or space work because it has now become clear that our rate of economic growth is increasingly dependent upon technological development. All the technology meetings noted the increased dependence of the economic growth rate on technological development. John T. Dunlop, the Harvard economist who edited the book on the Arden House symposium, said: "The industry of discovery opens up a new vista of the long future in which substantial resources in increasing amounts are devoted systematically to . . . reshaping the physical environment of mankind and to providing increased living standards and cultural opportunities . . . the rise of the industry of discovery suggests that we should be able to look forward to doubling productivity and living standards . . . every fifteen years (a rise from 3 to 5 percent in the yearly growth rate). These potentials underscore the common gains to be shared by increasing productivity and the possibilities of insuring adequately those who bear the costs of the adverse initial impacts of some technological changes. The industry of discovery also raises a host of issues and questions which are slowly coming to the fore. . . . *To what extent shall the direction of invention be left to the individual spirit and curiosity, to the market, and to what extent directed by priorities established by what bodies?*"

Thus the signs are accumulating that we are on the threshold of an increasingly hot and divisive national debate on this very question and that it may very well bring us to the brink of a constitutional crisis which cannot yet be precisely envisioned but will focus on the relations between the executive and legislative branches. It will be the central domestic issue of the 1960's and the 1970's. The manner in which the question is answered will determine our governmental framework for a generation, and especially the pattern of relationships between the national government and the other great power center, business, the administrator of the market system.

How distant, really, is the time when, as Robert Theobald stressed at Santa Barbara, the issues of biological and genetic control will be forced upon the agenda of government responsibilities under such prods as the population explosion of the senile and chronically ill, the possibilities of organ transplants, new miracle drugs and artificial insemination. Professor Somers cites the work of the British physician Ffrangcon Roberts, an expert on medical economics, who uses the wry term "medicated survival" to describe technology's accomplishments in forestalling death. He sees the market system as nourishing "antiplutic medicine," that is, treatment wherein society remains burdened despite treatment because the disease is congenital or the result of old age—"antiplutic" since the very success of the treatment exacerbates the cost to society. But the examples need hardly be so esoteric. The pressures are mounting behind such familiar questions . . . as whether a decentralized democracy traditionally infatuated with "local initiative" can cope with automotive congestion, originating across different state and city boundaries; or whether, as open land in metropolitan areas shrinks, we can devise institutions to prevent corrupting land uses; or whether the potential of television, now about to become international, is indefinitely to be determined by its effectiveness as a sales instrument for advertisers.

As the inadequacies of the market system become increasingly evident under the impact of technological change, there is a developing consensus that we are bound to witness a kind of intervention now feared by most Americans. Practically the only precedent we have for it is the Employment Act of 1946, which for the first time in Federal law stipulated that full employment and equitable income distribution were to become an explicit governmental concern rather than be left up to the market system. That law was passed in response to the national anxiety that the economy would falter with the end of wartime spending. (As it turned out, massive pent-up consumer demand more than compensated.) It was no radical dismissal of our system, but rather an acknowledgment that, in an age of technological disruption, supplementation of the market system by political action is essential for rational allocation of resources and the meeting of public needs. This year's Manpower Development and Training Act is the most important addition to the law so far.

Almost certainly we are also going to witness the development of a new kind of national economic budget going beyond annual Federal accounting (what we essentially do now) to set forth a five or six year projection of all our national resources viewed against our national goals. We will then have something close to national programming of explicit policies, in which the over-riding consideration will be the role of new technology.

Just what government body will emerge as the key agency for national planning no one could say now. But it could conceivably be the President's Council of Economic Advisers, a Council further strengthened by law and with vastly increased responsibilities and powers. It is such a body that must to a substantial extent fulfill the crucial function the European Economic Commission fulfills for the Common Market. One of the best prescriptions for such an agency as this is developed in the extraordinarily penetrating statement on automation issued by the Research Section of the Industrial Union Department, AFL-CIO. It calls for "A Permanent Commission on Technological Change" to act as "a central clearing house in which there will be gathered, analyzed, and evaluated, all pertinent information on public and private plans involving technological change." it would operate within the executive branch of the national government. Recently Arthur Burns, the former economic adviser to President Eisenhower, came forward with a surprisingly similar proposal.

The development of any such planning body and such a new kind of national economic budget to cope with technological change will no doubt create and be part of a great political ferment. But by then the domestic political context may also have been modified somewhat to ease the impact. For example, in the years immediately ahead we can anticipate some modernization of the organization of Congress. As the reapportionment movement slowly eliminates the most egregious abuses and begins to alter the complexion of our government, it may in time modify the American custom of putting local interests ahead of the national interest.

We will also witness the growing power of a new constituency in the electorate, a constituency created by technology itself. I refer to the burgeoning army of scientists and other intellectual workers of the new technological order. If Professor Daniel Bell of Columbia, a participant at the Boston symposium on technology where he first unveiled his now much-discussed vision of the "post-industrial society," is correct—and his statistically-awesome arguments were compelling—this new constituency will soon come to rival the dominant voice of the past, the business community. The rise of this constituency could be the most important single political development of the new technology. Dr. James R. Killian, Jr., Wiesner's predecessor as Presidential science adviser, has urged that scientists run for Congress. Noting that they have begun to appear in state legislatures, Killian suggested that a technological society must have scientists "in the public arena if it is to deal wisely with all the great policy matters arising out of science and technology."

In any event, one thing is clearer day by day. The American instinct for freedom, the talent of political inventiveness permitting a maximum of individual freedom combined with optimum collective performance, is to be put to a rugged test. To meet the test we will have to arrive at a far better comprehension of the full impact of technology. With planning to a much larger extent superseding the market mechanism as the director of our energies, there is bound to be much more discussion as to what worthy ends our political and social institutions should serve. There will be a growing consciousness that, as Robert Oppenheimer recently elaborated in his piece on science and culture in *Encounter*, whereas technology is a cumulative process ever building on its advances and thus moves only in the direction of progress, our moral and political life lacks cumulative growth and can at any time just as easily regress as progress. As of right now Americans are still floundering in a strange transitional state of mind, for the most part blindly addicted to the notion that the old market system will make everything come out all right; the rest uneasily awakening to the realization that only our resilience as a free people will see us through the crisis.

Max Ways
THE ERA OF RADICAL CHANGE

Within a decade or two it will be generally understood that the main challenge to U.S. society will turn not around the production of goods but around the difficulties and opportunities involved in a world of accelerating change and ever widening choices. Change has always been part of the human condition. What is different now is the pace of change, and the prospect that it will come faster and faster, affecting every part of life, including personal values, morality, and religion, which seem most remote from technology.

The condition is man-made; and everybody has some share of responsibility for it, not the least, the U.S. industrialist. For many changes come about through the business system, which has an active role to play between the discoverers on one hand and the consumers on the other. Within corporations hundreds of techniques, arising from scores of separate scientific and technological disciplines, are drawn together through complex management structures. Here all kinds of values arising from the individual initiative and responsibilities of corporate managers and specialists are somehow integrated. A larger and more intricate mediation of values and purposes occurs in "the market," meaning thousands of interconnected markets, where the public exercises ever increasing power through billions of daily decisions. The resultant of all these corporate and consumer decisions alters the very conditions of life.

So swift is the acceleration that trying to "make sense" of change will come to be our basis industry. Aesthetic and ethical values will be evolving along with the choices to which they will be applied. The question about progress will be how good rather than how much. Already this shift away from purely materialist and quantitative criteria is well advanced. Change is called "excessive" when it appears to outrun ethical or aesthetic patterns. In the conflicts that arise on this point there are dangers not only for the business system but also for the democratic

From Max Ways, "The Era of Radical Change," *Fortune*, LXIX, No. 5 (May 1964). Reprinted by permission. Mr. Ways is assistant managing editor of *Fortune* magazine.

constitutional state and for the hope that the spirit of individual man can enlarge its freedom.

Not long ago Alvin Pitcher, of the University of Chicago's divinity-school faculty, writing with anguished eloquence in the *Harvard Business Review*, asked, "How much flux can man stand?" Not this much, he said, calling for a slowdown of automation and other socially disruptive and "needless" changes. Pitcher's anxiety was broader than the usual fear of such economic consequences as unemployment. He associated the present unprecedented mobility of American society with juvenile delinquency, with the dissolution of communities, with a barrenness in individual life. Man, who needs a measure of order and stability, is being dehumanized, he said, by excessive change.

Most American political and social issues today arise, like Pitcher's protest, out of concern over the pace and quality of change. In many cases, the protest is accompanied by proposals that government restore order by taking some additional degree of control. Historically, it would be ironic if the long struggle of the individual vs. the state should issue as a program for protecting the individual by having government take charge of change. Practically, it is quite hopeless to expect a central government to perform well a task requiring a high degree of flexibility, decentralization, and willingness to accept risk. But the argument against statism will not prevail as long as we think that responsibility for coping with change must be assigned either to the government or else to the naked, isolated individual.

"The Middle Tier"

This way of framing the choice is set up by a Jeffersonian tradition (endorsed by Lincoln, Richard Nixon, and Lyndon Johnson, among others), which holds that the government should do only those things that the people cannot do for themselves. But in the American society of 1964, what can the people as individuals do for themselves? Each man can grasp only a few of the disciplines in which knowledge is divided. No individual, by himself, can sustain his present level of living. Most obviously of all, no individual can cope with radical change. If it's a choice between the isolated individual and government—then government had better do it.

But, of course, that isn't the real choice. In Jefferson's day organizations other than government were thin on the ground, small and simple. In the last hundred and fifty years they have proliferated in numbers, grown huge in size, and, most important, have so evolved as to widen the scope of individuals working within them and of individuals dealing with them from outside. Organizations making up this "third area" or "middle tier" include, in addition to business corporations, local government services, voluntary organizations, labor unions, philanthropic foundations, and universities. These last generate in their research centers most of the scientific discovery that is later transferred into technological change. They also educate nearly all the managers of the sister organizations and the intellectuals who try to express the patterns of value emerging in the society—or to improve those patterns by criticism.

No judgment can be made that even the amazing organizational fertility of recent American society is or will be adequate to cope with radical change. The point is simply that if this "middle tier" of institutions is bypassed or fails, society will fail. Shifting the venue of the struggle by putting the responsibility on government does not solve the problem, because socialism, too, would need criteria on which to decide how much change was "excessive" or "needless" and what kind of change was "disruptive." The police power works well only where norms are settled. . . .

Robert Oppenheimer has expressed the break with former eras quite succinctly. "This world of ours," he said, "is a new world, in which the unity of knowledge, the nature of human communities, the order of society, the order of ideas, the very notions of society and culture have changed, and will not return to what they have been in the past. What is new is new not because it has never been there before, but because it has changed in quality. One thing that is new is the prevalence of newness, the changing scale and scope of change itself, so that the world alters as we walk in it, so that the years of man's life measure not some small growth or rearrangement or moderation of what he learned in childhood, but a great upheaval."

Charles de Gaulle in Mexico put it more succinctly: "It so happens that the world is undergoing a transformation to which no change that has yet occurred can be compared, either in scope or in rapidity."

Historian Marshall M. Fishwick recalls that the Angel Gabriel in *Green Pastures* put it still more succinctly, "Everything nailed down is coming loose."

Yet there is a danger in that word "everything." If it means the particular works of man as we see them around us, it is true: most of these (e.g., old buildings, old machines) will quickly disappear; some (e.g., methods of work and education) will be modified; and the greatest (e.g., high achievements of art and intellect) will remain, unchanged in themselves, though perceived somewhat differently by future decades. But if "everything" is taken to include, say, the continuity of man's quest for order and right and truth and harmony, then it is not true. There are, indeed, two different ways in which we can blind ourselves to the meaning of the radical change around us: either we comfort ourselves with some such piece of obsolescent wisdom as "the more it changes, the more it stays the same," or else—and this is worse—we assume that the flux is total, that past, present, and future have nothing to do with one another, that no patterns are discernible, that no purpose is feasible because the "winds of change" are beyond control and, anyway, human values now have no endurance, no footing. Both these escapes from thinking tend to deny or diminish human responsibility, the first by assuming that the order "built into" society is beyond man's ability to destroy or improve, the second by confusing radical change with absolute randomness. To speak of change, however radical, presupposes some constants, some continuities, some patterns in that which is changing. The greater the change, the harder the reach needed to establish the patterns.

In looking for patterns, we do not start from scratch. Neither men nor society determine objective truth, and a change in society will not change truth. But the perception of truth by men—what they perceive and how they perceive it—is surely affected by changes in society. Many truths of history, science, philosophy, and religion have been perceived as transcending change. In a time of great social flux the truths perceived as transcendent may be fewer—and therefore more precious. They may be perceived as more abstract—and therefore harder to apply to actual life. A tremendous effort will be required to build the intermediate links between the novel patterns of a changing society and abstract, enduring truth. The "middle-tier" organizations of American society are trying to forge such links out of the new values and purposes that emerge in the course of practical operations. . . .

Nigel Calder
TOMORROW'S POLITICS: THE CONTROL AND USE OF TECHNOLOGY

Suppose a politician sought election on the following platform: I offer you a richer and more hectic world, with more people,

Nigel Calder, "Tomorrow's Politics: The Control and Use of Technology," *The Nation*, 200 (Jan. 4, 1965), 3–5. Reprinted by permission. Mr. Calder is the editor of *New Scientist*, London.

more noise, more automobile accidents, more neuroses and stress diseases than your wildest dreams evoke. Vote for me and I shall waken you each night with the exciting bang of passing supersonic air liners. I shall foment yet harsher economic and political nationalism. I shall lead you to glory in shooting up unruly people of lands whose standard of living is rising far more slowly than yours; we shall fight, too, for possession of the riches of the deep ocean. Together we shall banish wild animals to the museums where they belong and create an entirely man-made world. I offer you prostheses so potent that the day will come when we cannot tell man from machine. Our technocrats will continue to catch you unawares with new inventions. By such means we shall strengthen the power of central government and, through our national computer network, we shall be watching your every action, transaction and misdemeanor with a brotherly eye.

If anyone were bold enough (or honest enough) to declare such intentions he would doubtless be supposed to have committed political suicide. Certainly any tolerably well-intentioned politician would be honestly shocked to have it suggested that such was *his* program. And yet we are heading now to approximately the world I have described—under our benign leaders. It is the unwitting program of the technically advanced nations of the world, because politicians show a remarkable fatalism, or blind enthusiasm, for the application of new scientific and technological knowledge—attitudes that are deplorable, but not beyond remedy.

It is true that politicians have (belatedly) come to recognize the importance of science, but they have carefully enshrined it as a peripheral activity for government. Those who are readiest with the cliché par excellence of the 20th century—the one about science and technology offering unlimited opportunities for good or ill—are often the last to get down to cases and answer the question: "What do you think is good, and what ill, in the present tendencies in applied science?" (Antibiotics and the H-bomb won't do as answers—they are part of the cliché.)

Sometimes, the politician counter-attacks by saying that people are trying to drag science into party politics—to get politicians and parties to favor this and disfavor that sphere of scientific activity. That is precisely what I am doing. Ho, ho, comes the rejoinder, the spirit of science must not be enslaved; that was the error of the dictators. . . .

The obvious distinction that must be drawn is between scientific inquiry and the uses made of scientific knowledge so acquired. The former, I agree, must not be enslaved by society; but society is already in the thrall of the latter—not of any person or group of people (e.g., "the scientists,") but of the principle that says, if we can do it, we shall.

As one British Nobel Prize-winner has observed, we can regret nuclear weapons without regretting the knowledge that made them possible. The inability to resist a bright idea is often justified by the argument, "If we don't do it, somebody else will." There are fears for the prestige, military power and economic strength that underpin a nation's way of life. My fear is for the way of life, which may itself succumb to attempts to defend it by sacrifices to the god of efficiency and by remorseless and unthinking application of science in a sort of technological nationalism. Things that radically change everyday life, like television and automation to name but two, are brought casually into being. We have allowed automobiles to ruin the centers of our cities; we have turned our countryside into a two-dimensional chemical plant. The fact that all nations are following the same path does not prove it to be the right one.

Perhaps at this point I should affirm my own enthusiasm for human ingenuity, lest any reader suppose I am in some way "anti-science." Some of the impending applications of science fill me with delight; these include the desalination of water, the revolution in information-handling and communication promised by the big new computers, and the ability to treat mental disease and virus disease chemically. About others—air-cushion vehicles which can overcome the lack of roads in underdeveloped countries and provide 300 mph railways for advanced countries, or the automation of such demeaning work as clerking and mining—I complain that programs to apply them are going too slowly. I look forward hopefully to the day when food can be made artificially, when we shall have energy without limit by controlled nuclear fusion, when we shall have economic ways of winning minerals from low-grade ores. What I abjure is my right (or anyone's right) to say, "Let these things be done," without their being first subjected to the proper democratic tests of public approval and to a review of priorities. If they come unbidden, then democracy is powerless in matters touching the lives of everyone.

But how can we relate such matters to party politics? In principle it is very simple; in practice it will require unaccustomed thought on the part of politicians. To begin with, all technological proposals should, as a matter of course, be energetically opposed by someone, if only so that the dilemmas or uncertainties surrounding them can be exposed, and the complex technical and social issues aired. It is astonishing, for example, that in the United States "national goals in space" were not adequately contested before irreversible decisions had been taken and a substantial part of the nation's resources and scientific manpower committed to landing a few men on our barren satellite. Similarly, the Anglo-French supersonic air-liner project was started without any public debate.

That first requirement is minimal, and rather negative. The second and bigger step that party politicians must take will come from their realization that technological change is at least as full of consequence for the character of society as are the traditional preoccupations of politics. Different combinations of technology will produce different kinds of society. I have already outlined, in the fictional manifesto at the outset, the kind of society toward which we appear to be heading, out of control. A moment's reflection shows that we could do much better, and that in fact we have choices.

If politicians seriously attempted to evaluate current technological opportunities in the light of their political beliefs, they would find that different social views would tend to favor different items, and that they could, in effect, translate a large part of their policy into technological terms. If, for example, you believe in a strong, vigorous central government dedicated to a great technological leap into the future, you should favor big technical projects, big computers and power units, and the development of ocean resources; you should demand a large investment in preventive medicine, building and urban research, and the social sciences.

If, on the other hand, you are concerned with support for the "small man," local private enterprise and the well-being of the individual at home and abroad, you ought to prefer, for example, small-scale projects, energy sources and computers, better transport and communications, versatile production methods, natural products research and rural development, new technical methods of fighting crime, and a general bias toward improving the old technologies, rather than superseding them with new ones.

There are many ways of shuffling the pack to produce combinations of technologies that would match the particular set of beliefs of a given party. I leave it as an exercise for the reader to consider what, in the light of his own political beliefs, he favors and disfavors in current scientific possibilities. There are, of course, many more elements in the scene than I have mentioned; and where there are apparent gaps, the program maker is quite entitled to dream up new research projects.

If I may say so as a foreigner, a special responsibility falls on Americans. The United States is the pace-setter in technology, and latent in the present work of its scientists and engineers are many new wonders which will transform the world at an ever-accelerating rate. America has —in comparison with Britain, for example—the incalculable advantage of well-tried executive and legislative machinery for reviewing scientific matters, and an academic community well accustomed to serving the nation. If the United States should decide to exercise some choice, in what it encourages and what it rejects, the common man in every land who feels that he is being swept along helplessly in a torrent of innovation would be forever grateful.

Time is man's sternest discipline, unless he chooses to ignore it. In the present there are many possible futures, good and bad, for each of us as an individual and for the world at large. But when time passes and the future becomes the present, it is unique and there is no choice. *The* future, the one we or our children will actually inhabit, is too serious a matter to be left to science fiction, too much a concern of humane politics to be left to the blind drive of technology.

Aldous Huxley
OVER-ORGANIZATION

The shortest and broadest road to the nightmare of Brave New World leads, as I have pointed out, through over-population and the accelerating increase of human numbers—twenty-eight hundred millions today, fifty-five hundred millions by the turn of the century, with most of humanity facing the choice between anarchy and totalitarian control. But the increasing pressure of numbers upon available resources is not the only force propelling us in the direction of totalitarianism. This blind biological enemy of freedom is allied with immensely powerful forces generated by the very advances in technology of which we are most proud. Justifiably proud, it may be added; for these advances are the fruits of genius and persistent hard work, of logic, imagination and self-denial—in a word, of moral and intellectual virtues for which one can feel nothing but admiration. But the Nature of Things is such that nobody in this world ever gets anything for nothing. These amazing and admirable advances have had to be paid for. Indeed, like last year's washing machine, they are still being paid for—and each installment is higher than the last. Many historians, many sociologists and psychologists have written at length, and with a deep concern, about the price that Western man has had to pay and will go on paying for technological progress. They point out, for example, that democracy can hardly be expected to flourish in societies where political and economic power is being progressively concentrated and centralized. But the progress of technology has led and is still leading to just such a concentration and centralization of power. As the machinery of mass production is made more efficient it tends to become more complex and more expensive—and so less available to the enterpriser of limited means. Moreover, mass production cannot work without mass distribution; but mass distribution raises problems which only the largest producers can satisfactorily solve. In a world of mass production and mass distribution the Little Man, with his inadequate stock of working capital, is at a grave disadvantage. In competition with the Big Man, he loses his money and finally his very existence as an independent producer; the Big Man has gobbled him up. As the Little Men disappear, more and more economic power comes to be wielded by fewer and fewer people. Under a dictatorship the Big Business, made possible by advancing technology and the consequent ruin of Little Business, is controlled by the State—that is to say, by a small group of party leaders and the soldiers, policemen and civil servants who carry out their orders. In a capitalist democracy, such as the United States, it is controlled by what Professor C. Wright Mills has called the Power Elite. This Power Elite directly employs several millions of the country's working force in its factories, offices and stores, controls many millions more by lending them the money to buy its products, and, through its ownership of the media of mass communication, influences the thoughts, the feelings and the actions of virtually everybody. To parody the words of Winston Churchill, never have so many been manipulated so much by so few. We are far indeed from Jefferson's ideal of a genuinely free society composed of a hierarchy of self-governing units—"the elementary republics of the wards, the county republics, the state republics and the Republic of the Union, forming a gradation of authorities."

We see, then, that modern technology has led to the concentration of economic and political power, and to the development of a society controlled (ruthlessly in the totalitarian states, politely and inconspicuously in the democracies) by Big Business and Big Government. But societies are composed of individuals and are good only insofar as they help individuals to realize their potentialities and to lead a happy and creative life. How have individuals been affected by the technological advances of recent years? Here is the answer to this question given by a philosopher-psychiatrist, Dr. Erich Fromm:

Our contemporary Western society, in spite of its material, intellectual and political progress, is increasingly less conducive to mental health, and tends to undermine the inner security, happiness, reason and the capacity for love in the individual; it tends to turn him into an automaton who pays for his human failure with increasing mental sickness, and with despair hidden under a frantic drive for work and so-called pleasure.

Our "increasing mental sickness" may find expression in neurotic symptoms. These symptoms are conspicuous and extremely distressing. But "let us beware," says Dr. Fromm, "of defining mental hygiene as the prevention of symptoms. Symptoms as such are not our enemy, but our friend; where there are symptoms there is conflict, and conflict always indicates that the forces of life which strive for integration and happiness are still fighting." The really hopeless victims of mental illness are to be found among those who appear to be most normal. "Many of them are normal because they are so well adjusted to our mode of existence, because their human voice has been silenced so early in their lives, that they do not even struggle or suffer or develop symptoms as the neurotic does." They are normal not in what may be called the absolute sense of the word; they are normal only in relation to a profoundly abnormal society. Their perfect adjustment to that abnormal society is a measure of their mental sickness. These millions of abnormally normal people, living without fuss in a society to which, if they were fully human beings, they ought not to be adjusted, still cherish "the illusion of individuality," but in fact they have been to a great extent deindividualized. Their conformity is developing into something like uniformity. But "uniformity and freedom are incompatible. Uniformity and mental health are incompatible too. . . . Man is not made to be an automaton, if he becomes one, the basis for mental health is destroyed."

In the course of evolution nature has gone to endless trouble to see that every individual is unlike every other individual. We reproduce our kind by bringing the father's genes into contact with the mother's. These hereditary factors may be combined in an almost infinite number of ways. Physically and mentally, each one of us is unique. Any culture which, in the interests of efficiency or in the name of some political or religious dogma, seeks to standardize the human individual, commits an outrage against man's biological nature.

Science may be defined as the reduction of multiplicity to unity. It seeks to explain the endlessly diverse phenomena of nature by ignoring the uniqueness of particular events, concentrating on what they have in common and finally abstracting some kind of "law," in terms of which they make sense and can be effectively dealt with. For examples, apples fall from the tree and the moon moves across the sky. People had been observing these facts from time immemorial. With Gertrude Stein they were convinced that an apple is an apple is an apple, whereas the moon is the moon is the moon. It remained for Isaac Newton to perceive what these very dissimilar phenomena had in common, and to formulate a theory of gravitation in terms of which certain aspects of the behavior of apples, of the heavenly bodies and indeed of everything else in the physical universe could be explained and dealt with in terms of a single system of ideas. In the same spirit the artist takes the innumerable diversities and uniquenesses of the outer world and his own imagination and gives them meaning within an orderly system of plastic, literary or musical patterns. The wish to impose order upon confusion, to bring harmony out of dissonance and unity out of multiplicity is a kind of intellectual instinct, a primary and fundamental urge of the mind. Within the realms of science, art and philosophy the workings of what I may call this "Will to Order" are mainly beneficent. True, the Will to Order has produced many premature syntheses based upon insufficient evidence, many absurd systems of metaphysics and theology, much pedantic mistaking of notions for realities, of symbols and abstractions for the data of immediate experience. But these errors, however regrettable, do not do much harm, at any rate directly—though it sometimes happens that a bad philosophical system may do harm indirectly, by being used as a justification for senseless and inhuman actions. It is in the social sphere, in the realm of politics and economics, that the Will to Order becomes really dangerous.

Here the theoretical reduction of unmanageable multiplicity to comprehensible unity becomes the practical reduction of human diversity to subhuman uniformity, of freedom to servitude. In politics the equivalent of a fully developed scientific theory or philosophical system is a totalitarian dictatorship. In economics, the equivalent of a beautifully composed work of art is the smoothly running factory in which the workers are perfectly adjusted to the machines. The Will to Order can make tyrants out of those who merely aspire to clear up a mess. The beauty of tidiness is used as a justification for despotism.

Organization is indispensable; for liberty arises and has meaning only within a self-regulating community of freely co-operating individuals. But, though indispensable, organization can also be fatal. Too much organization transforms men and women into automata, suffocates the creative spirit and abolishes the very possibility of freedom. As usual, the only safe course is in the middle, between the extremes of *laissez-faire* at one end of the scale and of total control at the other.

During the past century the successive advances in technology have been accompanied by corresponding advances in organization. Complicated machinery has had to be matched by complicated social arrangements, designed to work as smoothly and efficiently as the new instruments of production. In order to fit into these organizations, individuals have had to deindividualize themselves, have had to deny their native diversity and conform to a standard pattern, have had to do their best to become automata.

The dehumanizing effects of over-organization are reinforced by the dehumanizing effects of over-population. Industry, as it expands, draws an ever greater proportion of humanity's increasing numbers into large cities. But life in large cities is not conducive to mental health (the highest incidence of schizophrenia, we are told, occurs among the swarming inhabitants of industrial slums); nor does it foster the kind of responsible freedom within small self-governing groups, which is the first condition of a genuine democracy. City life is anonymous and, as it were, abstract. People are related to one another, not as total personalities, but as the embodiments of economic functions or, when they are not at work, as irresponsible seekers of entertainment. Subjected to this kind of life, individuals tend to feel lonely and insignificant. Their existence ceases to have any point or meaning.

Biologically speaking, man is a moderately gregarious, not a completely social animal—a creature more like a wolf, let us say, or an elephant, than like a bee or an ant. In their original form human societies bore no resemblance to the hive or the ant heap; they were merely packs. Civilization is, among other things, the process by which primitive packs are transformed into an analogue, crude and mechanical, of the social insects' organic communities. At the present time the pressures of over-population and technological change are accelerating this process. The termitary has come to seem a realizable and even, in some eyes, a desirable ideal. Needless to say, the ideal will never in fact be realized. A great gulf separates the social insect from the not too gregarious, big-brained mammal; and even though the mammal should do his best to imitate the insect, the gulf would remain. However hard they try, men cannot create a social organism, they can only create an organization. In the process of trying to create an organism they will merely create a totalitarian despotism.

Brave New World presents a fanciful and somewhat ribald picture of a society, in which the attempt to re-create human beings in the likeness of termites has been pushed almost to the limits of the possible. That we are being propelled in the direction of Brave New World is obvious. But no less obvious is the fact that we can, if we so desire, refuse to co-operate with the blind forces that are propelling us. For the moment, however, the wish to resist does not seem to be very strong or very widespread. As Mr. William Whyte has shown in his remarkable book, *The Organization Man*, a new Social Ethic is replacing our traditional ethical system—the system in which the individual is primary. The key words in this Social Ethic are "adjustment," "adaptation," "socially orientated behavior," "belongingness," "acquisition of social skills," "team work," "group living," "group loyalty," "group dynamics," "group thinking," "group creativity." Its basic assumption is that the social whole has greater worth and significance than its individual parts, that inborn biological differences should be sacrificed to cultural uniformity, that the rights of the collectivity take precedence over what the eighteenth century called the Rights of Man. According to the Social Ethic, Jesus was completely wrong in asserting that the Sabbath was made for man. On the contrary, man was made for the Sabbath, and must sacrifice his inherited idiosyncrasies and pretend to be the kind of standardized good mixer that organizers of group activity regard as ideal for their purposes. This ideal man is the man who displays "dynamic conformity" (delicious phrase!) and an intense loyalty to the group, an unflagging desire to subordinate himself, to belong. And the ideal man must have an ideal wife, highly gregarious, infinitely adaptable and not merely resigned to the fact that her husband's first loyalty is to the Corporation, but actively loyal on her own account. "He for God only," as Milton said of Adam and Eve, "she for God in him." And in one important respect the wife of the ideal organization man is a good deal worse off than our First Mother. She and Adam were permitted by the Lord to be completely uninhibited in the matter of "youthful dalliance."

> Nor turned, I ween,
> Adam from his fair spouse, nor Eve the rites
> Mysterious of connubial love refused

Today, according to a writer in the *Harvard Business Review*, the wife of the man who is trying to live up to the ideal proposed by the Social Ethic, "must not demand too much of her husband's time and interest. Because of his single-minded concentration on his job, even his sexual activity must be relegated to a secondary place." The monk makes vows of poverty, obedience and chastity. The organization man is allowed to be rich, but promises obedience ("he accepts authority without resentment, he looks up to his superiors"—*Mussolini ha sempre ragione*) and he must be prepared, for the greater glory of the organization that employs him, to forswear even conjugal love.

   It is worth remarking that, in *1984*, the members of the Party are compelled to conform to a sexual ethic of more than Puritan severity. In *Brave New World*, on the other hand, all are permitted to indulge their sexual impulses without let or hindrance. The society described in Orwell's fable is a society permanently at war, and the aim of its rulers is first, of course, to exercise power for its own delightful sake and, second, to keep their subjects in that state of constant tension which a state of constant war demands of those who wage it. By crusading against sexuality the bosses are able to maintain the required tension in their followers and at the same time can satisfy their lust for power in a most gratifying way. The society described in *Brave New World* is a world-state, in which war has been eliminated and where the first aim of the rulers is at all costs to keep their subjects from making trouble. This they achieve by (among other methods) legalizing a degree of sexual freedom (made possible by the abolition of the family) that practically guarantees the Brave New Worlders against any form of destructive (or creative) emotional tension. In *1984* the lust for power is satisfied by inflicting pain; in *Brave New World*, by inflicting a hardly less humiliating pleasure.

The current Social Ethic, it is obvious, is merely a justification after the fact of the less desirable consequences of over-organization. It represents a pathetic attempt to make a virtue of necessity, to extract a positive value from an unpleasant datum. It is a very unrealistic, and therefore very dangerous, system of morality. The social whole, whose value is assumed to be greater than that of its component parts, is not an organism in the sense that a hive or a termitary may be thought of as an organism. It is merely an organization, a piece of social machinery. There can be no value except in relation to life and awareness. An organization is neither conscious nor alive. Its value is instrumental and derivative. It is not good in itself; it is good only to the extent that it promotes the good of the individuals who are the parts of the collective whole. To give organizations precedence over persons is to subordinate ends to means. What happens when ends are subordinated to means was clearly demonstrated by Hitler and Stalin. Under their hideous rule personal ends were subordinated to organizational means by a mixture of violence and propaganda, systematic terror and the systematic manipulation of minds. In the more efficient dictatorships of tomorrow there will probably be much less violence than under Hitler and Stalin. The future dictator's subjects will be painlessly regimented by a corps of highly trained social engineers. "The challenge of social engineering in our time," writes an enthusiastic advocate of this new science, "is like the challenge of technical engineering fifty years ago. If the first half of the twentieth century was the era of the technical engineers, the second half may well be the era of the social engineers"—and the twenty-first century, I suppose, will be the era of World Controllers, the scientific caste system and Brave New World. To the question *quis cusodiet custodes?*—Who will mount guard over our guardians, who will engineer the engineers?— the answer is a bland denial that they need any supervision. There seems to be a touching belief among certain Ph.D.'s in sociology that Ph.D.'s in sociology will never be corrupted by power. Like Sir Galahad's, their strength is as the strength of ten because their heart is pure—and their heart is pure because they are scientists and have taken six thousand hours of social studies.

Alas, higher education is not necessarily a guarantee of higher virtue, or higher political wisdom. And to these misgivings on ethical and psychological grounds must be added misgivings of a purely scientific character. Can we accept the theories on which the social engineers base their practice, and in terms of which they justify their manipulations of human beings? For example, Professor Elton Mayo tells us categorically that "man's desire to be continuously associated in work with his fellows is a strong, if not the strongest human characteristic." This, I would say, is manifestly untrue. Some people have the kind of desire described by Mayo; others do not. It is a matter of temperament and inherited constitution. Any social organization based upon the assumption that "man" (whoever "man" may be) desires to be continuously associated with his fellows would be, for many individual men and women, a bed of Procrustes. Only by being amputated or stretched upon the rack could they be adjusted to it.

Again, how romantically misleading are the lyrical accounts of the Middle Ages with which many contemporary theorists of social relations adorn their works! "Membership in a guild, manorial estate or village protected medieval man throughout his life and gave him peace and serenity." Protected him from what, we may ask. Certainly not from remorseless bullying at the hands of his superiors. And along with all that "peace and serenity" there was, throughout the Middle Ages, an enormous amount of chronic frustration, acute unhappiness and a passionate resentment against the rigid, hierarchical system that permitted no vertical movement up the social ladder and, for those who were bound to the land, very little horizontal movement in space. The impersonal forces of over-population and over-organization, and the social engineers who are trying to direct these forces, are pushing us in the direction of a new medieval system. This revival will be made more acceptable than the original by such Brave-New-Worldian amenities as infant conditioning, sleep-teaching and drug-induced euphoria; but, for the majority of men and women, it will still be a kind of servitude.